PROGRESS IN

Nucleic Acid Research
and Molecular Biology

Volume 35

PROGRESS IN
Nucleic Acid Research and Molecular Biology

edited by

WALDO E. COHN
Biology Division
Oak Ridge National Laboratory
Oak Ridge, Tennessee

KIVIE MOLDAVE
University of California
Santa Cruz, California

Volume 35

ACADEMIC PRESS, INC.
Harcourt Brace Jovanovich, Publishers

San Diego   New York   Berkeley   Boston
London   Sydney   Tokyo   Toronto

ACADEMIC PRESS, INC.
1250 Sixth Avenue
San Diego, California 92101

United Kingdom Edition published by
ACADEMIC PRESS INC. (LONDON) LTD.
24-28 Oval Road, London NW1 7DX

LIBRARY OF CONGRESS CATALOG CARD NUMBER: 63-15847

ISBN   0-12-540035-7   (alk. paper)

PRINTED IN THE UNITED STATES OF AMERICA
88 89 90 91   9 8 7 6 5 4 3 2 1

QP
551
.P695
V.35

Contents 1988

Complementary Use of Chemical Modification and Site-Directed Mutagenesis to Probe Structure–Activity Relationships in Enzymes

Albert T. Profy and Paul Schimmel

Mechanisms of the Antiviral Action of Interferons

Charles E. Samuel

Modulation of Cellular Genes by Oncogenes

Russell M. Lebovitz and Michael W. Lieberman

DNA Damage Produced by Ionizing Radiation in Mammalian Cells: Identities, Mechanisms of Formation, and Reparability

J. F. Ward

Human Ferritin Gene Expression

James W. Drysdale

Molecular Biology of the Insulin Receptor

Robert E. Lewis and Michael P. Czech

Cap-Binding Proteins of Eukaryotic Messenger RNA: Functions in Initiation and Control of Translation

Nahum Sonenberg

Physical Monitoring of Meiotic and Mitotic Recombination in Yeast

James E. Haber, Rhona H. Borts, Bernadette Connolly, Michael Lichten, Norah Rudin, and Charles I. White

Early Signals Underlying the Induction of the c-*fos* and c-*myc* Genes in Quiescent Fibroblasts: Studies with Bombesin and Other Growth Factors

Enrique Rozengurt and James Sinnett-Smith

Abbreviations and Symbols

All contributors to this Series are asked to use the terminology (abbreviations and symbols) recommended by the IUPAC-IUB Commission on Biochemical Nomenclature (CBN) and approved by IUPAC and IUB, and the Editors endeavor to assure conformity. These Recommendations have been published in many journals (*1, 2*) and compendia (*3*) and are available in reprint form from the Office of Biochemical Nomenclature (OBN); they are therefore considered to be generally known. Those used in nucleic acid work, originally set out in section 5 of the first Recommendations (*1*) and subsequently revised and expanded (*2, 3*), are given in condensed form in the frontmatter of Volumes 9–33 of this series. A recent expansion of the one-letter system (*5*) follows.

SINGLE-LETTER CODE RECOMMENDATIONS[a] (5)

Symbol	Meaning	Origin of designation
G	G	Guanosine
A	A	Adenosine
T(U)	T(U)	(ribo)Thymidine (Uridine)
C	C	Cytidine
R	G or A	puRine
Y	T(U) or C	pYrimidine
M	A or C	aMino
K	G or T(U)	Keto
S	G or C	Strong interaction (3 H-bonds)
W[b]	A or T(U)	Weak interaction (2 H-bonds)
H	A or C or T(U)	not G; H follows G in the alphabet
B	G or T(U) or C	not A; B follows A
V	G or C or A	not T (not U); V follows U
D	G or A or T(U)	not C; D follows C
N	G or A or T(U) or C	aNy
Q	Q	Queuosine (nucleoside of queuine)

[a] Modified from *Proc. Natl. Acad. Sci. U.S.A.* **83**, 4 (1986).

[b] W has been used for wyosine, the nucleoside of "base Y" (wye).

Enzymes

In naming enzymes, the 1984 recommendations of the IUB Commission on Biochemical Nomenclature (*4*) are followed as far as possible. At first mention, each enzyme is described *either* by its systematic name *or* by the equation for the reaction catalyzed *or* by the recommended trivial name, followed by its EC number in parentheses. Thereafter, a trivial name may be used. Enzyme names are not to be abbreviated except when the substrate has an approved abbreviation (e.g., ATPase, but not LDH, is acceptable).

REFERENCES

1. *JBC* **241**, 527 (1966); *Bchem* **5**, 1445 (1966); *BJ* **101**, 1 (1966); *ABB* **115**, 1 (1966), **129**, 1 (1969); and elsewhere.† General.
2. *EJB* **15**, 203 (1970); *JBC* **245**, 5171 (1970); *JMB* **55**, 299 (1971); and elsewhere.†
3. "Handbook of Biochemistry" (G. Fasman, ed.), 3rd ed. Chemical Rubber Co., Cleveland, Ohio, 1970, 1975, Nucleic Acids, Vols. I and II, pp. 3–59. Nucleic acids.
4. "Enzyme Nomenclature" [Recommendations (1984) of the Nomenclature Committee of the IUB]. Academic Press, New York, 1984.
5. *EJB* **150**, 1 (1985). Nucleic Acids (One-letter system).†

Abbreviations of Journal Titles

Journals	*Abbreviations used*
Annu. Rev. Biochem.	ARB
Annu. Rev. Genet.	ARGen
Arch. Biochem. Biophys.	ABB
Biochem. Biophys. Res. Commun.	BBRC
Biochemistry	Bchem
Biochem. J.	BJ
Biochim. Biophys. Acta	BBA
Cold Spring Harbor	CSH
Cold Spring Harbor Lab	CSHLab
Cold Spring Harbor Symp. Quant. Biol.	CSHSQB
Eur. J. Biochem.	EJB
Fed. Proc.	FP
Hoppe-Seyler's Z. physiol. Chem.	ZpChem
J. Amer. Chem. Soc.	JACS
J. Bacteriol.	J. Bact.
J. Biol. Chem.	JBC
J. Chem. Soc.	JCS
J. Mol. Biol.	JMB
J. Nat. Cancer Inst.	JNCI
Mol. Cell. Biol.	MCBiol
Mol. Cell. Biochem.	MCBchem
Mol. Gen. Genet.	MGG
Nature, New Biology	Nature NB
Nucleic Acid Research	NARes
Proc. Nat. Acad. Sci. U.S.	PNAS
Proc. Soc. Exp. Biol. Med.	PSEBM
Progr. Nucl. Acid. Res. Mol. Biol.	This Series

† Reprints available from the Office of Biochemical Nomenclature (W. E. Cohn, Director).

Some Articles Planned for Future Volumes

The Structural and Functional Basis of Collagen Gene Diversity
  P. BORNSTEIN

UV-Induced Crosslinks in Nucleoproteins
  E. I. BUDOWSKY

Molecular Structure and Transcriptional Regulation of the Proline-Rich Multigene Protein Complexes of the Salivary Gland
  D. M. CARLSON

Molecular Biology of β-Glucuronidase Regulation
  K. PAIGEN

Structural Organization and Regulation of Human Histone Genes
  G. STEIN AND J. STEIN

Complementary Use of Chemical Modification and Site-Directed Mutagenesis to Probe Structure–Activity Relationships in Enzymes

ALBERT T. PROFY* AND
PAUL SCHIMMEL†

* Repligen Corporation
Cambridge, Massachusetts 02139
† Department of Biology
Massachusetts Institute of
Technology
Cambridge, Massachusetts 02139

Chemical modification studies are used routinely to identify functionally important amino-acid residues in enzymes (1–4). When covalent modification of a particular residue results in a loss of enzymatic activity, it is often assumed that its side-chain functional groups are "essential" for catalysis. However, the validity of this conclusion is weakened by several well-known limitations inherent to chemical modification. Most modification reagents, for example, react with more than one residue in an enzyme, and rather drastic structural changes are often introduced.

Recently, it has become possible to make defined amino-acid substitutions at specific positions in enzymes. Using the technique of site-directed mutagenesis (5–8), preselected codon changes can be introduced into the coding region of a cloned gene such that the expressed protein contains the corresponding amino-acid replacement. This alternative method of perturbing protein structure has become popular for enzyme structure–function studies because it overcomes many of the limitations associated with chemical modification (9, 10). In par-

1

ticular, the amino-acid substitutions are limited to defined positions, and the differences between the native and altered protein are more subtle. However, in order to perform a site-directed mutagenesis experiment, it is necessary to identify regions of the enzyme where the effects of amino-acid changes will be interesting and interpretable.

In the many cases where a three-dimensional structure is unavailable, there are clear advantages to combining the techniques of chemical modification and site-directed mutagenesis for the study of enzyme function. Classical chemical modification data can play a necessary role in locating amino-acid residues that may participate in catalysis. Then, on the basis of this information, site-directed mutagenesis can be used to construct mutant proteins that contain amino-acid substitutions at these positions. The functional importance of the altered residues can then be assessed in a relatively unambiguous way by comparing the properties of the mutants to those of the native enzyme.

The purpose of this article is to show how chemical modification and site-directed mutagenesis can be effectively combined to answer structure–function questions. We first consider the rationale for using each technique to overcome limitations of the other, and then review several examples that illustrate the various types of information that can be obtained using this approach. We finish by discussing the somewhat surprising observation that catalytically important residues can often be replaced without completely abolishing enzymatic activity.

I. Rationale for the Combined Use of Chemical Modification and Site-Directed Mutagenesis

A. Chemical Modification of Enzymes: Goals and Limitations

Probably the main purpose of most chemical modification experiments is to identify amino-acid residues that comprise the active site of an enzyme of interest. Classically, these residues contain the side-chain functional groups that participate in bond-making or bond-breaking reactions (1). However, because catalysis and binding are not necessarily separable (10, 11), amino acids involved in substrate, transition state, or product binding may also be included. It is usually assumed that these amino acids are essential for catalysis.

In a typical experiment, an enzyme is treated with a reagent that produces a known covalent change, and the catalytic properties of the modified enzyme are analyzed. If the modification results in a loss of activity, it can be suggested that one or more of the labeled residues are required for catalysis. The rate of modification provides additional information about the reactivity of the important amino acid and, in some situations, the residue can be located in the primary structure of the protein by peptide mapping.

However, this approach is subject to a number of inherent limitations that complicate the interpretation of results. The most important of these are (1) the limited number of structural changes that can be produced, (2) the incomplete specificity of modification reagents, (3) the possibility that modification has not been quantitative, and (4) the possibility that modification results in a global structural change rather than a local perturbation.

Although a large number of chemical modification reagents have been designed, only a few types of amino-acid residues are susceptible to labeling. The most common reaction sites are the side chains of cysteine, lysine, histidine, tyrosine, arginine, tryptophan, and methionine. Unfortunately, there are no suitable reagents for labeling other residues, particularly those of glycine, valine, leucine, isoleucine, and phenylalanine. Although it can be argued that these residues are unlikely to participate in catalysis, they do occur in active-site regions, and may therefore be of interest.

Like the selection of side chains that can be attacked, the types of structural changes that can be introduced by chemical modification are limited. Almost invariably, labeling results in an increase in side-chain size, and this can lead to ambiguity in the interpretation of functional results. For example, creatine kinase is inactivated when a conserved cysteine residue is modified by 5,5'-dithiobis(2-nitrobenzoic acid), which greatly increases side-chain bulk (12). However, when the inactive enzyme was converted to the S-cyano derivative by reaction with KCN, the loss of steric bulk was accompanied by a restoration of 75% of the activity:

Other enzymes that are known to be inactivated by bulky reagents, but not by small ones, include glutamate dehydrogenase (13), NAD-malate enzyme (14), and luciferase (15).

Another limitation of chemical modification is that reagents rarely label a unique residue in an enzyme of interest. The most common reagents react predominantly with one type of side-chain, but complete specificity for a given type is rare. Thus, 5,5'-dithiobis(2-nitrobenzoic acid) modifies only cysteine sulfhydryl groups, while acetic anhydride reacts with lysine, tyrosine, histidine, and cysteine side chains (3). Even when the reagent is highly side-chain specific, several side-chains of the corresponding type may be modified. If activity is lost in this case, it may be postulated that a residue of a particular type is essential, but the actual residue may be unidentifiable.

In certain situations, the specificity of chemical modification is greater. Sometimes, the structure of the native enzyme enhances the reactivity of active-site residues so that they are labeled much more quickly than other residues of the same type. A classic example of this is the selective phosphorylation of the active-site serine residue in chymotrypsin with diisopropylfluorophosphate (16).

It is also possible to design modification reagents that bind to the active site before they react. These "affinity labels" (17–20) may react directly with residues at the binding site, or may be activated in situ (e.g., by photolysis) to label nearby side chains. A class of affinity labels, the mechanism-based inhibitors, are activated for covalent modification by undergoing part of the normal catalytic reaction (21). It is also possible to label an active-site residue specifically by trapping a covalent enzyme–substrate complex through chemical treatment. In a classic example, a lysine residue in aldolase was labeled by reducing an intermediate Schiff's base with sodium borohydride (22).

Despite these methods for improving specificity, most modifications lead to the labeling of more than one amino acid in an enzyme. It is sometimes possible to correlate the rate of inactivation to the rate of appearance of a peptide that contains the labeled residue, but when several residues react at the same rate, the important one cannot be identified.

In addition to the specificity of labeling, functional conclusions are limited by the extent of modification. If a particular side-chain has not been quantitatively derivatized, conclusions about its role in catalysis are weakened by the possibility of contamination by unreacted enzyme. A good deal of effort must be expended to show that labeling is quantitative (4).

In all chemical modification experiments, even those in which specific, quantitative modification is achieved, the interpretation of a loss of activity remains to some extent ambiguous. This is due to the difficulty in determining whether inactivation results from the derivatization of a catalytically essential side chain, or from the disruption of the spatial arrangement of active-site atoms following a global structural change. Such a structural change could occur upon modification of residues near to or distant from the active site, and could arise from, for example, the loss of a hydrogen bond or the introduction of steric bulk. It is also possible that inactivation of an enzyme results from the introduction of steric bulk at a nonessential residue near the active site. Although this modification may not alter the orientation of active-site groups, it may physically block substrate binding. This problem is exacerbated by the fact that most modifications lead to an increase in side-chain size.

Because of these limitations, conclusions based on chemical modification evidence have at best been tentative, and it has been desirable to support the identification of important residues with corroborating data. Recently, it has become possible to use site-directed mutagenesis for this purpose. The methodological details of this technique, and its advantages for structure-function studies, are discussed in the following sections.

B. Methods for Introducing Amino-Acid Substitutions by Site-Directed Mutagenesis

A site-directed mutagenesis experiment aimed at probing the structure–function relationship in an enzyme requires a cloned, sequenced gene that codes for the enzyme, a system for expressing the mutant gene in the absence of a wild-type or homologous copy, and a source of synthetic oligonucleotides. The methods used for the construction of specific mutants have been the subject of excellent reviews (5–8), and are discussed only briefly here. Usually, some modification of the procedure of Zoller and Smith (23) is followed. A fragment of the gene containing the sequence to be mutated is inserted into a vector derived from the genome of bacteriophage M13. This is then used to transform a suitable host, and single-stranded phage DNA is isolated. A complementary oligonucleotide containing mismatched bases at the intended sites of mutation is synthesized, purified, and used to prime DNA synthesis on the single-stranded M13 template. The heteroduplex formed by primer extension and ligation is then used to transform a competent host, and single-stranded DNA from the resulting phage particles is screened for the presence of the mutation. In a popular screening method, the DNA is blotted on nitrocellulose and probed with the mutagenic oligomer after it has been labeled with ^{32}P (24). Because the melting temperature of the oligomer–mutant duplex is higher than that of the corresponding wild-type duplex, the latter can be dissociated under conditions where the former remains labeled. Yields of mutant phage are often only a few percent, but they can be increased by a variety of methods (25–27).

M13 DNA that screens positive must be sequenced to confirm that the desired mutation is present and that unwanted changes have not occurred. The mutant fragment is then transferred from the double-stranded M13 replicative form to a suitable expression vector. In order to obtain unambiguous functional information on the mutant protein, it is essential to express the mutant in a host that contains neither a wild-type copy of the gene nor a homologous sequence. If a wild-type copy is present, it is difficult to determine whether the phenotype of the host or the activity of the purified enzyme arises from the intended amino-acid substitution or from contamination by wild-type enzyme.

In selecting an oligonucleotide sequence, it is important to avoid complementarity with other parts of the single-stranded template, as this could result in the introduction of unwanted mutations. Several nucleotide substitutions can be introduced simultaneously by the same oligonucleotide. This can be used, for example, to introduce multiple codon changes or to introduce or remove restriction sites that can be used to confirm the presence of a desired mutation.

Specific mutations can also be introduced by the technique of "cassette mutagenesis" (28). In this method, a short fragment of duplex DNA is removed from the region of interest and replaced by a synthetic duplex that contains the desired changes. The process is simpler to perform than oligonucleotide-directed mutagenesis, but requires the presence of convenient restriction sites.

C. Advantages of Site-Directed Mutagenesis

The rationale for the use of site-directed mutagenesis to probe enzyme structure–function relationships is identical to that for chemical modification experiments: the structure of the enzyme is perturbed by a defined chemical change and the effect on the catalytic properties (or some other function) is measured. Furthermore, the same logic is used to interpret the results: the absence of enzymatic activity in a mutant suggests that the replaced residue is required for catalysis.

There are, however, important advantages to the use of site-directed mutagenesis that overcome the principal limitations associated with chemical modification. Most important is that alterations introduced by site-directed mutagenesis are *specific* and *quantitative*. A single amino-acid residue can be changed by mutating the corresponding codon, and (disregarding errors in translation) all of the proteins expressed from the gene will contain the change. This overcomes the problem of side reactions that plague chemical modification experiments. Furthermore, if care is taken to express the mutant protein in a host that lacks a copy of the wild-type gene or a homolog, the problems associated with incomplete reaction in chemical modification experiments will be avoided. Because of these advantages, functional alterations can be attributed with confidence to a change at a defined position.

A second major advantage of site-directed mutagenesis is that a wider variety of chemical changes can be made. Particularly significant is that smaller side-chains can be introduced at desired positions. As discussed above, chemical modification leads, almost without exception, to an increase in side-chain size, and this opens the possibility for unintended steric effects that compromise the interpretation of functional data. Although smaller residues may also affect structural integrity, the possibility of steric occlusion of the active site is eliminated.

In a similar way, site-directed mutagenesis can be used to generate more subtle structural changes. By appropriate selection of amino-acid replacements, the effect of changing only one or a few atoms can be studied. Thus, Tyr → Phe and Ser → Ala changes can be used to determine the role of specific hydroxyl groups, and Glu → Gln and Asp → Asn changes can probe the importance of the negatively charged carboxylate groups. In a study of the function of His-48 in tyrosyl-tRNA synthetase, Lowe et al. (29) argued that asparagine and glutamine substitutions could test whether the histidine π- or τ-N is involved in hydrogen bonding.

The possible replacements, of course, are limited to the other 19 amino acids. However, it is possible to introduce a residue such as cysteine that can be derivatized by a rich assortment of chemical modification reagents. The properties of these labeled mutants can be revealing.

Despite these advantages, site-directed mutagenesis does suffer from certain limitations. As in chemical modification experiments, it is often unclear whether a change in enzymatic activity results from the replacement of an essential side-chain functional group or from a global structural change. The latter seems less likely in site-directed mutagenesis experiments because the modifications are more subtle and specific. Indeed, X-ray crystal structures of mutant dihydrofolate reductase (30) and trypsin (31) molecules show that structural changes are, for the most part, limited to the substitution site. Nevertheless, the possibility of global structural change is difficult to rule out without some structural information.

Other limitations are unique to site-directed mutagenesis. Obviously, a sequenced clone of the gene of interest must be available, as well as a suitable host for expression of the altered enzyme. A potential problem is that the introduced mutation may destabilize the protein so that it does not accumulate in the host cell. In these situations, it is sometimes possible to use the "maxicell" technique to acquire the unstable protein (32).

Even when a clone is available, it is usually not possible to identify, simply by inspection of the sequence, appropriate sites at which to perform mutagenesis. Additional information is required to make this selection. Usually, this information has been obtained from X-ray diffraction, sequence homology, or chemical modification data.

The wealth of information present in high-resolution structures based on X-ray crystallographic data has prompted the most informative site-directed mutagenesis experiments. These include work on tyrosyl-tRNA synthetase (24, 29, 33–42), dihydrofolate reductase (30, 43–45), aspartate transcarbamoylase (46–49), tryptophan synthase (50, 51), subtilisin (52–54), triosephosphate isomerase (55–57), trypsin (31, 58–61), staphylococcal nuclease (62, 63), T4 lysozyme (64, 65), and DNA binding proteins (66–69). Unfortunately, high-resolution structures are not always available for the enzyme under study.

When the gene of interest can be compared to a number of homologous sequences, the importance of conserved amino-acid residues can be tested by site-directed mutagenesis. The selection of appropriate conserved residues is often aided by secondary structure predictions. This has been employed to study mercuric ion reductase (70), isoleucyl-tRNA synthetase (71, 72), and the reverse transcriptase from HIV (73).

As we show, data from chemical modification experiments can also be used to select appropriate targets for site-directed mutagenesis. When evidence exists that a modified residue is functionally important, it is of interest to probe its role in more detail by studying the functional consequences of replacing it with other amino acids. This complementary use of chemical modification and site-directed mutagenesis, and the interesting results that have been obtained, are illustrated by the examples that follow.

II. Examples of the Combined Use of Chemical Modification and Site-Directed Mutagenesis

To illustrate the combined use of chemical modification and site-directed mutagenesis, investigations of seven enzymes are discussed.

The key features of these examples are outlined in Table I. In cases A–E, chemical modification data in combination with peptide mapping or X-ray crystallographic evidence were used to locate potentially important residues in the protein primary structure. Both affinity labels and reagents selectively modifying side-chains were used. In examples F and G, chemical modification results suggested only that a particular type of side-chain was important for catalysis. In these cases, site-directed mutagenesis coupled with chemical modification of the mutant enzymes enabled identification of the potentially essential residue. In every example, kinetic analysis of the mutant proteins provided new insights into the functional importance of the replaced residues.

A. β-Lactamase

β-Lactamases protect bacteria from penam and cephem antibiotics by catalyzing the hydrolytic cleavage of β-lactam rings. A number of β-lactamase inhibitors form acyl-enzyme intermediates during the catalytic reaction (74), and Fisher *et al.* (75) found that inactivation of the *E. coli* β-lactamase by the mechanism-based inhibitor quinacillin sulfone was accompanied by the labeling of a unique serine residue, Ser-70.

Because the sequenced *amp* gene for β-lactamase was readily available on plasmid pBR322, the essential Ser-70 became an early target for site-directed mutagenesis. By the use of restriction enzymes, the native AGC codon was converted to TGC, which codes for cysteine (76). Cells harboring the mutant plasmid were less resistant to ampicillin than those containing pBR322, but more resistant than cells that contained neither plasmid. Later, the kinetic properties of the purified mutant enzyme were compared to those of the native form, and were found to depend on the substrate (Table II) (77). For benzylpenicillin and ampicillin, the K_ms of the mutant and wild type are similar, but the k_{cat} of the mutant is only 1–2% of the wild-type value. On the other hand, for the reactive cephalosporin nitrocefin, k_{cat} for the mutant is similar to that of the wild-type enzyme, but the K_m of the former is 10-fold greater. Presumably, with the standard substrates, attack on the β-lactam ring is the rate-limiting step, and the cysteine sulfhydryl group reacts more slowly than the serine hydroxyl. However, in the case of the more labile substrate, formation of the acyl-enzyme intermediate is no longer rate-limiting for either the wild-type or mutant enzyme.

Additional work with thiol β-lactamase illustrates the use of chemical modification to probe mutant enzymes. As expected, the enzyme

TABLE I

Examples of Combined Use of Chemical Modification and Site-Directed Mutagenesis

Enzyme	Modification reagent that inactivates enzyme	Essential amino acid identified by chemical modification	Substitution by site-directed mutagenesis	Properties of mutant enzyme	References
A. β-Lactamase	Affinity labels	Ser-70	Cys-70	Residual activity, inactivated by p-chloromercuribenzoic acid, not inhibited by boric acid	76, 77
B. Ribulose-bisphosphate carboxylase	Affinity labels, trinitrobenzenesulfonate	Lys-175[a]	Thr-70	Inactive	82, 83
			Arg-166	0.02% native activity	95
			Ser-166	0.02% native activity	95
			His-166	2.0% native activity	95
	Affinity labels, trinitrobenzenesulfonate	Lys-334[a]	Gly-329	Inactive	96
			Ala-329	Inactive	96
			Ser-329	Inactive	96
			Glu-329	Inactive	96
			Cys-329	Inactive, activity reaction with bromoethylamine	96, 97
C. Aspartate transcarbamoylase	Diethyl pyrocarbonate	His-291	Ala-291	40% native activity	100
	Tetranitromethane	Tyr-160	Ser-160	25% native V_{max}	46
	Pyridoxal-phosphate trapping, trinitrobenzenesulfonic acid	Lys-84	Gln-84	Inactive	47
	Trinitrobenzenesulfonic acid	Lys-83	Gln-83	Native activity	47
D. Triosephosphate isomerase	Affinity labels	Glu-165	Asp-165	1/240th of native k_{cat}, labeled by bromohydroxyacetone phosphate	56, 57
E. Carboxypeptidase A	Acetylimidazole, tetranitromethane, 5-amino-1H-tetrazole	Tyr-248	Phe-248	Native k_{cat} for hydrolysis of peptide and ester substrates	116, 117

10

				Effect	Ref.
	Tetranitromethane	Tyr-198	Phe-198	Approximately native activity for different substrates	118
			Phe-248, Phe-198	Additive effects on K_ms	118
F. Glycyl-tRNA synthetase	N-Ethylmaleimide (MalNEt)	β-Subunit cysteines	Ala-98	Native activity, inactivated by MalNEt	121
			Ala-395	Native activity, not inactivated by MalNEt	121
			Ala-450	Native activity, inactivated by MalNEt	121
			Gln-395	<10% native activity	121
G. *lac* permease	Diethyl pyrocarbonate	Histidines	Arg-35	Native activity	125
			Arg-39	Native activity	125
			Arg-205	Inactive for transport	125
			Asn-205	Native activity	126
			Gln-205	Native activity	126
			Arg-322	Inactive for uphill transport	125
			Asn-322	Inactive for transport	126
			Gln-322	Inactive for transport	126
	N-Ethylmaleimide (MalNEt)	Cys-148	Ser-148	Native activity; resistant to MalNEt inactivation	131
			Gly-148	1/15th native V_{max}; resistant to MalNEt inactivation	129, 130
	N-Ethylmaleimide	Other cysteines	Ser-154	10% native transport rate	132
			Gly-154	Inactive for transport	132
			Ser-176	80% native activity	133
			Ser-234	70% native activity	133
			Ser-117	70% native activity	134
			Ser-333	Native activity	134
			Ser-353, Ser-355	>50% native activity	134

a Lys-166 and Lys-329 in the *R. rubrum* enzyme.

TABLE II
HYDROLYSIS OF β-LACTAMS BY WILD-TYPE (Ser-70) AND Cys-70 β-LACTAMASE[a]

Substrate	K_m (mM)		k_{cat} (s^{-1})	
	Cys-70	wt	Cys-70	wt
Benzylpenicillin	0.06	0.05	20	1700
Ampicillin	0.12	0.05	50	2000
Cephaloridine	1.8	1.0	2	1700
Nitrocefin	>2.5	0.11	>400	900

[a] From (77).

containing Cys-70 is inactivated by the thiol reagent p-chloromercuri-benzoic acid, while native β-lactamase is not (76). Conversely, although the native enzyme is competitively inhibited by boric acid, the mutant is not (77). This supports an early proposal that boric acid forms a covalent complex with an active-site hydroxyl group (78).

Although this mutagenesis study confirmed the identification of the Ser-70 hydroxyl group as the active-site nucleophile, it demonstrated that the similar thiol nucleophile at this position could also support catalysis. Thus, while it is almost certain that Ser-70 participates in cleavage of the β-lactam ring, it is not essential for activity. A similar result was reported by Ghosh et al. (79) who observed catalysis (albeit with a change in rate-limiting step) when the active-site Ser-102 of E. coli alkaline phosphatase was converted to a cysteine residue by oligonucleotide-directed mutagenesis. Interestingly, the conversion of the active-site hydroxyl of subtilisin to a sulfhydryl by chemical methods also afforded an active enzyme (80, 81).

After an active-site residue is identified in the amino-acid sequence of a protein, nearby residues can be probed by site-directed mutagenesis. The class-A β-lactamases contain a conserved threonine residue at position 71, adjacent to the essential Ser-70. To probe the role of this residue mutants were constructed that contain every permutation of serine and threonine at the two positions (82, 83). Mutants that contained threonine at position 70 were inactive, but the Ser-70, Ser-71 mutant showed 15% of the wild-type activity (83). To better understand the importance of position 71, the technique of cassette mutagenesis was used to substitute each of the other 19 amino acids for the native threonine (84). Surprisingly, 14 of the substitutions each provided ampicillin resistance to the strains that carried them, although all of the mutant proteins appeared to be less stable than the wild-type enzyme. Thr-71, therefore, seems to be conserved for the maintenance of structural integrity.

B. Ribulose-bisphosphate Carboxylase

Ribulose-bisphosphate carboxylase (EC 4.1.1.39) is an important enzyme that catalyzes the first step in photosynthetic CO_2 fixation. The spinach and *Rhodospirillum rubrum* enzymes have been cloned and sequenced, and their homologous primary structures have been aligned (85–87). A host of affinity labels have been used to probe the active sites of both enzymes, and on the basis of the studies, Lys-175 and Lys-334 of the spinach enzyme (Lys-166 and Lys-329 of the *R. rubrum* protein) were judged to be essential (88–93). Furthermore, Lys-166 in *R. rubrum* and Lys-334 in spinach ribulose-bisphosphate carboxylase are specifically modified by trinitrobenzenesulfonate. The former shows a particularly low pK_a of 7.9, suggesting that it may play a catalytic role (94).

Site-directed mutagenesis shows that both conserved lysine residues are important for activity. All position 166 mutants of the *R. rubrum* enzyme are severely deficient in carboxylase activity; the most active of those examined (Ser-166) exhibits only 0.2% of wild-type activity (95). As in the case of β-lactamase, the presence of low activity in certain mutants is interesting: although Lys-166 seems to be involved in catalysis, other residues at this position can support slight activity. The inactivity of the arginine mutant, and the competence in binding of phosphorylated ligands by other mutants, suggest that Lys-166 is not required for an electrostatic interaction, while the low but measurable activity of some mutants is consistent with a proton-transfer role for Lys-166.

Site-directed mutagenesis has also been used to substitute Lys-329 of the *R. rubrum* carboxylase with glycine, alanine, serine, arginine, glutamic acid, and cysteine residues (96). The purified mutant proteins formed dimers like the native enzyme, but showed no activity, and did not form a well-known complex with CO_2, Mg^{2+}, and the transition-state analog carboxyarabinitol bisphosphate.

The mutant carboxylase containing Cys-329 was used in an interesting chemical modification experiment. Treatment of the mutant with bromoethylamine resulted in the recovery of 25% of the native activity. This derivative shows K_m values similar to that of the wild-type enzyme, and forms a stable CO_2/Mg^{2+}/carboxyarabinitol-bisphosphate complex. Presumably, the S-aminoethylcysteine residue sufficiently resembles a lysine residue to restore activity (97):

$$R\text{—}CH_2\text{—}SH + Br\text{—}CH_2\text{—}CH_2\text{—}NH_2 \longrightarrow$$

$$R\text{—}CH_2\text{—}S\text{—}CH_2\text{—}CH_2\text{—}NH_2 + HBr$$

Although site-directed mutagenesis experiments confirmed that
Lys-166 and Lys-329 participate in catalysis, this was not the case for
His-291. Modification of the spinach enzyme with diethyl pyrocarbonate suggested that the enzyme contains one essential histidine residue
(98), and this was later shown by peptide mapping to be the conserved
His-298 (99). To test this, the homologous His-291 of the R. rubrum
enzyme was replaced by an alanine residue using oligonucleotide-
directed mutagenesis of the gene (100). Kinetic analysis of the purified enzymes showed that the Ala-291 mutant retained considerable
activity, and the latter formed a stable CO_2/Mg^{2+}/carboxyarabinitol-
bisphosphate complex. This experiment suggests that His-291 need
not participate in the catalytic mechanism, but that increasing its
steric bulk may perturb the active-site conformation (100).

C. Aspartate Transcarbamoylase

Aspartate transcarbamoylase catalyzes the first committed reaction
in pyrimidine biosynthesis, and the E. coli enzyme has been inten-
sively studied. The pyrB gene has been cloned and sequenced, and,
with the aid of X-ray crystallographic data, a number of site-directed
mutagenesis studies have probed the catalytic and regulatory properties of the enzyme (46–49). Some of these studies were also based on
the results of chemical modification experiments. For example, nitration of the enzyme with tetranitromethane led to inactivation, although protection was afforded by substrates. Both Tyr-160 and Tyr-
213 were labeled in this experiment, but because Tyr-213 could be
specifically labeled without loss of activity, it was concluded that Tyr-
160 was the essential residue (101). Oligonucleotide-directed mutagenesis was therefore used to replace Tyr-160 with a serine residue.
Interestingly, the Ser-160 mutant showed activity, albeit at a reduced
level: V_{max} was reduced to 25% of the wild-type rate, K_m for aspartate
increased 12-fold, and the allosteric properties were altered (46). Although Tyr-160 seems to be important for catalysis, it is not absolutely
required. It would be interesting to study mutants with other substitutions, such as Phe, at position 160.

It is worth noting that, in these and other studies, a 10-fold change
in a K_m or k_{cat} is a relatively small change in the free energy of binding
or of transition-state stabilization. For this reason, the significance of
changes of this magnitude should not be overemphasized.

Other chemical studies show that inactivation of aspartate transcarbamoylase follows labeling of Lys-84 by pyridoxal phosphate (102,

103), or modification of both Lys-84 and Lys-83 by bromosuccinate (*104*) or trinitrobenzenesulfonic acid (*105*). Site-directed mutagenesis experiments confirm that Lys-84 is essential—mutant enzymes containing glutamine or arginine residues at this position show virtually no activity (*47*), and this is consistent with the crystallographic data showing the Lys-84 side-chain in contact with a substrate analog. Lys-83, on the other hand, is unnecessary for catalysis. A mutant containing glutamine at this position exhibited appreciable activity, both as the holoenzyme and as the isolated catalytic subunit (*47*).

D. Triosephosphate Isomerase

Affinity labeling (*106–108*) and X-ray crystallographic (*109*) evidence identified an essential active-site residue in triosephosphate isomerase (Glu-165). In order to analyze the effect of shortening the essential side-chain, site-directed mutagenesis was performed to replace the glutamic acid with an aspartic acid residue (*56, 57*). A kinetic analysis of the mutant enzyme showed that turnover numbers for the forward and reverse reactions were, respectively, 1/240th and 1/1500th those of the wild type, but the K_m values were not dramatically different. To rule out the possibility that the mutant enzyme indirectly catalyzes proton transfer through an intervening water molecule, it was shown that reactions performed in D_2O showed no isotope effect and that Asp-165 is modified by the affinity label bromohydroxyacetone phosphate (*57*). Although Glu-165 appears to be involved in catalysis, it can be replaced by a residue of similar structure without complete loss of activity.

E. Carboxypeptidase A

Early chemical modification experiments showed that four tyrosine residues of bovine carboxypeptidase A are acylated by acetylimidazole (*110*). Two of these are cleaved by hydroxylamine more rapidly than the others, and are protected from labeling by 3-phenylpropionate. Later, it was found that Tyr-248 is selectively labeled by tetranitromethane (*111, 112*) and 5-amino-1*H*-tetrazole (*112, 113*). These modifications reduce the rate of peptide hydrolysis by an order of magnitude but do not reduce the rate of ester cleavage. X-Ray diffraction data for a carboxypeptidase A–potato inhibitor complex (*114*) helped to explain these results. Tyr-248 was discovered to be within contact distance of the inhibitor's cleaved peptide bond, and it was suggested that the phenolic hydroxyl group is required for protonation of the incipient imine anion formed during amide hydrolysis (*115*). It was assumed that, in the case of ester hydrolysis, protonation of the more stable alkoxide is unnecessary, and therefore Tyr-248 is not required.

To assess more rigorously the catalytic role of the Tyr-248 hydroxyl group, site-directed mutagenesis was used to construct a phenylalanine codon at position 248 in the rat cDNA (116). Both wild-type and Phe-248 zymogens were expressed in yeast, cleaved to the active forms, and purified. The results of a detailed kinetic analysis (116, 117) are summarized in Table III. Surprisingly, mutant and wild-type proteases showed similar k_{cat} values for the hydrolysis of both peptide and ester substrates. This contradicts the proposed involvement of Tyr-248 in amide cleavage. However, K_m values and the K_I value for the potato inhibitor were 6- to 70-fold higher in the mutant. Therefore, Tyr-248 seems to play a role in binding.

The effect of tetranitromethane modification on the Phe-248 mutant was interesting. Although nitration of the cloned, wild-type rat enzyme led to the expected decrease in peptidase activity and increase in esterase activity, the activities of the mutant were unaffected (Fig. 1) (116). This confirms that the effect of nitration arises from reaction at Tyr-248, but does not explain the associated kinetic changes, which remain unclear.

When Tyr-248 is labeled by 5-amino-1H-tetrazole, Tyr-198 of carboxypeptidase A becomes sufficiently reactive to undergo nitration (113). To test the catalytic significance of this residue, a Phe-198 mu-

TABLE III
HYDROLYSIS OF SUBSTRATES BY WILD-TYPE (Tyr-248) AND Phe-248
CARBOXYPEPTIDASE A[a]

Substrate	K_m (μM)		k_{cat} (s^{-1})	
	Phe-248	wt	Phe-248	wt
Peptides				
Bz-Gly-Phe[b]	199	39.2	21.2	17.7
Cbz-Gly-Gly-Phe[c]	194	27.1	23.1	51.6
Esters				
ClCnPhLac[d]	252	26.3	4.13	17.5
Bz-Gly-PhLac[e]	136	95.6	1138	1194

[a] From (116).
[b] Benzoylglycyl-L-phenylalanine.
[c] Carbobenzoxyglycylglycyl-L-phenylalanine.
[d] O-($trans$-p-chlorocinnamoyl)-L-phenyllactic acid.
[e] O-Benzoylglycyl-DL-phenyllactic acid.

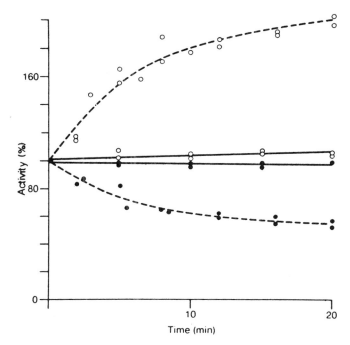

FIG. 1. Effect of tetranitromethane on wild-type (Tyr-248) and Phe-248 carboxypeptidase A. Activities for peptide (Cbz-Gly$_2$-Phe) hydrolysis: (–––) wild-type; (——) Phe-248 mutant. Activities for ester (Bz-Gly-PhLac) hydrolysis: (O–––O) wild-type; (O——O) Phe-248 mutant. Reprinted from (116).

tant, as well as a Phe-198, Phe-248 double mutant, was constructed (118). Kinetic analysis of the purified single mutant showed that k_{cat} values for most substrates were reduced relative to the native enzyme, but K_m values were similar. The K_m values for the double mutant equaled the summed changes for the single mutants, demonstrating that the effects of each mutation were independent (9). The decreased k_{cat} values for the Phe-198 mutant suggest that this residue participates in transition-state binding for some substrates, but it is clear that neither Tyr-198 nor Tyr-248 is essential for catalysis (118).

The three carboxypeptidase mutants were also used to clarify the effects of modification by acetylation. After treatment with acetylimidazole, each single mutant contained only one highly labile acetyltyrosine, and the double mutant contained none. Furthermore, the functional affect of acetylation on the Phe-198 mutant was identical to the affect on the native enzyme. Thus, acetylated Tyr-198 and Tyr-248 must be the two labile residues in the wild-type, and the modification of Tyr-248 must be responsible for the observed kinetic changes (118).

F. Glycyl-tRNA Synthetase

Glycyl-tRNA synthetase catalyzes the formation of glycyl adenylate and the subsequent transfer of the activated amino acid to tRNA^{Gly}. Upon modification of the *E. coli* enzyme by reaction with *N*-ethylmaleimide (MalNEt), glycyl-tRNA synthesis is inactivated, but the rate of glycyl adenylate formation is increased (119). The inactivation followed first-order kinetics, and the site of modification was localized to the β-subunit, but the actual labeled residue was not identified.

Cloning and sequencing of the *glyS* gene showed that the β subunit of *E. coli* glycyl-tRNA synthetase contains three cysteine residues: Cys-98, Cys-395, and Cys-450 (120). In order to identify the residue that, when labeled, causes inactivation, site-directed mutagenesis was used to construct three mutants, each expressing an alanine residue in place of one of the β-subunit cysteines (121). Surprisingly, all of these mutants catalyzed aminoacylation at the wild-type rate, suggesting that none of the β-subunit cysteine residues is essential (Table IV). Furthermore, a cysteine-free β-subunit containing alanine residues at all three positions supported significant aminoacylation activity. Presumably, *N*-ethylmaleimide alkylation leads

TABLE IV
ACTIVITIES OF ALTERED GLYCYL-tRNA SYNTHETASES[a,b]

β-Subunit amino-acid changes	Relative activities	
	Aminoacylation[c]	Adenylate synthesis[d]
Wild-type[e]	1.0	1.0
Ala-98	1.0	0.7
Ala-395	0.8	0.9
Ala-450	0.6	0.7
Ala-98, Ala-395, Ala-450	0.3	0.9
Gln-395	0.08	1.1

[a] From (121).

[b] Activities were measured in extracts from *glyS* null strain TM202 containing plasmid-encoded mutant *glyS* alleles and were normalized to β-lactamase levels, as described in the text.

[c] Uncertainty is 20%.

[d] Uncertainty is 30%.

[e] Wild-type enzyme has a Cys at positions 98, 395, and 450.

to a structural or steric defect that is not generated by the smaller alanine side-chain.

Chemical modification of the mutant synthetases was used to identify the site that, when alkylated by N-ethylmaleimide, causes inactivation. N-Ethylmaleimide treatment inactivated the Ala-98 and Ala-450 enzymes at the same rate as the wild-type enzyme, but the Ala-395 mutant lost activity at one-fifth the rate (Fig. 2). It can therefore be concluded that it is necessary to label Cys-395 in order to produce the observed activity loss. To show that a lesion at position 395 is *sufficient* to cause inactivation, and to determine if large side-chains are tolerated at this position, site-directed mutagenesis was

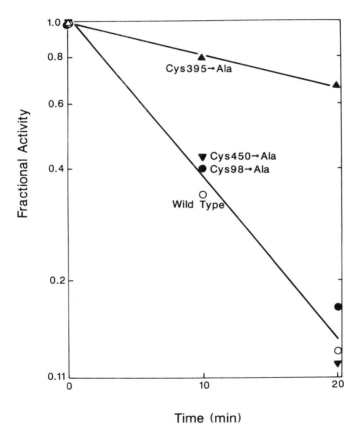

FIG. 2. Kinetics for inactivation of wild-type and mutant glycyl-tRNA synthetases by N-ethylmaleimide. From (121).

used to replace Cys-395 with a glutamine residue, which to some extent resembles the alkylated cysteine (121). As expected, the properties of the mutant were similar to the N-ethylmaleimide-modified wild-type enzyme: aminoacylation activity was greatly reduced, but glycyl adenylate formation occurred at the same rate as the native enzyme (Table IV). Thus, a lesion at position 395 is *sufficient* to cause activity loss.

G. lac Permease

The *lac* permease of *E. coli* catalyzes the symport of β-galactosides and protons. The histidine-selective reagent diethyl pyrocarbonate inactivates permease-catalyzed lactose transport by modifying a single residue with a pK_a of 6.0–6.5, though the actual residue was not identified (122–124). Because the modification did not affect substrate binding, it was suggested that the labeled histidine is involved in proton transfer (123).

To identify the modified histidine residue, each of the four histidine codons in the *lacY* gene was converted to an arginine codon by site-directed mutagenesis (125). Although mutants that contained Arg-35 or Arg-39 exhibited native activity, the Arg-205 and Arg-322 mutants were each inactivated for uphill lactose transport. The latter, though, retained the ability to facilitate downhill transport. To better understand the functional roles of His-205 and His-322 in the native permease, each residue was replaced by an asparagine or glutamine (126, cf. 29). Both the Asn-205 and Gln-205 mutants displayed normal activity, suggesting that the residue at this position participates in hydrogen bonds that are involved in substrate binding or the maintenance of structure. Conversely, the Asn-322 and Gln-322 mutants are devoid of activity and, in conjunction with the results for the Arg-322 mutant, it was suggested that His-322 participates in proton transport, and may be the residue modified by diethyl pyrocarbonate (126).

Chemical modification and site-directed mutagenesis were also combined to identify important cysteine residues in *lac* permease. N-Ethylmaleimide treatment abolishes symport activity in a first-order reaction, but substrates afford protection (127). The site of labeling is Cys-148 (128). In an attempt to show that Cys-148 is essential, site-directed mutagenesis was used to construct Gly-148 (129, 130) and Ser-148 (131) permeases. As in the case of glycyl-tRNA synthetase, the different substitutions affected the rate of lactose transport differently: V_{max} for the Gly-148 protein was 1/15th that of the native permease, but the Ser-148 mutant catalyzed transport at the wild-type rate. In other characteristics, such as steady-state lactose levels, K_m

(app) for lactose, and K_D for p-nitrophenylgalactopyranoside, both mutants resembled the wild-type enzyme. On the basis of these results, it is clear that Cys-148 is not required for activity.

Chemical modification experiments on the *mutant* permeases, however, led to the suspicion that another cysteine residue may be essential for permease activity. As expected, both the Gly-148 and Ser-148 proteins were resistant to rapid inactivation by N-ethyl-maleimide, but both were completely inactivated after a long reaction time (*129–131*). Significantly, a substrate analog did not protect the mutants from inactivation, although it did completely protect the native enzyme. In order to assess the roles of the other six cysteine residues in *lac* permease, site-directed mutagenesis was performed at each of these positions (*132–134*). The results suggest that of these residues, only Cys-154 is important for lactose transport.

Cys-154 was already known to be partially labeled by N-ethyl-[^{14}C]maleimide in the wild-type enzyme (*132*). A Gly-154 mutant showed essentially no transport activity, which argues for the importance of Cys-154, but a Ser-154 mutant did transport lactose, albeit at only 10% of the wild-type rate (*132*). These results suggest that a side-chain nucleophile may be necessary at position 154. Alternatively, the expression of a helix-breaking glycine residue at position 154 may have destabilized an α-helical structure predicted to occur in this region (*135*). It is worth noting that the importance of position 154 could be realized only after the reactive but unnecessary Cys-148 was removed by site-directed mutagenesis.

III. Conclusions

On the basis of these examples, a few generalizations can be made about the combined use of chemical modification and site-directed mutagenesis. Clearly, site-directed mutagenesis provides a useful test of the validity of conclusions based on chemical modification experiments. Not surprisingly, a number of putative "essential" residues can be replaced without a substantial activity loss. This was particularly true when the initial identifications were based on labeling by common, side-chain-selective modification reagents. Thus, His-291 in ribulose-bisphosphate carboxylase, Cys-395 in glycyl-tRNA synthetase, Cys-148 in *lac* permease, and even Tyr-248 in carboxypeptidase A are expendable. The surprising result in the carboxypeptidase Tyr-248 case demonstrates the power of site-directed mutagenesis as a structure–function probe.

It was also expected that replacement of some "essential" amino acids would cause a dramatic loss in enzymatic activity, thereby confirming their importance. This was generally observed when the initial assignment was based on affinity labeling, such as in the case of Ser-70 in β-lactamase, Lys-166 and Lys-329 in ribulose-bisphosphate carboxylase, Lys-84 in aspartate transcarbamoylase, and Glu-165 of triosephosphate isomerase. These results confirm that affinity labeling is a much more reliable way to identify active-site amino acids than is modification by common side-chain-selective reagents.

An important new result is the demonstration that catalysis can still be observed when residues evidently important for catalysis are replaced by amino acids of similar structure. This was true in the Ser-70 $\rightarrow$ Cys mutant of β-lactamase, the Lys-166 $\rightarrow$ His mutant of ribulose-bisphosphate carboxylase, and the Glu-165 $\rightarrow$ Asp mutant of triosephosphate isomerase, where the native residues almost certainly participate in catalysis. Thus, instead of thinking in terms of essential amino-acid residues, it is more appropriate to consider essential functionality, and it is now possible to address this experimentally using site-directed mutagenesis.

For the biochemist interested in discovering the functional role of a particular amino-acid residue, the observation of residual activity in mutant proteins may provide a useful new tool. If replacement of a suspected residue by one of similar structure produces a mutant with low but measurable activity, while its replacement by other amino acids results in inactive mutants, then the residue may well be involved in catalysis. Indeed, this was the case for Ser-70 of β-lactamase and for Glu-165 of triosephosphate isomerase. It is possible, of course, that this result would be obtained in other situations—a residue may be important for maintaining secondary structure, for example.

In other cases, the interpretation of site-directed mutagenesis experiments may be more ambiguous. If a number of structurally similar replacements produce partially active mutants, or if some mutants show native activity, it is unlikely that the residue participates in catalysis. If, on the other hand, substitutions by structurally dissimilar amino acids do not affect activity, it is clear that the residue of interest is not essential for catalysis. In these situations, however, certain substitutions may still produce an inactive enzyme: this was observed with β-lactamase and glycyl-tRNA synthetase.

More site-directed mutagenesis studies will be required before the kinetic properties of mutant enzymes can be interpreted with confidence. Furthermore, more effort should be expended to characterize mutants that have already been constructed (10). The utility that classical chemical modification has shown, both for the selection of appropriate substitutions and for the characterization of the mutants, ensures that this approach will continue to be important in future studies.

ACKNOWLEDGMENT

This work was supported in part by National Institutes of Health Grant No. GM 15539.

REFERENCES

1. B. L. Vallee and J. F. Riordan, *ARB* **38**, 733 (1969).
2. L. A. Cohen, *in* "The Enzymes" (P. D. Boyer, ed.), 3rd ed., Vol. 1, p. 147. Academic Press, New York, 1970.
3. G. E. Means and R. E. Feeney, "Chemical Modification of Proteins." Holden-Day, San Francisco, California, 1971.
4. R. L. Lundblad and C. M. Noyes, "Chemical Reagents for Protein Modification." CRC Press, Boca Raton, Florida, 1984.
5. M. Smith, *ARGen* **19**, 423 (1985).
6. D. Botstein and D. Shortle, *Science* **229**, 1193 (1985).
7. C. S. Craik, *BioTechniques* **3**, 12 (1985).
8. P. Carter, *BJ* **237**, 1 (1986).
9. G. K. Ackers and F. R. Smith, *ARB* **54**, 597 (1985).
10. J. R. Knowles, *Science* **236**, 1252 (1987).
11. J. B. S. Haldane, "Enzymes." MIT Press, Cambridge, Massachusetts, 1965.
12. Y. Degani and C. Degani, *Bchem* **18**, 5917 (1979).
13. Y. Degani, F. M. Veronese and E. L. Smith, *JBC* **249**, 7929 (1974).
14. D. M. Kiick, B. L. Allen, J. G. S. Rao, B. G. Harris and P. F. Cook, *Bchem* **23**, 5454 (1984).
15. S. C. Alter and M. DeLuca, *Bchem* **25**, 1599 (1986).
16. E. F. Jansen, M.-D. F. Nutting, R. Jang and A. K. Balls, *JBC* **185**, 209 (1950).
17. S. J. Singer, *Adv. Protein Chem.* **22**, 1 (1967).
18. E. Shaw *in* "The Enzymes" (P. D. Boyer, ed.), 3rd ed., Vol. 1, p. 91. Academic Press, New York, 1970.
19. F. Wold, *Methods Enzymol.* **46**, 3 (1977).
20. V. Chowdhry and F. H. Westheimer, *ARB* **48**, 293 (1979).
21. C. T. Walsh, *ARB* **53**, 493 (1984).
22. J. C. Speck, Jr., P. T. Rowley and B. L. Horecker, *JACS* **85**, 1012 (1963).
23. M. J. Zoller and M. Smith, *Methods Enzymol.* **100**, 468 (1983).
24. P. J. Carter, G. Winter, A. J. Wilkinson and A. R. Fersht, *Cell* **38**, 835 (1984).
25. W. Kramer, K. Schughart and H.-J. Fritz, *NARes* **10**, 6475 (1982).
26. M. J. Zoller and M. Smith, *DNA* **3**, 479 (1984).
27. P. Carter, H. Bedouelle and G. Winter, *NARes* **13**, 4431 (1985).
28. K.-M. Lo, S. S. Jones, N. R. Hackett and H. G. Khorana, *PNAS* **81**, 2285 (1984).
29. D. M. Lowe, A. R. Fersht and A. J. Wilkinson, *Bchem* **24**, 5106 (1985).
30. E. E. Howell, J. E. Villafranca, M. S. Warren, S. J. Oatley and J. Kraut, *Science* **231**, 1123 (1986).
31. S. Sprang, T. Standing, R. J. Fletterick, R. M. Stroud, J. Finer-Moore, N.-H. Xuong, R. Hamlin, W. J. Rutter and C. S. Craik, *Science* **237**, 905 (1987).

32. M. Jasin, L. Regan and P. Schimmel, *Nature* **306**, 441 (1983).
33. A. R. Fersht, J.-P. Shi, A. J. Wilkinson, D. M. Blow, P. Carter, M. M. Y. Waye and G. P. Winter, *Angew. Chem., Int. Ed. Engl.* **23**, 467 (1984).
34. G. Winter, A. R. Fersht, A. J. Wilkinson, M. Zoller and M. Smith, *Nature* **299**, 756 (1982).
35. A. J. Wilkinson, A. R. Fersht, D. M. Blow, P. Carter and G. Winter, *Nature* **307**, 187 (1984)
36. A. R. Fersht, J.-P. Shi, J. Knill-Jones, D. M. Lowe, A. J. Wilkinson, D. M. Blow, P. Brick, P. Carter, M. M. Y. Waye and G. Winter, *Nature* **314**, 235 (1985).
37. D. H. Jones, A. J. McMillan and A. R. Fersht, *Bchem* **24**, 5852 (1985).
38. R. J. Leatherbarrow, A. R. Fersht and G. Winter, *PNAS* **82**, 7840 (1985).
39. T. N. C. Wells and A. R. Fersht, *Bchem* **25**, 1881 (1986).
40. C. K. Ho and A. R. Fersht, *Bchem* **25**, 1891 (1986).
41. M. D. Jones, D. M. Lowe, T. Borgford and A. R. Fersht, *Bchem* **25**, 1887 (1986).
42. T. N. C. Wells, C. K. Ho and A. R. Fersht, *Bchem* **25**, 6603 (1986).
43. J. E. Villafranca, E. E. Howell, D. H. Voet, M. S. Strobel, R. C. Ogden, J. N. Abelson and J. Kraut, *Science* **222**, 782 (1983).
44. R. E. London, E. E. Howell, M. S. Warren, J. Kraut and R. L. Blakley, *Bchem* **25**, 7229 (1986).
45. K. M. Perry, J. J. Onuffer, N. A. Touchette, C. S. Herndon, M. S. Gittelman, C. R. Matthews, J.-T. Chen, R. J. Mayer, K. Taira, S. J. Benkovic, E. E. Howell and J. Kraut, *Bchem* **26**, 2674 (1987).
46. E. A. Robey and H. K. Schachman, *JBC* **259**, 11180 (1984).
47. E. A. Robey, S. R. Wente, D. W. Markby, A. Flint, Y. R. Yang and H. K. Schachman, *PNAS* **83**, 5934 (1986).
48. S. A. Middleton and E. R. Kantrowitz, *PNAS* **83**, 5866 (1986).
49. S. R. Wente and H. K. Schachman, *PNAS* **84**, 31 (1987).
50. A. M. Beasty, M. R. Hurle, J. T. Manz, T. Stackhouse, J. J. Onuffer and C. R. Matthews, *Bchem* **25**, 2965 (1986).
51. M. R. Hurle, N. B. Tweedy and C. R. Matthews, *Bchem* **25**, 6356 (1986).
52. J. A. Wells and D. B. Powers, *JBC* **261**, 6564 (1986).
53. P. Bryan, M. W. Pantoliano, S. G. Quill, H.-Y. Hsiao and T. Poulos, *PNAS* **83**, 3743 (1986).
54. J. A. Wells, D. B. Powers, R. R. Bott, T. P. Graycar and D. A. Estell, *PNAS* **84**, 1219 (1987).
55. G. A. Petsko, R. C. Davenport, Jr., D. Frankel and U. L. Rajbhandary, *Biochem. Soc. Trans.* **12**, 229 (1984).
56. D. Straus, R. Raines, E. Kawashima, J. R. Knowles and W. Gilbert, *PNAS* **82**, 2272 (1985).
57. R. T. Raines, E. L. Sutton, D. R. Straus, W. Gilbert and J. R. Knowles, *Bchem* **25**, 7142 (1986).
58. C. S. Craik, Q.-L. Choo, G. H. Swift, C. Quinto, R. J. MacDonald and W. J. Rutter, *JBC* **259**, 14255 (1984).
59. C. S. Craik, C. Largman, T. Fletcher, S. Roczniak, P. J. Barr, R. Fletterick and W. J. Rutter, *Science* **228**, 291 (1985).
60. L. Graf, C. S. Craik, A. Patthy, S. Roczniak, R. J. Fletterick and W. J. Rutter, *Bchem* **26**, 2616 (1987).
61. C. S. Craik, S. Roczniak, C. Largman, and W. J. Rutter, *Science* **237**, 909 (1987).
62. D. W. Hibler and J. A. Gerlt, *FP* **45**, 1875 (1986).
63. E. H. Serpersu, D. Shortle and A. S. Mildvan, *Bchem* **26**, 1289 (1987).
64. L. J. Perry and R. Wetzel, *Science* **226**, 555 (1984).

65. L. J. Perry and R. Wetzel, *Bchem* **25**, 733 (1986).
66. M. H. Hecht, J. M. Sturtevant and R. T. Sauer, *PNAS* **81**, 5685 (1984).
67. H. C. M. Nelson and R. T. Sauer, *Cell* **42**, 549 (1985).
68. R. T. Sauer, K. Hehir, R. S. Stearman, M. A. Weiss, A. Jeitler-Nilsson, E. G. Suchanek and C. O. Pabo, *Bchem* **25**, 5992 (1986).
69. S. J. Eisenbeis, M. S. Nasoff, S. A. Noble, L. P. Bracco, D. R. Dodds and M. H. Caruthers, *PNAS* **82**, 1084 (1985).
70. P. G. Schultz, K. G. Au and C. T. Walsh, *Bchem* **24**, 6840 (1985).
71. R. M. Starzyk, T. Webster and P. Schimmel, *Science* **237**, 1614 (1987).
72. N. Clarke, D. Lien and P. Schimmel, unpublished.
73. B. A. Larder, D. J. M. Purifoy, K. L. Powell and G. Darby, *Nature* **327**, 716 (1987).
74. J. Fisher, J. G. Belasco, S. Khosla and J. R. Knowles, *Bchem* **19**, 2895 (1980).
75. J. Fisher, R. L. Charnas, S. M. Bradley and J. R. Knowles, *Bchem* **20**, 2726 (1981).
76. I. S. Sigal, B. G. Harwood and R. Arentzen, *PNAS* **79**, 7157 (1982).
77. I. S. Sigal, W. F. DeGrado, B. J. Thomas and S. R. Petteway, Jr., *JBC* **259**, 5327 (1984).
78. P. A. Kiener and S. G. Waley, *BJ* **169**, 197 (1978).
79. S. S. Ghosh, S. C. Bock, S. E. Rokita and E. T. Kaiser, *Science* **231**, 145 (1986).
80. L. Polgar and M. Bender, *Bchem* **6**, 610 (1967).
81. K. E. Neet, A. Nanci and D. E. Koshland, Jr., *JBC* **243**, 6392 (1968).
82. G. Dalbadie-McFarland, L. W. Cohen, A. D. Riggs, C. Morin, K. Itakura and J. H. Richards, *PNAS* **79**, 6409 (1982).
83. G. Dalbadie-McFarland, J. J. Neitzel and J. H. Richards, *Bchem* **25**, 332 (1986).
84. S. C. Schultz and J. H. Richards, *PNAS* **83**, 1588 (1986).
85. G. Zurawski, B. Perrot, W. Bottomley and P. R. Whitfeld, *NARes* **9**, 3251 (1981).
86. F. Narang, L. McIntosh and C. Somerville, *MGG* **193**, 220 (1984).
87. F. C. Hartman, C. D. Stringer and E. H. Lee, *ABB* **232**, 280 (1984).
88. I. L. Norton, M. H. Welch and F. C. Hartman, *JBC* **250**, 8062 (1975).
89. C. D. Stringer and F. C. Hartman, *BBRC* **80**, 1043 (1978).
90. J. V. Schloss, C. D. Stringer and F. C. Hartman, *JBC* **253**, 5707 (1978).
91. B. Fraij and F. C. Hartman, *JBC* **257**, 3501 (1982).
92. C. S. Herndon, I. L. Norton and F. C. Hartman *Bchem* **21**, 1380 (1982).
93. B. Fraij and F. C. Hartman, *Bchem* **22**, 1515 (1983).
94. F. C. Hartman, S. Milanez and E. H. Lee, *JBC* **260**, 13968 (1985).
95. F. C. Hartman, T. S. Soper, S. K. Niyogi, R. J. Mural, R. S. Foote, S. Mitra, E. H. Lee, R. Machanoff and F. W. Larimer, *JBC* **262**, 3496 (1987).
96. T. S. Soper, F. W. Larimer, R. J. Mural, R. Machanoff, R. S. Foote, E. H. Lee and F. C. Hartman, *FP* **46**, 1976 (1987).
97. H. B. Smith and F. C. Hartman, *FP* **46**, 1976 (1987).
98. C. Peach, *Bchem* **24**, 3194 (1985).
99. Y. Igarashi, B. A. McFadden and T. El-Gul, *Bchem* **24**, 3957 (1985).
100. S. K. Niyogi, R. S. Foote, R. J. Mural, F. W. Larimer, S. Mitra, T. S. Soper, R. Machanoff and F. C. Hartman, *JBC* **261**, 10087 (1986).
101. A. M. Lauritzen, S. M. Landfear and W. N. Lipscomb, *JBC* **255**, 602 (1980).
102. P. Greenwell, S. L. Jewett and G. R. Stark, *JBC* **248**, 5994 (1973).
103. T. D. Kempe and G. R. Stark, *JBC* **250**, 6861 (1975).
104. A. M. Lauritzen and W. N. Lipscomb, *JBC* **257**, 1312 (1982).
105. R. S. Lahue and H. K. Schachman, *JBC* **259**, 13906 (1984).
106. F. C. Hartman, *JACS* **92**, 2170 (1970).
107. A. F. W. Coulson, J. R. Knowles, J. D. Priddle and R. E. Offord, *Nature* **227**, 180 (1970).

108. S. G. Waley, J. C. Miller, I. A. Rose and E. L. O'Connell, *Nature* **227**, 181 (1970).
109. T. Alber, D. W. Banner, A. C. Bloomer, G. A. Petsko, D. Phillips, P. S. Rivers and
I. A. Wilson, *Philos. Trans. R. Soc. London, Ser. B* **293**, 159 (1981).
110. R. T. Simpson, J. F. Riordan and B. L. Vallee, *Bchem* **2**, 616 (1963).
111. G. Muszynska and J. F. Riordan, *Bchem* **15**, 46 (1976).
112. J. F. Riordan, M. Sokolovsky and B. L. Vallee *Bchem* **6**, 3609 (1967).
113. L. Cueni and J. F. Riordan, *Bchem* **17**, 1834 (1978).
114. D. C. Rees and W. N. Lipscomb, *PNAS* **77**, 4633 (1980).
115. D. C. Rees and W. N. Lipscomb, *PNAS* **78**, 5455 (1981).
116. S. J. Gardell, C. S. Craik, D. Hilvert, M. S. Urdea and W. J. Rutter, *Nature* **317**, 551
(1985).
117. D. Hilvert, S. J. Gardell, W. J. Rutter and E. T. Kaiser, *JACS* **108**, 5298 (1986).
118. S. J. Gardell, D. Hilvert, J. Barnett, E. T. Kaiser and W. J. Rutter, *JBC* **262**, 576
(1987).
119. D. L. Ostrem and P. Berg, *Bchem* **13**, 1338 (1974).
120. T. A. Webster, H. Tsai, M. Kula, G. Mackie and P. Schimmel, *Science* **226**, 1315
(1984).
121. A. T. Profy and P. Schimmel, *JBC* **261**, 15474 (1986).
122. E. Padan, L. Patel and H. R. Kaback, *PNAS* **76**, 6221 (1979).
123. M. L. Garcia, L. Patel, E. Padan and H. R. Kaback, *Bchem* **21**, 5800 (1982).
124. L. Patel, M. L. Garcia and H. R. Kaback, *Bchem* **21**, 5805 (1982).
125. E. Padan, H. K. Sarkar, P. V. Viitanen, M. S. Poonian and H. R. Kaback, *PNAS* **82**,
6765 (1985).
126. I. B. Püttner, H. K. Sarkar, M. S. Poonian and H. R. Kaback, *Bchem* **25**, 4483 (1986).
127. C. F. Fox and E. P. Kennedy, *PNAS* **54**, 891 (1965).
128. K. Beyreuther, B. Bieseler, R. Ehring and B. Müller-Hill, *in* "Methods in Protein
Sequence Analysis" (M. Elzina, ed.), p. 139. Humana Press, Clifton, New Jersey,
1982.
129. W. R. Trumble, P. V. Viitanen, H. K. Sarkar, M. S. Poonian and H. R. Kaback,
BBRC **119**, 860 (1984).
130. P. V. Viitanen, D. R. Menick, H. K. Sarkar, W. R. Trumble and H. R. Kaback,
Bchem **24**, 7628 (1985).
131. H. K. Sarkar, D. R. Menick, P. V. Viitanen, M. S. Poonian and H. R. Kaback, *JBC*
261, 8914 (1986).
132. D. R. Menick, H. K. Sarkar, M. S. Poonian and H. R. Kaback, *BBRC* **132**, 162
(1985).
133. R. J. Brooker and T. H. Wilson, *JBC* **261**, 11765 (1986).
134. D. R. Menick, J. A. Lee, R. J. Brooker, T. H. Wilson and H. R. Kaback, *Bchem* **26**,
1132 (1987).
135. D. L. Foster, M. Boublik and H. R. Kaback, *JBC* **258**, 31 (1983).

Mechanisms of the Antiviral Action of Interferons

Charles E. Samuel

Section of Biochemistry and
  Molecular Biology
Department of Biological Sciences
University of California,
  Santa Barbara
Santa Barbara, California 93106

What are interferons? How do they function to reduce the efficiency of virus replication? Considerable progress has been made toward answering these and many other important questions concerning interferons and their actions since they were discovered by Isaacs and Lindenmann in 1957 (1). It is now clear that interferons (IFNs) are a multigene family of regulatory proteins (2, 3). There appear to be two major types of IFNs present in most, if not all, mammalian species: the type-I or viral IFNs, which include α (leukocyte) IFN and β (fibroblast) IFN; and the type-II or immune IFN, γ IFN. The characteristics of the human IFNs and their genes are summarized in Table I (2–4).

Interferons exert their actions through specific cell surface receptors. The expression of at least two dozen different cellular genes appears to be modulated by IFNs. The products encoded by the

27

TABLE I
CHARACTERISTICS OF HUMAN TYPE-I AND TYPE-II INTERFERONS

	Type I	Type II
Designation	α: leukocyte; viral β: fibroblast	γ: immune
Genes	Chromosome 9, short arm No introns α: more than 20 genes β: probably 1 gene	Chromosome 12, long arm Three introns One gene and one mRNA
Proteins	165–166 amino-acid monomer α: some glycosylated functional monomer β: glycosylated functional dimer	146 amino-acid monomer Glycosylated functional tetramer
Receptors	α/β receptor Chromosome 21	γ receptor Chromosome 6
Biologic activities	Antiviral activity Cell growth inhibitory activity Immune regulatory activity	

IFN-regulated genes can profoundly affect a number of biologic activities that include virus multiplication, cell growth and differentiation, and the immune response (2–4). The antiviral activity of IFNs, the property that led to their discovery (1), remains one of the most widely studied aspects of IFN research. Both in cell culture and in animals, IFNs induce activities that cause the inhibition of virus multiplication (3–6).

A wide range of different RNA and DNA animal viruses is sensitive to the antiviral actions of IFNs (3–5). However, the antiviral properties of natural and molecularly cloned IFNs can differ for different viruses in different animal cell systems, suggesting that multiple molecular mechanisms of IFN action exist (4–6). Three lines of indirect evidence initially indicated that the mechanisms of action of type-I and type-II IFNs may be distinct from each other for a number of different animal viruses: the antiviral activities of type-I (α or β) and type-II (γ) IFNs are synergistic for the inhibition of multiplication of several different viruses (12–14); type-I and type-II IFNs bind to different classes of cell surface receptors (4, 15); and type-I IFN does not induce an antiviral state when introduced directly into cells (16, 17), whereas intracellular type-II IFN can induce an antiviral state (18). The notion that type-I viral and type-II immune interferons indeed may inhibit the replication of viruses by different molecular mechanisms is directly supported by the results of detailed biochemical studies of the inhibition of vesicular stomatitis virus replication in human cells by purified, molecularly cloned IFNs (7–11).

For most animal virus–host cell combinations that have been examined, the stage of the virus multiplication cycle inhibited by treatment with type-I IFNs is the synthesis of viral macromolecules. As reviewed in Section II, viruses whose macromolecular synthesis is affected by IFN treatment include the picornaviridae, rhabdoviridae, orthomyxoviridae, reoviridae, poxviridae, adenoviridae, herpesviridae, and retroviridae. The inhibition of macromolecular synthesis is often primarily exerted at the step of translation of viral mRNAs into viral polypeptides. However, not all animal viruses are inhibited by all IFNs at the level of viral macromolecular synthesis. Exceptions have been identified in which the virus multiplication cycle is apparently affected by IFN either at an early stage which includes penetration and uncoating (reviewed in Section I), or at a late stage, which includes the assembly and release of progeny virions (reviewed in Section III).

Several comprehensive reviews dealing with many different aspects of interferon research have been published (2–6, 19, 20). However, many developments have occurred since these reviews appeared. These developments have provided both new insights and a better understanding of earlier observations concerning various aspects of the antiviral actions of interferons. It is now clear that multiple molecular mechanisms of IFN action are responsible for the IFN-mediated inhibition of virus replication. The specific molecular mechanism principally responsible for the inhibition of infectious progeny virion production seems dependent upon the particular combination of virus, cell, and IFN examined. In this review, I consider studies that pertain to the mechanisms by which virus replication may be inhibited in interferon-treated cells.

I. Interferon Effects on Early Stages of Viral Multiplication Cycles

The earliest stages of a viral multiplication cycle at which IFN could conceivably act would be those involving the initiation of infection, that is, virion attachment to cells, penetration into cells, and uncoating within cells.

A. Papovaviridae

The replication of simian virus 40 (SV40), a member of the papovaviridae, appears to be inhibited by IFN in permissive monkey cells at the stage of uncoating of the parental SV40 virions, a block that prevents the subsequent formation of active early transcriptional complexes. This effect of IFN on the initiation of SV40 infection of permissive cells appears to represent an exception to most of the evidence obtained with several other animal viruses. As summarized in Section II, the early stages of the viral multiplication cycle, for most animal viruses, are generally not affected by treatment of cells with natural or molecularly cloned IFNs.

The results of several independent studies leading to the conclusion that IFN inhibits the uncoating of parental SV40 virions to yield active early transcription complexes may be summarized as follows. First, attachment and penetration of SV40 virions do not seem to be affected by IFN treatment because the amount of input SV40 genome present in untreated and IFN-treated cells is comparable at early times after infection (21; W.-Q. Zeng and C. E. Samuel, unpublished results, 1981). Second, both the accumulation of SV40 early RNA and the synthesis of early viral T- and t-antigen polypeptides are markedly reduced in monkey cells treated with IFN *before* infection with virions (21, 23–31). Third, the kinetics of SV40 early RNA decay for untreated and IFN-treated cells are comparable as determined by both pulse–chase hybridization (27) and protein synthesis (29) techniques. However, SV40-infected, IFN-treated cells do contain 2′,5′-oligoadenylates, although they do not activate cleavage of RNA (32). Fourth, in contrast to the results obtained with cells treated with IFN before infection, with one exception (26), neither the accumulation of early RNA nor the synthesis of T antigen is significantly inhibited in monkey cells treated with IFN either *after* infection with virions (23, 26, 30) or *before* transfection with free SV40 DNA (25). IFN treatment late in the SV40 lytic cycle also does not affect the accumulation or polyadenylation of late SV40 RNA, although the internal N^6-methylation of adenosine and the formation of 5′-terminal cap-II structures are increased (26, 33); the biologic significance of the increased methylation is still unclear (33). IFN shows very little antiviral activity against SV40 when treated permissive simian cells are transfected with free infectious SV40 genome DNA rather than infected with SV40 virions (25), in contrast to the results observed earlier in conceptually similar poliovirus-genome RNA-transfection experiments (34, 35), or when a VSV cDNA of the G gene is expressed under the control of the SV40 late promoter (36). Fifth, expression of SV40 early genes also is not inhibited by IFN in IFN-sensitive SV40-transformed cells (28, 30, 31, 37, 38). The results summarized above are all consistent with an effect of IFN in monkey cells at a very early step of SV40 infection following virion attachment and penetration, but prior to early transcription, a step perhaps involved in the uncoating of SV40 virions.

SV40 temperature-sensitive group-D mutants in untreated cells have some properties analogous to those of wild-type virus in cells treated with IFN before infection (23, 30). The SV40 tsD mutants have an unusual property in that the first cycle of SV40 multiplication is *not* temperature-sensitive when infection is carried out with free viral DNA rather than with intact virions (39, 40). The SV40 tsD mutants, which map within the late genes encoding the virion proteins VP2 and VP3, appear to be defective in virion-infected cells at an early step following virion attachment and penetration, but prior to viral macromolecular synthesis (41). The tsD mutants behave as though they contain a tightly bound repressor of transcription (42), possibly the consequence of an aberrant or inefficient removal of VP2/VP3 during the uncoating process. Conceivably, IFN treatment of monkey cells prior to infection with wild-type virions affects either the expression of cellular genes or the organization of cell ultrastructure required for the efficient removal of capsid proteins VP2 and or VP3 during virion uncoating, thus preventing the synthesis of SV40 early RNA in IFN-treated cells. However, it is also possible that SV40 may in addition encode or induce factors that antagonize the antiviral effects of the IFN system, factors that may, for example, prevent IFN-mediated inhibition of SV40 protein synthesis once uncoating and transcription of early viral mRNA have occurred (43). Such an antagonistic factor of IFN-mediated inhibition of translation, virus-associated VA RNA, is indeed observed in wild-type adenovirus-infected cells (44).

B. Virus Families Other Than Papovaviridae

With the possible exception of SV40, numerous studies carried out with a variety of different RNA and DNA viruses indicate that IFN treatment does not significantly affect virion attachment, penetration, or uncoating under conditions where the production of infectious progeny virions is drastically reduced by IFN.

Neither "naked" viruses (i.e., lacking a lipoprotein membrane envelope), such as reovirus (45, 46) and poliovirus (34, 35), nor enveloped viruses—such as vaccinia virus (47, 48), vesicular stomatitis virus (7, 10), influenza virus (49), Western (34) and Eastern (50) equine encephalomyelitis viruses, and Sindbis virus (51, 52)—is significantly inhibited by IFN at the early stages of their multiplication cycles. The nature of the experimental evidence that indicates no significant effect of IFN treatment on the attachment, penetration, and uncoating of many viruses under conditions where the production of infectious progeny is drastically reduced by IFN is both direct and indirect.

In the cases of reovirus (45, 46), vaccinia virus (47, 48), vesicular stomatitis virus (7, 10), influenza virus (49), and Sindbis virus (51, 52), the attachment of radioactively labeled virions or their uncoating to yield either subviral particles or nucleocapsids has been examined directly. With other viruses, such as poliovirus (34, 35) and Western (34) and Eastern (50) equine encephalomyelitis viruses, an effect of IFN treatment on certain steps of viral macromolecular synthesis appeared under conditions where earlier steps of the viral multiplication cycle had been circumvented. These results (34, 35, 50) have been interpreted to mean that the IFN treatment affected none of the early steps of multiplication such as attachment, penetration, and uncoating, steps that would have had to occur prior to the specific macromolecular process examined during the course of a standard infection.

Although most studies reveal that neither type-I nor type-II IFN treatment significantly affects the early stage of viral multiplication cycles (7, 10, 34, 35, 45–52), an effect of IFN on virus penetration by endocytosis has been described (53, 54). IFN treatment inhibits pinocytosis as measured by the uptake either of a virus, vesicular stomatitis virus (53), or of horseradish peroxidase (54). Pinocytosis is inhibited in IFN-treated mouse, human, and chick embryo fibroblasts treated with homologous but not with heterologous IFN preparations. However, the IFN-mediated inhibition of pinocytosis requires higher doses of natural IFN (IFN concentration; time of IFN treatment) than normally is required to elicit a significant antiviral response. This may reflect a relative quantitative insensitivity of the pinocytosis response to IFN, or alternatively, the requirement for a specific subspecies of IFN normally present in natural preparations only in low amounts. Thus, it is possible that a reduction in virion uptake as the result of inhibition of pinocytosis could, under certain conditions, represent a contribution to the overall antiviral response that typically is undetected because the apparent sensitivity of the pinocytosis effect is normally much less than that of the other IFN-sensitive steps of virus multiplication.

II. Interferon Effects on Viral Macromolecular Synthesis

The synthetic phase of a virus multiplication cycle, during which macromolecular synthesis occurs, commences following virion penetration and uncoating. It is during this stage of the multiplication cycle that viral mRNA synthesis, viral polypeptide synthesis, and progeny genome synthesis occur (55). With most animal virus–host cell systems studied, IFN treatment of the host cell prior to infection causes a significant reduction in virus-specific macromolecular synthesis, often without adversely affecting overall host macromolecular synthesis (3–5). Several studies involving animal viruses representative of a wide array of different virus families reveal that the synthesis of viral polypeptides is inhibited in IFN-treated cells. However, identification of a single, principal biochemical mechanism accounting for the selective inhibition in synthesis of viral polypeptides in IFN-treated cells has not been achieved. It has variously been reported that IFN treatment affects a component of the cellular translational machinery that causes a direct inhibition of viral mRNA translation or, alternatively, that IFN treatment affects a step in either the synthesis, modification, or degradation of viral messenger RNAs that then leads to a reduction in viral polypeptide synthesis.

Depending upon the genetic system of the virus, the uncoating of the input parental virions, which must occur in order for viral macromolecular synthesis to begin, is either partial or complete. Partial uncoating yields a subviral particle or nucleocapsid structure containing an activated virion-associated viral transcriptase; complete uncoating yields the free virion genome in a form suitable either for direct translation or for transcription by cellular enzymes (55, 56). The effect of IFN treatment on viral protein and nucleic acid synthesis and degradation has been examined in many different animal virus/host cell systems (3–5, 19, 20). Among the specific animal viruses studied in great detail with regard to the mechanisms by which IFN acts to inhibit viral macromolecular synthesis are vesicular stomatitis virus, influenza virus, reovirus, and vaccinia virus, all of which possess a virion-associated RNA polymerase, and encephalomyocarditis (EMC) virus, which does not possess a virion-associated polymerase.

A. Picornaviridae

Picornaviruses have a positive-strand RNA genome that, following complete uncoating, is directly translated to produce a large precursor polyprotein that undergoes a complex pattern of posttranslational cleavages. The posttranslational cleavages yield several mature polypeptides including capsid polypeptides and polypeptides required for virus-specific RNA polymerase activity. As a single isolated species, free picornavirus genome RNA is infectious. Picornavirus 35-S intracellular mRNA is polyadenylated, but unlike most eukaryotic mRNAs, is not capped and methylated but rather has a free 5'-terminus (57, 58).

Among the first studies published on the antiviral mechanism of

IFN action were those carried out with two picornaviruses, poliovirus (34, 35) and Mengovirus (59, 60). These studies, which included the transfection of nonpermissive chick cells with free infectious poliovirus genome RNA (34, 35) and the infection of permissive mouse cells with [³H]uridine-labeled Mengovirus virions (59), firmly established that the inhibitory action of IFN against a picornavirus is exerted, at least in part, at a step in the multiplication cycle following the complete uncoating of the virion genome. Furthermore, the studies performed with Mengovirus and mouse L-cells indicated that the step in the picornavirus multiplication cycle probably inhibited by type-I IFN treatment is the synthesis of viral polypeptides (59, 60). Later studies performed with EMC virus, also a picornavirus, likewise suggest that one of the primary mechanisms of type-I IFN action observed in EMC-infected mouse L-cells (61) and EMC-infected human HeLa cells (62) is the inhibition of viral protein synthesis (61). This conclusion was based on the observation that such inhibitors of protein synthesis as cycloheximide and anisomycin mimic IFN treatment in that they specifically inhibit the synthesis of EMC virus proteins under conditions where host cellular protein synthesis as well as cell viability are not severely reduced (61). This discriminatory effect on EMC protein synthesis may have as its basis the fact that EMC viral mRNA is a more efficient initiator than host cellular mRNAs at times in the infectious cycle well before those when virus-induced cytopathic effects are apparent (62).

Conceivably the reduction in synthesis of EMC virus proteins observed in type-I IFN-treated, virus-infected cells is caused by degradation of RNA. Several investigations of the antiviral effect of type-I IFNs against EMC virus have correlated the IFN-mediated inhibition of EMC virus multiplication with the activation of the IFN-induced 2′,5′-oligoadenylate synthetase system. A combination of sensitive radioimmune, radiobinding, and liquid chromatography assays together with analysis of RNA structure by gel electrophoresis shows that the synthesis of 2′,5′-oligo(A) and the activation of 2′,5′-oligo(A)-dependent RNase occur in mouse L-cells infected with EMC virus (63–66). In pathogen-free mice treated with the IFN inducer poly(rI)·poly(rC) or infected with EMC virus, the levels of 2′,5′-oligo(A) recovered from tissues are not directly proportional to the amount of 2′,5′-oligo(A) synthetase present, indicating that factors other than the level of synthetase control the amount of 2′,5′-oligo(A) present in tissues (77). In IFN-treated HeLa cells infected with EMC virus, the inhibition of EMC virus RNA accumulation closely parallels the induction of 2′,5′-oligo(A) synthetase activity, but occurs prior to the detection of increased levels of the IFN-induced protein kinase (68). Furthermore, in an embryonal carcinoma cell line which responds to IFN treatment with induction of the 2′,5′-oligo(A) synthetase but not the P1/eIF-2α protein kinase, EMC multiplication is sensitive to IFN treatment (69). The expression of the antisense RNA to the 2′,5′-oligo (A) synthetase in HOS cells eliminates enzymic activity and the resultant cells are not protected by type-I IFN from EMC virus infection (67). Conversely, constitutive expression of the synthetase cDNA in CHO cells confers resistance to Mengo virus infection (305). The replication of EMC virus is not significantly reduced by IFN treatment of NIH 3T3 cells which contain unusually low levels of 2′,5′-oligo(A)-dependent RNase; however, NIH 3T3 cells do acquire an antiviral state in response to treatment with IFN when measured with certain viruses other than EMC virus (70–72). These observations are consistent with the idea that the 2′,5′-oligo(A)-dependent RNase may play a role in the inhibition of EMC virus multiplication; however, the actual biologic significance of changes in 2′,5′-oligo(A) concentration and rRNA cleavages in the antiviral action of IFN remains to be established (73). It should also be noted that the P1/eIF-2α protein kinase is activated in IFN-treated HeLa cells infected with EMC virus, as measured by the increased level of phosphorylation of eIF-α (74), and that the rescue of EMC virus from the inhibitory actions of IFN in L-cells doubly infected with EMC and vaccinia viruses does not appear to involve a block in the 2′,5′-oligo(A) synthetase system but rather correlates with a vaccinia-mediated inhibition of the IFN-induced P1/eIF-2α protein kinase (75). Possibly EMC virus replication is inhibited in type-I IFN-treated cells by more than one molecular mechanism.

The actions of natural type-I and type-II mouse IFNs are synergistic for the inhibition of EMC virus replication in mouse DBT cells (76) and for Mengovirus repliction in mouse L929 cells (12). The simplest interpretation of the synergistic inhibition of picornavirus multiplication by combinations of type-I and type-II IFNs is that their molecular mechanisms of action are unique, although this is yet to be established for picornaviruses in biochemical terms. Fundamentally important information on the mechanism of IFN action has been obtained from studies of picornavirus-infected cells. However, most of the recent and more detailed information concerning the molecular mechanism of IFN antiviral action comes from studies of viruses other than picornaviruses, in part because of the broader host range of some of these viruses and also because of major advances in the understanding of their molecular biology, including in some cases the availability of virus stocks with temperature-sensitive mutations in functions important in considerations of the actions of IFN.

B. Rhabdoviridae

Vesicular stomatitis virus (VSV), a member of the rhabdoviridae family, has often been used as the challenge virus in studies of IFN production and action because of its relatively short multiplication time, its broad host range, and its acute sensitivity to the antiviral effects of IFN in cell lines of many animal species. VSV virions possess a virus-coded RNA-dependent RNA polymerase (EC 2.7.7.48) that transcribes the negative-stranded VSV genome, contained within a ribonucleoprotein complex, into a 47-nucleotide leader RNA and five messenger RNA species. The monocistronic VSV mRNAs are capped, methylated, and polyadenylated. Primary transcription catalyzed by the input parental virion-associated transcriptase can occur in the absence of protein synthesis; however, VSV genome replication has an absolute requirement for viral protein synthesis and occurs through the synthesis of a full-length 42-S positive-stranded intermediate that serves as the template for the synthesis of 42-S negative-stranded progeny genomes (78).

Genetic analysis has revealed that the antiviral mechanism of action of type-I IFNs, at least against VSV, is independent of cyclic AMP (79–81). Type-I IFN inhibits the synthesis of VSV proteins and the production of infectious VSV progeny virions in adenylate-cyclase-deficient and cAMP-dependent protein kinase-deficient variants of mouse S49 lymphoma cells (79), mouse J774.2 macrophage-like cells (80), and Chinese hamster ovary cells (81).

The identification of the precise step or steps of VSV macromolecular synthesis at which IFN exerts its principal antiviral effect has proven difficult. There is little agreement among the studies of the mechanism of IFN action against VSV. It has variously been reported that treatment with type-I IFNs inhibits VSV transcription (82–85), cap methylation of VSV transcripts (86), or translation of VSV mRNAs (7–9, 87–89). In addition to these possible actions of IFN directed against various steps of VSV macromolecular synthesis, IFN appears also to affect the glycosylation of VSV envelope glycoprotein G and to cause the production of VSV particles with reduced specific infectivity (90–92). The lack of agreement among these studies may, in part, reflect true differences among the various species and types of animal cells studied with regard to the molecular basis of the antiviral state induced by IFN against VSV. Alternatively, the differences may, in some cases, also be attributable to indirect assay methods, and to the use of natural IFN preparations of limited purity, composed of mixtures of IFN types and subspecies in unknown proportions as well as other proteins of unknown biologic activity.

Systematic biochemical studies of the effect of purified molecularly cloned type-I IFN-α on each stage of the multiplication cycle of VSV in two types of human cells, epithelial-like amnion U-cells (7–9) and fibroblastic GM2767 cells (82, 83) have clearly established that the major step of VSV replication inhibited by IFN is likely dependent upon the type of cell examined. The major, and possibly only, effect of IFN-αA on VSV multiplication in U-cells is translation inhibition (7–9). By contrast, the major effect of IFN-αA on VSV multiplication in GM2767 cells is the accumulation of primary mRNA transcripts (82, 83). With the VSV mutant tsG41, which is competent in primary RNA transcription but defective in RNA replication at the nonpermissive temperature, IFN-αA does not significantly inhibit the accumulation of primary transcripts in U cells, although the *in vivo* translation of the primary viral transcripts is greatly impaired as a function of IFN treatment (8, 9). Dot-blot (9) and "Northern" gel analysis (8, 9) of glyoxylated RNA using cDNA probes to individual VSV mRNAs revealed no detectable effect of IFN treatment on either the amount or the structural integrity of VSV primary transcripts synthesized in U-cells. Primary viral RNA synthesis in amnion U-cells remained unaltered over the course of IFN treatments that reduced primary protein synthesis to one-tenth or less (8, 9). These results, obtained in the absence of metabolic inhibitors such as cycloheximide, support some prior conclusions (87, 88, 93), but are at variance with other studies reporting an effect of IFN on primary viral transcription (84, 85). The apparent inhibition of primary transcription described in some earlier studies (84, 85) may possibly have come from a small IFN-induced difference in the uptake and uncoating of parental VSV virions (53) or, alternatively, from complications introduced by the use of cycloheximide (94) and actinomycin D together with methods of analysis that did not directly examine individual viral molecular species (84, 85). However, it is clear that IFN-αA may indeed cause a reduction in accumulation of VSV primary transcripts in human fibroblast cells (82, 83). With the VSV tsG41 mutant and in the absence of metabolic inhibitors, both dot-blot and Northern gel-blot analyses show that IFN-αA treatment of GM2767 fibroblasts causes a reduction in the accumulation of VSV primary transcripts synthesized by input parental virions (82, 83). Although the IFN-α treatment of GM2767 cells caused no detectable reduction in either the penetration or uncoating of parental VSV virions (83), it is as yet unclear as to whether the reduction in accumulation of primary transcripts arises from an effect on the synthesis or on the stability of the transcripts (82, 83).

The synthesis of VSV polypeptides is selectively inhibited in type-I IFN-treated cells without an adverse effect on the synthesis of cellular polypeptides. This selective inhibition of VSV polypeptide synthesis is observed both when the five VSV mRNAs are produced in virion-infected human U-cells (7, 8) as well as when a single VSV mRNA is produced in expression vector-transfected monkey COS cells (36). The synthesis of the five VSV polypeptides is uniformly inhibited in virion-infected cells; no single viral polypeptide differs significantly from the others in its sensitivity to IFN-induced inhibition of synthesis in human amnion (8) or HeLa (93) cells. The extent of the IFN-induced inhibition of VSV protein synthesis in U-cells is not as great as the resultant decrease in infectious virus for each time of treatment with either a saturating or low concentration of IFN-αA (8). Likewise, the amount of viral protein incorporated into assembled nucleocapsids is not reduced quite as rapidly by IFN-αA as is viral infectivity (7). In both cases, these disproportionate reductions probably reflect the fact that VSV assembly is a net multimolecular reaction, and IFN inhibition of translation reduces the concentration of all of the participating reactants, the progeny genome RNA and the five viral polypeptides. Thus, for any given dose of IFN, the total effect on the production of infectious units would be expected to decrease still further the synthesis of any single viral polypeptide.

In addition to the inhibition of VSV protein synthesis caused by IFN treatment, IFN treatment also prevents the VSV shutoff of cellular protein synthesis in static monolayer but not suspension culture. When human U-, monkey COS-1, and LLC-MK2 cells are grown in static monolayer culture, IFN treatment reverses the VSV-induced inhibition of protein synthesis. In contrast, when human HeLa and mouse S49 cells are grown in suspension culture, IFN treatment fails to prevent shutoff of host protein synthesis in VSV-infected cells (8, 88, 93).

The molecular mechanism by which type-I IFN treatment causes a selective inhibition in the synthesis of VSV polypeptides without inhibiting overall cellular protein synthesis is not yet clear. Several studies indicate a fundamentally important role of the IFN-induced P1/eIF-2α protein kinase (95, 96) and or the 2',5'-oligo(A) synthetase and nuclease (95, 97) in the antiviral action of IFN against VSV. Among the studies that suggest that the kinase may be important in the antiviral mechanism of type-I IFN is the observation that double infection of VSV-infected cells with vaccinia virus "rescues" the VSV from the inhibitory action of IFN (98–100). This vaccinia virus-mediated rescue of VSV virus yield is due to a release of the inhibition of VSV protein synthesis by IFN and is accompanied by the blockage of the IFN-induced protein kinase (74, 100).

Like poxviruses, certain human adenoviruses are not appreciably sensitive to the antiviral action of type-I IFNs in cell culture, and can rescue VSV from the inhibitory effects of IFN treatment in doubly infected cells (44, 102). The insensitivity of adenoviruses in single cells in culture to IFN appears to come from the expression of a small adenovirus-coded RNA, virus-associated (VA) RNA, which antagonizes the antiviral action of type-I IFNs by preventing the activation of the IFN-induced protein kinase (44, 103). Among the best evidence that the 2',5'-oligo(A) synthetase and nuclease may play an important role in the antiviral action of type-I IFN against VSV (95, 97, 104) is the observation that the loss of 2',5'-oligo(A) synthetase activity by production of antisense RNA complementary to 2',5'-oligo(A) synthetase cDNA results in a lack of protection by IFN from VSV infection (67). However, these experiments appear compromised (301).

In addition to the possible roles that the protein P1/eIF-2α kinase and the 2',5'-oligo(A) synthetase may play in the antiviral action of IFN against VSV, about 60% of the nonpolysomal viral mRNA synthesized in IFN-treated VSV-infected HeLa cells lacks the 7-methyl group in the 5'-terminal guanosine of the mRNA cap structure, and this mRNA does not bind as efficiently to reticulocyte ribosomes in an assay for the initiation of protein synthesis as nonpolysomal RNA from control cells [45% as compared to 73% bound, respectively (86)]. An increase in S-adenosylhomocysteine concentration and a concomitant change in the ratio of S-adenosylhomocysteine to S-adenosylmethionine occur in IFN-treated HeLa cells (105); it is possible that these metabolic changes are responsible for the inhibition of cap methylation of VSV mRNA observed in IFN-treated systems. It is well established that the 5'-terminal 7-methylguanosine modification greatly increases the efficiency of ribosome binding and translation of some viral mRNAs in some cell-free systems (106–109). However, the possible contribution of the reported changes in 5'-terminal guanosine methylation of VSV mRNAs to the total antiviral effect of IFN is not entirely clear. In vitro protein synthesis reveals no major difference in the functional integrity of VSV mRNA isolated from IFN-αA-treated U-cells as compared to untreated cells when examined in a wheat germ system under reaction conditions that would have distinguished an effect on cap methylation (8). Likewise, no IFN-mediated alteration was detected in the methylation of VSV mRNA synthesized *in vitro* by purified VSV added to extracts prepared from untreated as compared to IFN-treated chick cells (89); however, this result could indicate that if an IFN-induced component affects methylation, it is either a labile component and/or has a reaction requirement not fulfilled in the cell-free system. Finally, in contrast to the reduction in binding to reticulocyte ribosomes reported for VSV mRNA from IFN-treated HeLa cells unmethylated in the 5'-terminal guanosine, it appears that the 5'-terminal 7-methylguanosine is not essential for the translation of VSV mRNA in the reticulocyte system (108).

The antiviral activities of pure recombinant IFN-αA and recombinant IFN-γ are synergistic for the inhibition of VSV replication in human amnion U-cells (13). As mentioned earlier, the simplest interpretation of the synergistic inhibition of virus multiplication in cells treated with a combination of type-I and type-II IFNs is that their molecular mechanisms of action are unique. Subsequent systematic biochemical studies indeed established that the inhibition of the replication of VSV in human U-cells treated with type-I IFN-α (7–9) was by a molecular mechanism different from that by which type-II IFN-γ inhibited VSV replication in U-cells (10, 11). The evidence suggests that the principal cause of the IFN-induced inhibition of VSV protein synthesis in U-cells treated with IFN-αA is an alteration of a component of the translational machinery other than the viral mRNA template (7–9). However, in U-cells treated with IFN-γ, yields of progeny VSV particles are significantly reduced in the absence of a marked reduction in synthesis of either viral RNA or viral protein (10, 11). Thus, the molecular mechanism by which the multiplication of VSV is inhibited by IFN treatment appears to depend not only upon the kind of cell examined in the case of type-I IFN (7–9, 82, 83), but also upon the type of IFN used to induce the antiviral state in a given kind of cell, such as human U-cells treated with type-I IFN-α as compared to type-II IFN-γ (7–11, 13, 302, 303).

C. Orthomyxoviridae

Influenza virus, a member of the orthomyxoviridae, possesses a negative-stranded segmented RNA genome. Like other negative-stranded RNA viruses, an RNA-dependent RNA polymerase is associated with the enveloped virion. This polymerase transcribes the 8 genome segments into 8 RNAs with the polarity of mRNA. The RNA transcripts encode 10 different polypeptides; each of 2 transcripts codes for 2 separate polypeptides, and each of the remaining 6 appears to encode a single primary polypeptide. Primary transcription catalyzed by the input parental virion-associated RNA polymerase can occur in the absence of protein synthesis; however, protein synthesis is required for secondary transcription and for the synthesis of progeny genome segments. Influenza mRNAs are capped, methylated, and polyadenylated. The 5'-terminal methylated capped structure of influenza virus mRNAs is generated by an unusual mechanism. Cellular RNAs act as primers for the synthesis of influenza viral mRNAs. The virion, in addition to the RNA polymerase, contains unique cap-(m^7GpppN_m-) dependent endonuclease that cleaves cellular RNAs 10 to 14 nucleotides from the cap to generate the primers that initiate viral RNA transcription (*101*).

Influenza virus occupies a special place in the historical development of the IFN field. IFNs were discovered during studies performed with influenza virus on the mechanism of viral interference (*1*). Isaacs and Lindenmann observed that when heat-inactivated influenza virus was incubated with fragments of chick chorioallantoic membrane, an interfering activity appeared in the culture medium. The multiplication of infectious influenza virus was inhibited when fresh membrane fragments not previously exposed to virus were treated with the medium and then challenged with live virus. The term "interferon" was coined for this activity present in the medium that was responsible for the transfer of viral interference (*1*).

Genetic and biochemical analyses have established that, in the mouse, the antiviral state against influenza virus induced by type-I IFN is controlled by a host gene designated Mx that encodes a 75-kDa polypeptide (*110, 111*). The mouse Mx^+ gene is induced by type-I IFN-α and -β but not by type-II IFN-γ; the IFN-induced Mx protein accumulates in the nucleus of Mx^+ mouse cells (*112*). The gene Mx originates from the inbred mouse strain A2G, which has an inborn resistance to infection by influenza virus (*113*). Replication of influenza virus in peritoneal macrophages and in embryonic cells from mice bearing the gene Mx is efficiently inhibited by type-I IFN; the replication of influenza is not efficiently inhibited by type-I IFN in mouse cells lacking the Mx gene (*110, 111*). Although the IFN-induced inhibition of the influenza A and B orthomyxoviruses is dependent upon the Mx^+ allele in mice, other viruses including members of the paramyxo-, rhabdo-, picorna-, and herpesviridae are equally sensitive to the antiviral action of type-I IFNs in Mx^+ and Mx^- cells (*111*). Mx^- alleles derive from their Mx^+ counterpart by deletion (*111, 114*). The time course for induction of the antiviral state against influenza viris is comparable in cells with and without Mx and is similar to that observed for VSV; however, the decay of the antiviral state against influenza virus is markedly slower in cells bearing the Mx gene as compared to cells lacking Mx (115).

A preliminary study of the molecular mechanism of natural type-I IFN action in peritoneal macrophages from A2G Mx^+ mice revealed that the multiplication of mouse adapted influenza virus TUR of avian origin is blocked by IFN at a step following virion attachment and penetration, but prior to or including protein synthesis (116). A further systematic study was then undertaken comparing the effect of mouse type-I IFN on each stage of influenza multiplication in mouse macrophages from A2G Mx^+ mice and BALB/c Mx^- mice (117). About a 50% reduction in the accumulation of primary transcripts was observed in IFN-treated macrophages at the highest concentration of IFN tested, regardless of the Mx genetic constitution of the host cell. However, a marked inhibition of influenza virus polypeptide synthesis was observed in Mx^+ A2G macrophages when treated with type-I IFN. By contrast, no evidence was obtained for an inhibition of translation of influenza virus mRNA in type-I IFN-treated BALB/c macrophages which were Mx^-. Influenza virus primary mRNA transcripts isolated from IFN-treated A2G Mx^+ macrophage cells, while not translated in $vivo$ in the IFN-treated virus-infected cell, were functionally active when examined in an in $vitro$ cell-free protein-synthesizing system as measured by their ability to direct the synthesis of viral polypeptides with fidelity (117). These results of a quantitative, systematic examination of the effect of IFN-α and -β on influenza replication in Mx^+ as compared to Mx^- murine cells $(116, 117)$ are in agreement with a prior investigation on the antiviral mechanism of IFN action in A/WSN influenza virus-infected mouse fibroblast L-cells and chicken embryo fibroblast cells (87).

The analysis of A/WSN-infected L and CEF cells suggested that the site of IFN action against influenza virus was exerted at an intermediate step located between primary and secondary transcription, perhaps the translation of primary transcripts into polypeptides (87). However, other investigations into the possible mechanism of inhibition of influenza replication by IFN indicate that primary transcription $(118-120)$ rather than primary translation $(87, 116, 117)$ is probably inhibited by IFN treatment. For example, only two viral mRNAs were detected by Northern analysis and by translation in $vitro$ of poly(A)$^+$ RNA from infected Mx^+ A2G mouse cells in a wheat germ system: a reduced amount of the mRNA encoding the NS1 protein and an even lower amount of the mRNA encoding the M protein were detected, whereas other influenza mRNAs were not made in detectable amounts in IFN-treated Mx$^+$ mouse cells (118). In addition, the rate of primary viral mRNA synthesis catalyzed by the input parental virion-associated transcriptase was severely inhibited. By contrast, IFN treatment of Mx$^-$ mouse cells had little or no effect on the steady-state level of viral mRNAs (118). Influenza A/WSN primary transcription was also inhibited by treatment of MDBK cells with molecularly cloned IFN-α; the inhibition was restricted to transcripts of the P genes at doses of 10 units/ml, whereas higher doses such as 50 units/ml of IFN-α markedly inhibited the accumulation of all viral primary transcripts (119).

Although the exact molecular mechanism by which influenza virus replication is inhibited by IFN is not yet resolved (87, 116–120), what is clear is that the Mx protein alone may be sufficient to account for the inhibition of influenza virus by type-I IFNs. When a cDNA of the 3.5 kilobase mouse Mx$^+$ RNA is expressed in transfected Mx$^-$ mouse cells, influenza virus replication is inhibited whereas VSV replication is not affected (114). Influenza viruses are also sensitive to several different subspecies of molecularly cloned and natural IFNs in human diploid fibroblast cells (121). The sensitivity of influenza viruses FPV and WSN in human embryonic fibroblasts to both type-I and type-II human IFNs was comparable to that of VSV, which was taken as a reference (121). Presumably homologous IFN-γ may induce different antiviral states in human and mouse cells, as influenza is resistant to the antiviral action of IFN-γ in murine cells (122) but sensitive in human cells (121). An Mx-like protein appears to exist in human cells. Antibodies prepared against the mouse Mx protein recognize a protein induced by type-I IFN in human cells (123); furthermore, two types of human cDNA clones have been obtained to IFN-induced mRNA that display homology with the mouse Mx cDNA (C. E. Samuel, D. Thomas, M. Aebi and C. Weissmann, unpublished results, 1987). The mouse *Mx* gene is located on mouse chromosome 16 (125); the chromosomal location of the human *Mx*-like gene has not yet been determined.

D. Reoviridae

The genome of human reovirus, a member of the reoviridae, consists of 10 distinct segments of double-stranded RNA, each of which is transcribed into single-stranded RNA of the polarity of mRNA by a virion-associated RNA polymerase. The RNA transcripts, 9 of which appear to be monocistronic, encode 11 different polypeptides; the S1 segment is bicistronic and encodes two primary translation products (150). A twelfth polypeptide, a major component of the virion outer capsid shell, is generated by a posttranslational cleavage mechanism. Primary transcription of the reovirus genome catalyzed by the input virion-associated RNA polymerase can occur in the absence of protein synthesis, although protein synthesis is absolutely required for the synthesis of progeny genome dsRNA segments and for secondary transcription. Reovirus mRNAs are capped and methylated; however, they are unusual relative to most eukaryotic mRNAs in that they are not polyadenylated (126).

The Dearing strain of human reovirus serotype 3 has been extensively studied in an attempt to elucidate the antiviral mechanism of type-I IFN action. Natural and molecularly cloned type-I IFNs inhibit the replication of reovirus in a wide variety of cells, including mouse ascites tumor (127) and mouse fibroblast cells (45, 128–130), monkey kidney CV-1 (129), COS (J. A. Atwater, C. X. George and C. E. Samuel, unpublished results, 1987), and BSC-1 cells (23, 95). Surprisingly, however, the multiplication of human reovirus is not significantly inhibited by either natural or molecularly cloned human type-I α IFNs in either human amnion (95, 132), human fibroblast (133), or human HeLa (134) cells, although type-I IFN-β appears to exert an antiviral effect against reovirus in human HeLa cells (135) and human osteosarcoma HOS cells (67). The lack of inhibition of reovirus multiplication in human amnion and human fibroblast cells treated with human IFN-α is a property of the cell and not the virus or IFN, because the same stocks of reovirus are sensitive to the same preparations of human IFN-α in monkey (23, 95) and mouse (128) cells.

The step in the multiplication cycle of reovirus at which the type-I IFN-induced inhibition exerts its principal antiviral effect in IFN-sensitive mouse and monkey cells is the translation of primary mRNA transcripts into viral polypeptides. Treatment of cells with type-I IFN does not affect the early stages of the reovirus multiplication cycle, virion attachment to cells, penetration into cells, or uncoating within cells (45, 136). The effect of IFN on the accumulation and translation of early reovirus mRNAs synthesized in infected cells in the absence of cycloheximide has been studied by using the reovirus temperature-sensitive mutant ts447 (45, 129). At the nonpermissive temperature, essentially all viral mRNA transcribed in ts447-infected cells is synthesized by the virion-associated polymerase of parental subviral particles; this RNA, by definition, is early "primary" mRNA. IFN treatment of mouse L (45) or L$_{929}$ (129) fibroblasts causes a small IFN dose-dependent reduction in the accumulation of reovirus-specific early mRNA as measured by hybridization of ^{32}P- or ^{3}H-labeled RNA from infected cells with an excess of unlabeled purified genome dsRNA (45, 129). By contrast, the synthesis of reovirus polypeptides measured by SDS/PAGE analysis is drastically reduced in IFN-treated cells infected with either ts447 or wild-type reovirus (45, 127, 129). However, the synthesis of cellular polypeptides is not adversely affected by the IFN treatment (23, 45, 127, 129, 130). The inhibition of reovirus late functions dependent upon the translation of primary transcripts—that is, the synthesis of dsRNA (inhibited 75%), secondary transcription from progeny subviral particles, and the formation of infectious progeny virus (inhibited >90%)—are all progressively more sensitive to IFN than is the translation of early mRNA (45). This progressive increase in sensitivity of reovirus synthetic functions to inhibition by IFN is probably a consequence of mass action, as has been concluded for the inhibition of VSV in IFN-treated cells (7, 8). That is, because increasingly more reovirus gene products are presumably required as the replication cycle approaches production of the completely assembled infectious progeny virion, and because the concentration of all gene products that serve as the reactants in the pathway are reduced, it is not surprising that, as a function of IFN treatment, a progressively increasing sensitivity is observed as the process approaches the final product, infectious progeny virions.

Additional independent studies provided further evidence that the major effect of type-I IFN treatment on reovirus multiplication in murine and simian cells is the selective inhibition in synthesis of viral polypeptides without an adverse effect on the synthesis of cellular polypeptides (23, 127, 129, 130). However, it has been difficult to identify further the precise component involved in the biochemical mechanism of reovirus polypeptide synthesis that is functionally altered in type-I IFN-treated cells. It has variously been reported that treatment with type-I IFNs inhibits reovirus mRNA cap methylation (137), increases the degradation rate of reovirus mRNA (129, 138), or alters a component of the host's protein synthesis machinery (initiation factor eIF-2α), which is required for translation of the reovirus mRNA (130, 139–141).

The relative amount of reovirus mRNA with a "cap 2" structure—that is, mRNA 2'-O-methylated at the third nucleoside (which in reovirus mRNAs is cytidine), is 36 to 47% lower in mRNA from type-I IFN-treated mouse L_{929} cells as compared to mRNA from untreated cells (137). However, the methylation of the 5'-terminal and the penultimate G residue of the reovirus mRNAs is not diminished in IFN-treated as compared to untreated cells under conditions where the IFN treatment reduces the reovirus yield by >98% (137). Although the 5'-terminal cap and methylation can clearly affect the translational efficiency of reovirus mRNA in some cell-free protein-synthesizing systems (107, 109, 142), the role of the 5'-cap structure in the translational process *in vivo* is much less clear. Indeed, it has even been suggested that reovirus induces a modification in the cap dependence of the host translational apparatus such that uncapped reovirus mRNA is preferentially translated over capped cellular mRNA at late times after infection of untreated cells (143). Possible alterations in cap structure and function in IFN-treated (137) or reovirus-infected (143) cells are not accompanied by detectable structural changes in either eIF-4A or eIF-4B (141), two protein synthesis initiation factors that interact with mRNA at the 5'-cap during mRNA binding to the small ribosomal subunit (144). Thus, it is unclear at present what role, if any, the IFN-induced modifications in reovirus mRNA cap structure play in the inhibition of synthesis of reovirus polypeptides observed in IFN-treated cells.

Treatment of mouse L_{929} (129) or L (45) cell fibroblasts with homologous mouse IFN before infection with ts447 causes a small dose-dependent reduction in accumulation of reovirus primary mRNA transcripts. The kinetics of decay of reovirus mRNA has also been measured in IFN-treated and untreated mouse cells by pulse–chase and hybridization analysis (129, 138). Reovirus mRNA decayed more rapidly in IFN-treated than in untreated mouse fibroblast cells; the apparent average half-life ranged from about 4.5 to 5.3 hours in IFN-treated cells versus about 12.3 to 12.5 hours in untreated mouse cells (129, 138). These results suggest that the IFN-mediated reduction in accumulation of early reovirus-specific RNA in mouse cells may arise in part from an effect on RNA degradation rather than RNA synthesis.

The enhanced turnover of reovirus mRNA in IFN-treated cells may possibly be mediated by the 2',5'-oligo(A)-activated endoribonuclease. An increase in $(2',5')A_n$ concentration has been reported for IFN-treated as compared to untreated HeLa cells infected with reovirus (135). When RNA extracted from infected cells was analyzed by Northern blots, full-sized reovirus mRNAs were detected in untreated cells but not in IFN-treated cells; furthermore, at the time of increase in $(2',5')A_n$ concentration, an endoRNase was reported to be activated as demonstrated by the cleavage of rRNA, degradation of cellular mRNA, and polysome breakdown in the presence of emetine (135). Although total reovirus mRNA is greatly reduced in IFN-treated HeLa cells as compared to untreated cells infected with wild-type reovirus, Northern gel analysis revealed that the qualitative natures of the reovirus mRNAs detected in IFN-treated and untreated HeLa cells appear comparable (135). By contrast, the cleavage of nascent reovirus mRNA by localized activation of the 2′,5′-oligo(A)-dependent RNase has also been described (145). Finally, in contrast to the generally uniform observation of a small decrease in accumulation of reovirus primary transcripts in mouse fibroblasts (45, 129), the accumulation of reovirus-specific early RNA was not reduced by IFN treatment in monkey kidney CV-1 cells but rather appeared to be slightly increased in IFN-treated compared to untreated CV-1 cells, as measured by hybridization (129). The reason for the apparent increase in reovirus primary transcripts in IFN-treated monkey CV-1 cells is not known; an apparent increase in vaccinia virus early RNA has also been observed in IFN-treated vaccinia-infected mouse L cells (146).

Single reovirus mRNAs have been expressed in monkey COS cells transfected with an SV40 expression vector containing cDNA inserts of the reovirus S1, S3, and S4 genes (131). The expression of reovirus genes in transfected COS cells is mainly inhibited by IFN treatment at the level of protein synthesis; IFN treatment of transfected cells caused a reduction of less than half in accumulation of reovirus transcripts, and the reovirus transcripts were not detectably degraded in IFN-treated compared to untreated, transfected cells (J. A. Atwater, C. X. George and C. E. Samuel, unpublished results, 1987).

Phosphorylation and dephosphorylation of two proteins, ribosome-associated protein P1 and the α subunit of protein synthesis initiation factor eIF-2, appear to have important roles in the antiviral action of type-I IFN in mouse cells (96, 147). It has been demonstrated that the phosphorylation of protein P1 is increased in IFN-treated cells infected with reovirus (70). Furthermore, two-dimensional IEF/SDS/PAGE and immunoblotting techniques show that the extent of phosphorylation of eIF-2α is also increased in IFN-treated reovirus-infected cells (141). About 5 to 10% of the eIF-2α is phosphorylated in untreated, uninfected cells, whereas 25 to 30% is phosphorylated in IFN-treated, reovirus-infected cells. An intermediate level of phosphorylation, usually about 15%, is observed with either IFN treatment or reovirus infection (141). Likewise, the inhibition of protein synthesis observed upon infection of one HeLa cell line but not a second HeLa cell line with reovirus correlates with an increase in phosphorylation of eIF-2α in the β-IFN-treated cells (140).

Both the kinetics of induction and the kinetics of decay of the IFN-induced P1/eIF-2α kinase correlate with the induction and decay of the antiviral state against reovirus (128, 148). A large fraction of the reovirus mRNA is not associated with polysomes in IFN-treated compared to untreated L-cells, although the nonpolysomal viral mRNA can bind to ribosomes in vitro in a reticulocyte system (130). The binding of reovirus mRNA to ribosomes *in vivo* appears to be inhibited in IFN-treated cells by a discriminatory mechanism that does not affect the translation of cellular mRNA (*130*). Thus, most of the evidence is consistent with the notion that phosphorylation of eIF-2α, leading to an inhibition of reovirus mRNA translation at the step of initiation of polypeptide synthesis, may play an important role in the antiviral action of type-I IFNs.

The replication of human reovirus is not appreciably inhibited by human type-I IFN-α in most types of human cells so far examined, which include amnion U-cells and fibroblast GM2767 and FS4 cells (*132, 133*), in contrast to the results obtained with many different mouse cell lines. However, the replication of human reovirus is significantly inhibited by both natural and molecularly cloned human type-II IFN-γ in human amnion and fibroblast cells (*13, 133*). The molecular mechanism by which human IFN-γ inhibits the multiplication of reovirus in human cells is now being elucidated. Studies with the reovirus mutant *ts*447 suggest that neither attachment, nor penetration, uncoating, primary transcription, nor translation of the primary transcripts is significantly affected by IFN-γ treatment of human amnion cells, although the production of infectious progeny virions is greatly reduced (*149*). Thus, it appears that the antiviral mechanism by which type-II IFN-γ inhibits reovirus replication is different from that by which the type-I IFNs inhibit reovirus replication in sensitive cells.

E. Poxviridae

Vaccinia, a member of the poxviridae, has a large double-stranded DNA genome. The enveloped virion has associated with it a DNA-dependent RNA polymerase that catalyzes the synthesis of a family of early mRNAs that encode a number of enzymic activities involved in DNA synthesis. Vaccinia virus mRNAs are capped, methylated, and polyadenylated. A unique aspect of the poxviridae is that protein synthesis is required for the uncoating process, and also for late expression to occur. Late proteins include the virion-associated enzymes and a multitude of capsid proteins. The morphogenesis of poxviruses occurs in the cytoplasm, unlike most other families of DNA viruses in which assembly occurs in the nucleus (*151*).

One of the first studies published on the antiviral mechanism of IFN action concluded that the inhibitory action of natural mouse IFN on the replication of the WR strain of vaccinia virus in mouse L-cells is expressed principally at the step of synthesis of viral polypeptides (*146*). Several subsequent studies of poxvirus-infected mouse L-cells, chick embryo fibroblast cells, and human HeLa cells have confirmed and extended this conclusion (152–157). IFN does not decrease the rate of synthesis of vaccinia early mRNA; instead, the rate of formation of early viral mRNA is accelerated in some lines of IFN-treated L-cells (146, 153). However, the rate of protein synthesis can be drastically inhibited in L-cells (146, 153, 154) and CEF cells (155, 157). This inhibition of early protein synthesis leads to the inhibition of second-stage uncoating of the viral DNA contained within the cores as well as the inhibition of viral DNA synthesis (47, 146, 152). Several immediate early viral proteins have recently been identified in vaccinia WR-infected and cowpox virus-infected CEF cells by affinity chromatography on native DNA-cellulose and two-dimensional electrophoresis, and the synthesis of these viral proteins is inhibited by IFN treatment (155). The inhibition of viral protein synthesis in IFN-treated vaccinia-infected L-cells is characterized by a disaggregation of polysomes and by a lack of binding of vaccinia mRNA to ribosomes to form virus-specific polysomes (146, 154). These observations suggest that the initiation of vaccinia virus protein synthesis can be a principal site of the antiviral action of IFN in certain murine cell lines.

With poxviruses, like most other of the virus systems examined in interferon mechanism studies, it has been difficult to establish the specific nature of the molecular change induced by IFN that is principally responsible for the inhibition of poxvirus protein synthesis in IFN-treated cells. The relative sensitivity of poxvirus replication to IFN appears to be dependent in part upon the conditions of cell culture and the type of cell examined (146, 158–163). Vaccina virus replication and protein synthesis in some lines of L-cells are extremely sensitive to IFN (146, 153, 158, 159). Activation of the 2',5'-oligo(A)-dependent RNase and the cleavage of rRNA and viral RNA correlate with the inhibition of protein synthesis in mouse fibroblasts (158, 159, 164). Furthermore, blot hybridization analysis shows a generally reduced steady-state amount of vaccinia virus-specific early mRNA in IFN-treated chick embryo fibroblasts, although ribosomal RNA is not degraded in vaccina-infected IFN-treated CEF cells (157). By contrast, in other cell lines (including vaccinia virus-infected HeLa cells and IFN-treated, vaccinia virus-infected HeLa, CV1, and L929 cells), 2',5'-oligo(A) and related compounds accumulate to high concentrations even when vaccinia virus replication is not inhibited (160, 163, 165). Therefore, it seems that high levels of 2',5'-oligo(A) per se are not sufficient to cause an antiviral effect against vaccinia virus in these cell-culture systems (160, 163, 165). A virus-mediated ATPase and phosphatase have been associated with alterations of the 2',5'-oligo(A) system observed in vaccinia virus-infected cells (166). However, several reports suggest that the resistance of vaccinia virus replication to the antiviral effects of IFN is associated with a virus-mediated inhibitor of the P1/eIF-2α protein kinase (100, 160, 168, 170).

Vaccinia virus mRNA synthesized in IFN-treated cells does not differ significantly from that synthesized in untreated cells in terms of 3'-polyadenylation (171). A subtle IFN-induced reduction in 2'-O-methylation of the penultimate residue of the 5'-cap-I structure is observed for both viral and cellular mRNAs in CEF cells (172, 173); however, neither the overall methylation nor the 5'-terminal G7-methylation of vaccinia virus-specific mRNA is markedly affected under conditions of induction of an antiviral state (172, 173). It is unclear what role, if any, the change in 5'-cap ribose methylation may play in the IFN-induced inhibition of protein synthesis in vaccinia virus-infected cells, because 2'-O-methylation appears to play only a minor role, if any, compared to that of G7-methylation in initiation complex formation (174).

One study revealed that vaccinia virions produced by IFN-treated mouse L-cells are less effective in their ability to adsorb, penetrate, and uncoat than are virions produced by untreated control cultures (48). This defect may be the result of alterations in the composition of the capsid polypeptides of virions produced by IFN-treated cells (48). Likewise, an IFN-mediated decrease in the functional level of viral proteins involved in the synthesis of vaccinia DNA conceivably may also be responsible for the observed inhibition of viral DNA synthesis observed in IFN-treated L-cells (176).

F. Adenoviridae

Adenoviruses are "naked" icosahedral viruses that possess a linear double-stranded DNA genome of about 36 kilobases encoding about 50 different polypeptide products. Two temporal stages of viral gene expression, early and late, have been described for the productive infection of human cells by adenoviruses. The late stage commences, by definition, with the onset of viral DNA replication. Adenovirus DNA replication occurs in the nucleus and requires early region virus-encoded polypeptides. The host cell RNA polymerase II is responsible for the synthesis in the nucleus of adenovirus mRNAs from six independent regions of the genome: five early (E1A, E1B, E2, E3, and E4) and one late (L1–L5). Each of these transcription units generates a spectrum of mRNAs utilizing a single promoter and a complex pattern of processing that involves the use of multiple splicing and cleavage-polyadenylation sites. The 5'-termini of adenovirus mRNAs are also modified by 5'-methylated cap structures. The early E region gene products appear to play primarily regulatory roles and are involved in DNA replication, transformation, and other functions that remain to be elucidated. The late L region gene products are mainly viral capsid proteins. Two small virus-associated (VA) RNAs synthesized by host RNA polymerase III are located at about 30 map units on the adenovirus genome; the VA RNAs do not encode polypeptides (41, 167).

The human adenoviruses are generally weak IFN inducers (170) and they are more resistent to the antiviral action of type-I IFNs in cell culture than are other animal viruses (3). This resistance of adenovirus to the inhibitory actions of IFN appears to be caused by the production of the VA RNAs, which prevent the activation of the IFN-induced P1/eIF-2α protein kinase (44). The 160-nucleotide, highly structured VA RNAs are synthesized in large amounts at late times after infection. Deletion mutants of adenovirus that do not synthesize the major species of VA RNA are defective in late viral mRNA translation; this defect is located in an early step in the initiation of translation (177, 178). The characteristics of the inhibition of adenovirus translation in VA RNA deletion mutant-infected human 293 cells (177, 178) are somewhat similar to those of the inhibition of VSV mRNA translation in IFN-treated human U-cells (7–9). In human epithelial 293 cells that have an inducible P1/eIF-2α protein kinase, the adenovirus deletion mutant lacking VA RNA multiplies poorly relative to the parental virus, which synthesizes VA RNA. By contrast, the VA deletion mutant multiplies nearly as well as wild-type virus in human fibroblast cells that contain no detectable dsRNA-dependent, IFN-inducible P1/eIF-2α protein kinase (179). The protein kinase is activated and the function of initiation factor eIF-2 is impaired in extracts prepared from VA deletion mutant-infected cells (179–181). By contrast, the P1/eIF-2α kinase is not activated and eIF-2 function is not impaired in cells infected with wild-type adenoviruses that synthesize large amounts of VA RNA (179–181). The VA RNA binds to the protein kinase P1 selectively, both in vitro (103) and in vivo (169), and inhibits the activation of the kinase by dsRNA (44, 103). The growth phenotype of the VA mutant appears to correlate with the kinetics of kinase induction and activation, although active P1/eIF-2α per se may not be sufficient to inhibit viral protein synthesis in VA mutant dl331-infected cells (182). The growth of the adenovirus deletion mutant, which is unable to produce VA RNA, is inhibited by IFN (44); by contrast, the growth of the wild-type adenovirus parent, which produces large amounts of VA RNA, is not affected by IFN (44,

102). Furthermore, wild-type adenovirus will rescue vesicular stomatitis virus from the antiviral effects of IFN in IFN-treated cells coinfected with both viruses (*102*). Thus, the evidence is consistent with the proposition that the insensitivity of adenovirus to the antiviral effects of IFN in cell culture arise from the ability of the adenovirus-encoded VA RNA to inhibit the activation of the IFN-induced P1/eIF-2α protein kinase.

The IFN-induced expression of the major histocompatibility antigens conceivably may contribute to the antiviral and antiproliferative actions of IFN at the "cell–cell" level within intact animals (*4*), perhaps by enhancement of the antigen-specific lytic effect of cytotoxic T-lymphocytes directed against adenovirus-infected or -transformed cells (*183*). The cytotoxic T-cell response is virus-specific and histocompatibility-antigen restricted (*184, 185*). It is assumed that the major histocompatibility antigens function, at least in part, in the presentation of foreign antigens, including viral antigens or tumor antigens, to T-cells. If the basal level of the cell-surface histocompatibility antigens is below the threshold concentration normally required for efficient T-cell responses, the IFN-induced increase in levels of class-I and class-II antigens could represent an important component of the host's response to infections as well as to tumorigenic cells. This "cell–cell" aspect of an antiviral response may be especially important in the cases of viruses like adenovirus whose macromolecular synthesis is only poorly affected at the "cell" level by IFN treatment (*44, 102*). Interestingly, however, adenoviruses appear to possess a mechanism that permits them to evade immune surveillance (*186, 187*) as well as to antagonize the antiviral action of IFN (*44*).

G. Herpesviridae

The members of the family herpesviridae can be identified by the presence of double-stranded linear DNA in the core of the icosahedral virion, which possesses an envelope derived from the nuclear membrane (*188*). The expression of the 50 to 100 genes of herpesviruses is coordinately regulated and sequentially ordered in a cascade fashion. Viral DNA is transcribed in the nucleus by host RNA polymerase II, but with the participation of viral factors at all stages of the infection. Viral RNAs are capped, methylated, and polyadenylated, but only a relatively small proportion of the herpes mRNAs is derived by splicing. Replication of viral DNA takes place in the nucleus and requires several viral gene products (*188*). The herpesviruses are ubiquitous, and can produce many diseases of varying severity in humans. Much of the information on herpesviruses comes from studies of the two serotypes of herpes simplex viruses (HSV), HSV-1 and HSV-2. HSV replication is clearly inhibited by IFN in many types of human cells (14, 189–199). However, independent studies have reached contradictory conclusions with regard to the stage of HSV multiplication blocked by IFN. Conceivably, HSV replication is indeed inhibited by different types of IFNs in different cell types—for example, macrophages (189, 190) in contrast to fibroblasts (196, 197)—by different molecular mechanisms.

The yield of infectious HSV virions in human peripheral blood macrophages (189) or human monocyte cultures is reduced by treatment with IFN (199). Both natural and molecularly cloned IFN-α and IFN-β, but not IFN-γ, inhibit HSV replication in human macrophages (189). IFN-γ also did not cause a detectable synergistic antiviral effect with IFN-α or IFN-β in human macrophages (189), but in murine macrophages (191) and in human melanoma cells (14), synergistic anti-HSV activities were observed with combinations of type-II IFN-γ and type-I IFN-α or -β. The type-I IFNs appear to act early in macrophages to inhibit the synthesis of HSV α- and β-proteins (189). A variety of techniques, including direct measurement of enzymic activity, SDS/PAGE analysis of radioactively labeled polypeptides, and immunofluorescence, show that type-I IFNs inhibit the synthesis of HSV proteins (189–193), including the immediate early α-protein ICP4 (189), β-proteins including DNA polymerase and thymidine kinase (189, 192), and γ-proteins (189). The inhibition of HSV translation has also been observed in cells treated with the IFN inducer, poly(rI)·poly(rC) (195). Because the efficient expression of HSV β- and γ-proteins is dependent upon the presence of functional HSV α-protein ICP4 (188), the inhibitory effects of type-I IFNs on the synthesis of HSV β- and γ-proteins could be accounted for by an inhibition of either the accumulation or the translation of HSV mRNAs encoding the α gene products. When the effect of IFN-α/β on the expression of the HSV α genes was analyzed in murine macrophages, a strong inhibition of α-protein synthesis was observed under conditions where the synthesis of mRNA encoding the α-protein ICP4 was only moderately inhibited by IFN (190). By contrast, IFN treatment caused a strong inhibition of the accumulation HSV β mRNA and synthesis of HSV β-proteins (190). Thus, the evidence suggests that the principal cause of the IFN-mediated inhibition of HSV replication in macrophages (189–193) is the inhibition of translation of HSV α mRNA into HSV α polypeptide products. The molecular basis of the inhibition of

HSV mRNA translation is not yet clear. 2′,5′-Oligoadenylates accumulate in IFN-treated, HSV-infected cells (194), although their possible relation to the antiviral effect against HSV is not resolved.

Molecularly cloned human IFN-α and IFN-β appear to inhibit the replication of HSV-1 and HSV-2 in human fibroblasts (196, 197) by a mechanism probably different from that observed in macrophages (189, 190). HSV replication is blocked by type-I IFNs in human fibroblasts at a late stage in the cycle of viral infection; both release of total extracellular HSV virions and cell-to-cell fusion are inhibited by IFN treatment (196, 197). Neither type-I IFN has a significant inhibitory effect on the synthesis of the major HSV nucleocapsid proteins in fibroblasts, but the synthesis of specific glycoproteins as measured by immunoblot analysis is reduced or delayed (197). Electron microscope examinations of IFN-treated, HSV-infected fibroblasts reveal an apparently normal assembly of nucleocapsid particles within the nucleus, yet the release of mature progeny particles from the cells is significantly reduced (197). These results are consistent with an inhibitory effect of type-I IFNs on HSV replication in human fibroblasts at a late stage of morphogenesis that prevents the release of progeny virions (196, 197). By contrast, it has also been reported that IFN-α has no significant effect on either HSV-1 polypeptide synthesis or progeny virion assembly, but rather causes the release from cells of normal levels of noninfectious virus particles (198). Thus, type-I IFNs may possibly affect a late stage of HSV replication (196–198), either the production of defective virions (198) or the release of virions (196, 197). The molecular basis of these effects has not yet been elucidated.

HSV latency and reactivation have been studied using various treatments to inhibit the cytocidal potential of the virus. IFN plays a crucial role in maintaining persistent HSV infection of macrophages (175). An *in vitro* model for HSV latency was established by treatment of human fetus sensory neurons with a combination of human IFN-α and (E)-5-(2-bromovinyl)-2′-deoxyuridine (200). This combination of inhibitors blocked complete expression of the HSV genome, limited virus-specific cytopathic effect, and resulted in greater than 80% neuron survival. After removal of the inhibitors, latency was maintained for an interval of at least 9 days (200). Both molecularly cloned human IFN-αA/D (201), which is active in murine cells (128), and natural murine IFN-β (202) potentiate the antiviral activity of the acyclic nucleoside 9-(1,3-dihydroxy-2-propoxymethol)guanine against HSV-2 systemic infections of mice. Combinations of molecularly cloned human IFN-α and either acyclovir or (dihydroxypropoxy)methylguanine are highly synergistic against both HSV-1 and HSV-2 in cultured human fibroblasts (203). The molecular basis of the synergistic actions against HSV of IFN and nucleoside antiviral agents has not yet been resolved (201–203).

H. Retroviridae

The genome of retroviruses is a 60 S–70 S dimer complex of two identical subunits of positive-strand RNA that resemble mRNA in that they are capped and methylated at the 5'-termini and polyadenylated at their 3'-termini. Most replication-competent retroviruses contain three viral genes arranged (5')-gag-pol-env-(3') in the RNA genome. Replication as well as transformation by retroviruses requires the synthesis of a double-stranded DNA copy of the RNA genome and its integration into the host cell DNA. Retrovirus virions contain a virus-coded RNA-dependent DNA polymerase (reverse transcriptase) that catalyzes the first step in the replication cycle, synthesis of retroviral DNA from the template genomic RNA. Expression of viral genes encoded by the integrated provirus is by cellular machinery, and the mechanisms for obtaining mature gene products involve both the production of subgenomic mRNAs and the synthesis of polyproteins that undergo posttranslational cleavages (22, 124).

IFN treatment greatly reduces the production of infectious retrovirus particles, both in chronically infected cells and in acutely infected cells (94, 204–215). In addition to the well-established inhibition of the type-C retroviruses (206–213, 220–222), the replications of type-B (214, 215) and type-D (216) retroviruses are also inhibited by IFN treatment. Most investigations have involved the study of chronically infected cells, and, as discussed in detail in Section III, IFN inhibits the production of infectious retrovirions in these cells at a late stage of virus morphogenesis, either particle assembly or release and maturation. However, in an acute exogenous virus infection, IFN appears to act at an early stage in the retrovirus multiplication cycle, preventing either the synthesis or the integration of proviral DNA (217–221).

The replication of Rous sarcoma virus (RSV) in chick embryo fibroblasts (CEF) and the transformation of CEF cells by RSV are highly sensitive to low doses of homologous natural chick IFN (220). Exogenous infection of CEF with RSV is inhibited at an early stage of the retrovirus replication cycle, either at or before proviral DNA synthesis (220, 221). Cellular morphology, hexose transport, microfilament organization, and the phosphotyrosine content of vinculin and p36 (two apparent substrates of the pp60^{src} phosphotyrosine protein kinase) are indistinguishable between uninfected CEF and IFN-treated, RSV-infected CEF (222).

In studies of cell transformation by oncogenic murine retroviruses, it was observed that IFN treatment can prevent the transformation of murine fibroblasts by the Kirsten strain of murine sarcoma virus (217, 223). Further studies indicated that IFN probably does not act by inhibiting the adsorption, penetration, or uncoating of KiMSV (KiMLV), but rather blocks a stage after uncoating but before integration of the provirus (224). The synthesis of proviral DNA is also inhibited by IFN in NIH/3T3 cells exogenously infected with Moloney murine leukemia virus (218); however, there is no effect of IFN on the synthesis of proviral DNA in NIH/3T3 cells exogenously infected with Friend MLV (225). In normal rat kidney cells infected with Molony murine sarcoma virus, IFN treatment delays cytoplasmic viral DNA synthesis and the transport of the DNA to the nucleus, but the amount of DNA eventually synthesized and transported is comparable in IFN-treated and untreated NRK cells (219). However, there was no significant integration of the proviral DNA into cell DNA in IFN-treated NRK cells although the major portion of the viral DNA did become integrated in untreated cells. Alkaline sucrose gradient analysis revealed that the IFN treatment of NRK cells inhibited the supercoiling of Moloney MSV proviral DNA; the linear and open circular DNA forms that accumulated in the nucleus of IFN-treated cells were slowly degraded (219). If supercoiling of proviral DNA is indeed required for subsequent provirus integration into the host cell DNA (22), inhibition of supercoiling by IFN treatment would provide an explanation for the inhibition of provirus integration observed in exogenous retrovirus infections.

IFN treatment can affect the expression of v-*onc* and c-*onc* genes (226–236). For example, treatment of Daudi cells with type-I IFNs causes a significant decrease in the level of c-*myc* mRNA (226–231). In most cases the IFN treatment appears not to affect the c-*myc* transcription rate, but rather reduces the half-life of c-*myc* mRNA (226, 231). IFN treatment also reduces the amount of Ha-*ras* mRNA and protein in mouse RS485 cells (232) and in human RT4 cells (233), and c-*fos* mRNA in BALB/c 3T3 cells (235). IFN treatment also inhibits the oncogenic transformation and stable expression of genes of both viral and cellular origin, genes including v-Ha-*ras*, c-Ha-*ras*, and c-Ki-*ras*, after their transfection into rodent cells (235, 236). This inhibition appears to be exerted at the level of stabilization and/or integration of exogenous DNA sequences into the recipient cellular genome (235).

III. Interferon Effects on Late Stages of Viral Multiplication Cycles

The latest point in the multiplication cycle of a virus at which IFN could conceivably act would be virion morphogenesis and release from cells. A defect introduced at this level could possibly impair the infectivity of progeny virions that otherwise might have appeared to have escaped an IFN-induced inhibition of viral replication.

A. Retroviridae

The first viral genetic system described in which the antiviral effect of IFN is possibly manifested at a comparatively late stage in the viral multiplication cycle is that of the retroviruses (94, 204, 205). The inhibition of retrovirus multiplication in IFN-treated, chronically infected cells is observed in the absence of a significant reduction in viral macromolecular synthesis. Neither the synthesis of viral RNA nor the synthesis of the major viral envelope and core proteins is significantly inhibited in IFN-treated, retrovirus-infected cells (209, 210, 214–216, 237–240). During morphogenesis the virions of retroviruses acquire a lipoprotein membrane envelope from the host plasma membrane as the viral particles bud from the surface of infected cells; further maturation of extracellular retrovirus particles probably occurs following their release from the cell surface (22). IFN treatment either greatly reduces the number of retrovirus particles that are released from infected cells (206, 209, 212, 214–216, 241) or greatly reduces the specific infectivity of those extracellular virions released (210, 242). In some systems, both the number and the specific infectivity of the released virions are reduced in IFN-treated cells (210, 212). An increase in the number of viral particles associated with the host plasma membrane is also often observed in systems under conditions where the actual number of particles released is reduced by the IFN treatment (209, 214, 241).

The molecular mechanism by which the number and the specific infectivity of released retrovirus particles are decreased by IFN treatment is not yet clear. Studies with a Moloney murine leukemia virus (MuLV) mutant temperature-sensitive for virus assembly indicate that a major effect of IFN is exerted on a relatively early step in virion assembly (243). IFN treatment might directly affect a viral component such as the processing of a viral precursor polyprotein or the post-translational modification of a viral polypeptide; alternatively, the structure and function of a cellular membrane component that plays a role in retrovirus morphogenesis may be the entity altered rather than a direct effect on the production of a viral gene product. No clear, uniform mechanistic picture has yet emerged to account for the effect of IFN on the late stages of retrovirus multiplication.

Early studies performed with Moloney MuLV and Rauscher MuLV indicated that IFN treatment may affect the processing of viral precursor polyproteins (244, 245). Subsequent studies with Moloney MuLV indicated that the inhibition of production of infectious progeny particles could be attributed to an inhibition of viral protein glycosylation observed in chronically infected NIH/3T3 cells (238). However, more recent studies with mink cell focus-inducing virus in a cell line with a slow rate of *env* gene processing indicated that IFN treatment causes the formation of defective virions of low specific infectivity deficient in virion envelope glycoprotein gp70; no evidence was obtained for the inhibition of viral protein synthesis, processing, or modification by glycosylation (211). Likewise, an earlier study with Rauscher MuLV also detected no IFN effect on the synthesis of the major core protein or envelope glycoprotein or the post-translational cleavage processing of the precursors to these proteins (240).

The production of Gazdar murine sarcoma virus, a retrovirus lacking *env* proteins and containing an uncleaved *gag* precursor polyprotein, is also inhibited by IFN treatment (246). This result with Gz-MSV indicates that the IFN-induced inhibition of retroviruses, in general, is not principally the consequence of either a defective interaction between viral nucleoprotein cores and viral envelope proteins or a defect in the proteolytic processing of the *gag* polyprotein, because these processes do not occur during the morphogenesis of Gz-MSV particles, and their production is IFN-sensitive. The mechanism by which retrovirus production is inhibited by IFN may involve IFN-induced alterations in cellular components of the plasma membrane or cytoskeleton. Among the IFN-induced alterations observed in cell structure is a significant decrease in membrane fluidity (247). Such changes could alter a variety of membrane-associated functions. For example, it is known that IFN treatment suppresses cell fusion (247, 248) and recent results suggest that the mechanisms underlying the inhibition of fusion and the inhibition of retrovirus production may be closely related and distinct from those antiviral mechanisms involved in the inhibition of such viruses as vesicular stomatitis virus or encephalomyocarditis virus (248). Naturally occurring IFNs inhibit cell

fusion or multinucleate cell formation in human cells induced by Ma-
son-Pfizer monkey virus (MPMV), a D-type retrovirus (249). Although
cell fusion mediated by MPMV is independent of virus replication
(250), the hybrid human IFN-αA/D, active on heterologous cell species (128), blocks the replication of MPMV in both human and nonhu-
man primate cells (216). The block in MPMV replication appears to be
at the stage of release of infectious virus particles because few extracellular particles are observed even though normal levels of intracyto-
plasmic A particles are found in the IFN-treated cells (216). Although
the antiviral mechanisms by which retroviruses are inhibited by type-
I IFNs are different from those by which VSV and EMC virus are
inhibited, the antiviral activities of molecularly cloned human IFNs
αA and αD and hybrids derived from them are, in general, proportional against these three viruses in feline, human, and murine cells
(251).

Of particular interest is the finding that the replication of immunosuppressive retroviruses can be blocked by treatment of cells with
molecularly cloned type-I (252) and type-II (253, 254) IFNs. Human
type-I IFN-αA has a suppressive effect on the replication of human
immunodeficiency virus (HIV/HTLV-III) in vitro (252). When type-II
IFN-γ was added prior to acute HIV/HTLV-III infection, reverse
transcriptase activity was reduced by 90 to 100%, and viral antigen
expression was nearly eliminated when the IFN was maintained in
the culture medium (253). Furthermore, an inverse relationship has
been observed between constitutive IFN-γ production and HTLV
expression in cultured T-lymphocytes (254). Little information exists
concerning the molecular mechanism by which the HIV/HTLV retroviruses are inhibited by IFN treatment.

B. Virus Families Other Than Retroviridae

IFN treatment also causes the production of defective progeny
virions in the case of murine and human cells infected by three quite
different enveloped viruses: vesicular stomatitis (91, 92, 255–259),
vaccinia (48), and herpes simplex (196, 197). VSV, a negative-strand
RNA virus, derives its lipoprotein envelope from an altered region of
the host's plasma membrane by a budding process that excludes host
membrane proteins from the virion envelope (260). Vaccinia, a double-strand DNA virus, also contains an envelope, but the virion structure of vaccinia is far more complicated than that of VSV. The complex
membrane envelope structure of vaccinia is synthesized de novo and
assembled within the host's cytoplasm where virion maturation occurs (261). The defective VSV and vaccinia virions produced from

IFN-treated cells are characterized by alterations in polypeptide composition and apparent reductions in specific infectivity as compared to progeny virion particles produced from untreated cells.

In the case of VSV, treatment of certain murine cell lines with natural mouse IFN has been reported to cause a selective reduction in the incorporation of two viral proteins, the transmembrane glycoprotein G and the peripheral membrane protein M, into assembled virions (91, 255–257). In addition, G protein present in virions released from IFN-treated cells is underglycosylated to an extent similar to that brought about by the glycosylation inhibitor tunicamycin (92). As little as a 0.5% yield of infectious VSV progeny was observed when mouse fibroblasts were treated with doses of natural mouse IFN that reduced the yield of VSV particles to about 10%, suggesting that IFN-treated cells produce VSV progeny particles with low infectivity (91, 258). Human GM2504 fibroblast cells, but not human HeLa cells, produce VSV particles of reduced specific infectivity when treated with molecularly cloned human IFN-α prior to infection (259). The general biologic significance of these observations (91, 92, 255–259) in terms of the antiviral activity of IFN in VSV-infected cells is not yet clear, because they appear to be highly dependent upon the nature of the cell lines and IFN preparations examined. For example, no alteration of either the specific infectivity or the polypeptide composition of VSV virions was detected in human amnion cells treated with molecularly cloned human leukocyte IFN derived from E. coli even though the yield of infectious progeny virions was reduced to less than 1% (7). Furthermore, no IFN-induced inhibition of glycosylation of either cellular or viral glycoproteins was observed in a variety of independent studies including the following: when human immunoglobulin G-producing RPMI 8226 cells were treated with natural human α or β IFN (262); when human HeLa cells treated with IFN were infected with VSV (134, 262); when the VSV G gene was expressed in COS cells transfected with a eukaryotic expression vector containing the G gene cDNA insert (36); when retrovirus envelope glycoprotein gp70 was examined in natural mouse IFN-treated murine SC-1 cells chronically infected with mink cell focus-inducing AK-13 virus (211); when VSV G protein modification was reexamined in murine L-cells treated with natural IFN and infected with VSV (263); or when the glycosylation of fibronectin and IgG were examined in IFN-treated murine NIH/3T3 cells and P3X63XAg8 plasmacytoma cells, respectively (263). Although the envelope glycoprotein G is essential for VSV infectivity (264) and inhibition of glycosylation can impede its passage to the cell surface and incorporation into VSV virions (265), lack of glycosylation per se in assembled virions does not appear to affect VSV infectivity. Virions from tunicamycin-treated cells containing nonglycosylated G protein (265, 266), virions from swainsonine-treated cells containing G protein with unprocessed high mannose residues (267), and neuraminidase-treated virions containing unsialylated G protein (268) all have a specific infectivity similar to that of VSV containing fully glycosylated G protein.

Defective vaccinia virus particles are produced by mouse L-cells treated with natural mouse IFN (48). With vaccinia virus, both the phosphorylation and the glycosylation of certain virion polypeptides (measured by labeling with $^{32}P_i$ or [^{3}H]glucosamine) are significantly reduced in virions purified from IFN-treated cells. The alterations in vaccina virion polypeptide modification were observed with doses of IFN that did not appear to alter the overall polypeptide composition of the purified virions as measured by the pattern of [^{35}S]methionine-labeled polypeptides. The defective vaccinia particles purified from IFN-treated cells appeared to attach, penetrate, and uncoat less efficiently than normal virions purified from untreated cells (48).

The replication of herpes simplex virus also appears to be blocked by type-I IFNs in human fibroblasts at a late stage in the virus multiplication cycle (196, 197). Electron microscope examinations of IFN-treated, HSV-infected fibroblasts revealed an apparently normal assembly of viral nucleocapsids within the host nucleus, yet the release of mature progeny HSV virions from the infected cells was significantly reduced (197).

There are many different changes in the structure and function of the plasma membrane and cell surface of IFN-treated animal cells in the absence of virus infection (5, 247, 269). These changes may reflect an "anticellular" effect of IFN. It is possible that some of these changes also affect the ability of certain cells to serve as host for the multiplication of certain viruses, particularly in those cases where either the initiation of infection or the assembly/release of progeny virions is dependent upon a particular aspect of the host cell ultrastructure.

In those viruses whose replication may be inhibited by IFN at more than one stage of the multiplication cycle (for example, "early" during virion penetration or "late" during virion morphogenesis in addition to specific and selective effects on viral protein synthesis), the effects at the early or late stages of the multiplication cycle may reflect the "non-antiviral/anticellular activity" of IFN rather than its "antiviral activity." Depending upon the rate of virus replication and the specific biochemical mechanisms involved in viral macromolecular synthesis, the relative contribution of the "antiviral activity" as compared to the "anticellular activity" on the production of infectious progeny may vary among different virus–host systems. The apparent lack of agreement among some of the studies of the effect of IFN on VSV virion morphogenesis, or equally well upon virion penetration, may arise in part from marked differences in the IFN dose (time and concentration) required to induce each of the individual biochemical changes, as well as from significant differences among the various induced biochemical changes in terms of their individual contribution to the overall final reduction in infectious virus yield.

IV. Cellular Messenger RNAs and Proteins Regulated by Interferon

Enzymes of the P1/eIF-2α protein kinase (4, 96, 139) and the 2′,5′-oligoadenylate synthetase systems (4, 270, 271) as well as the protein Mx (111, 114) are all induced by IFN. These cellular gene products, as

TABLE II

CELLULAR MESSENGER RNAs AND PROTEINS REGULATED BY INTERFERONS

Cellular gene	Reference
A. Increased expression in IFN-treated cells	
1. P1/eIF-2α Protein Kinase	4, 96, 139
2. 2′,5′-Oligo(A) synthetase	4, 270, 271
3. 2′,5′-Oligo(A)-dependent RNase	272
4. 2′,5′-Phosphodiesterase	273
5. Protein Mx	111, 114
6. Class-I major histocompatibility antigens	274–278
7. Class-II major histocompatibility antigens	278–281
8. Class-III major histocompatibility proteins	282
9. β_2-Microglobulin	275, 276, 279
10. Guanylate binding proteins	283
11. Xanthine oxidase	284, 285
12. Indoleamine 2,3-dioxygenase	286, 287, 304
13. Glutathione transferase	296
14. Metallothionein-II	288
15. Thymosin B4	288
16. Tumor necrosis factor receptor	289–291
B. Decreased expression in IFN-treated cells	
1. c-*myc*	226, 229, 231
2. c-*fos*	234
3. Collagen	292, 293
4. Epidermal growth factor receptor	294
5. Transferrin receptor	295

discussed in Section II, have been implicated in the antiviral actions of interferons directed against either a specific virus family, for example, orthomyxoviridae (*111, 114*), or against multiple virus families (*4, 96, 270*). In addition to the enzymes associated with the kinase and the synthetase systems (*4, 96, 139, 270–273*), the expression of a number of other cellular genes is also regulated by IFN (*226, 229, 231, 234, 274–296*).

The steady-state concentrations of about two dozen different cellular gene products whose biochemical functions have been identified are either increased (*96, 139, 270–291*) or decreased (*226, 229, 231, 234, 292–296*) by IFN treatment (Table II). Some of these gene products [for example, the major histocompatibility antigens (*4, 183–185, 297–300*)] appear to play an important role in the antiviral actions of IFNs in whole animals. However, the possible importance and role of many of the IFN-regulated proteins in the IFN response directed against viruses so far are unknown. It is possible that many different IFN-regulated proteins play a role in the reduced replication of animal viruses, and that the specific cellular protein(s) primarily important in mediating the inhibition of virus multiplication is (are) dependent upon the virus and the cell studied, and whether the animal virus–cell combination is examined in cell culture or in the intact animal.

V. Conclusion

The finding that the multiplication of most viruses appears to be inhibited by IFN at the level of protein synthesis may not be surprising. Translation of viral mRNA by the host protein-synthesizing machinery clearly plays a central role in all viral multiplication cycles. By contrast, the various mechanisms and subcellular sites of viral genome replication and transcription used by animal viruses can differ substantially between the major families of animal viruses. In some cases, host, and in other cases, viral-coded enzymes are utilized in the biogenesis of viral mRNA. However, not all viruses are inhibited by IFN at the level of translation; this finding also may not be surprising in view of the fact that interferons are indeed a *family* of regulatory proteins (Table I) that regulate the expression of several cellular genes (Table II).

Many studies have implicated either the P1/eIF-2α protein kinase system or the 2′,5′-oligoadenylate system, or both systems, in the antiviral action of IFNs and the inhibition of protein synthesis commonly observed in IFN-treated, virus-infected cells. However, other cellular proteins whose synthesis is regulated by IFN may also play roles in the antiviral action of IFN. The identity of only a few of the proteins whose expression is regulated by IFN is known; many IFN-regulated cellular genes are as yet simply characterized as unidentified protein bands on polyacrylamide gels or as unidentified cDNA clones to mRNAs whose steady-state level is regulated by IFN.

The most direct evidence for the role of a specific IFN-regulated cellular gene product in the antiviral action of IFN has been obtained by the expression in transfected cells of antisense RNA to the $2',5'$-oligoadenylate synthetase in recipient synthetase-positive cells, or the expression of the murine Mx protein in recipient Mx-negative cells. The results of these experimental approaches are consistent with involvement of the $2',5'$-oligoadenylate system and the Mx protein in the antiviral action of IFN against some kinds of viruses in some types of cell culture systems. However, other antiviral mechanisms involving other IFN-regulated proteins cannot entirely be excluded for other virus–cell combinations. Furthermore, the antiviral response to IFN within the whole animal is most probably the result of a combination of mechanisms, both those operative in single cells and those, such as cellular immune responses, which are the product of multiple cell interactions. In all likelihood, the principal mechanism by which virus replication is inhibited by IFN treatment will indeed depend upon all three primary components: the nature of the host cell, the type and perhaps subspecies of the IFN, and the kind of virus that infects the IFN-treated cells. As the functions of the many IFN-regulated proteins become identified, the possibilities offered by the expression of cDNAs or antisense RNAs in cell culture systems as well as transgenic animals will hopefully broaden our understanding of the antiviral mechanisms of interferons.

Acknowledgments

The work from the author's laboratory was supported in part by Research Grants AI-12520 and AI-20611 from the National Institute of Allergy and Infectious Diseases.

References

1. A. Isaacs and J. Lindenmann, *Proc. R. Soc. London, Ser. B* 147, 258 (1957).
2. C. Weissmann and H. Weber, *This Series* 33, 251 (1986).
3. W. E. Stewart, II, "The Interferon System." Springer-Verlag, Berlin and New York, 1979.
4. S. Pestka, J. A. Langer, K. A. Zoon and C. E. Samuel, *ARB* 56, 727 (1987).
5. L. Pfeffer (ed.), "Mechanisms of Interferon Actions." CRC Press, Boca Raton, Florida, 1987.
6. C. E. Samuel, *in* "Mechanisms of Interferon Actions" (L. Pfeffer, ed.), Chapter 8, pp. 111–130. CRC Press, Boca Raton, Florida, 1987.

7. P. S. Masters and C. E. Samuel, *JBC* **258**, 12019 (1983).
8. P. S. Masters and C. E. Samuel, *JBC* **258**, 12026 (1983).
9. P. S. Masters and C. E. Samuel, *BBRC* **119**, 326 (1984).
10. N. Ulker and C. E. Samuel, *JBC* **260**, 4319 (1985).
11. N. Ulker and C. E. Samuel, *JBC* **260**, 4324 (1985).
12. W. R. Fleischmann, Jr., J. A. Georgiades, L. C. Osborne and H. M. Johnson, *Infect. Immun.* **26**, 248 (1979).
13. C. E. Samuel and G. S. Knutson, *Virology* **130**, 474 (1983).
14. C. W. Czarniecki, C. W. Fennie, D. B. Powers and D. A. Estell, *J. Virol.* **49**, 490 (1984).
15. A. A. Branca and C. Baglioni, *Nature* **294**, 768 (1981).
16. Y. Higashi and Y. Sokowa, *J. Biochem.* **91**, 2021 (1982).
17. G. Huez, M. Silhol and B. Lebleu, *BBRC* **110**, 155 (1983).
18. J. Sanceau, P. Sondermeyer, F. Beranger, R. Falcoff and C. Vaquero, *PNAS* **84**, 2906 (1987).
19. I. Gresser (ed-in-chief), "Interferon," Vols. 1–8. Academic Press, New York, 1979–1987.
20. S. Baron, F. Dianzani, G. J. Stanton and W. R. Fleischmann (eds.), "The Interferon System to 1987." Univ. of Texas Press, Austin, 1987.
21. D. H. Metz, M. J. Levin and M. N. Oxman, *J. Gen. Virol.* **32**, 227 (1976).
22. R. Weiss, N. Teich, H. Varmus and J. Coffin (eds.), "Molecular Biology of Tumor Viruses: RNA Tumor Viruses," 2nd ed., Cold Spring Harbor Laboratory, Cold Spring Harbor, New York, 1982.
23. K. A. Daher and C. E. Samuel, *Virology* **117**, 379 (1982).
24. M. N. Oxman and M. J. Levin, *PNAS* **68**, 299 (1971).
25. K. Yamamoto, N. Yamaguchi and K. Oda, *Virology* **68**, 58 (1975).
26. E. Yakobson, C. Prives, J. R. Hartman, E. Winocour and M. Revel, *Cell* **12**, 73 (1977).
27. S. M. Kingsman and C. E. Samuel, *Virology* **101**, 458 (1980).
28. S. M. Kingsman, M. D. Smith and C. E. Samuel, *PNAS* **77**, 2419 (1980).
29. K. A. Daher and C. E. Samuel, *BBRC* **101**, 697 (1981).
30. M. B. Brennan and G. R. Stark, *Cell* **33**, 811 (1983).
31. M. A. Garcia-Blanco, P. K. Ghosh, B. M. Jayaram, S. Ivory, P. Lebowitz and P. Lengyel, *J. Virol.* **53**, 893 (1985).
32. C. L. Hersh, R. E. Brown, W. K. Roberts, E. A. Swyryd, I. M. Kerr and G. R. Stark, *JBC* **259**, 1731 (1984).
33. C. Kahana, E. Yakobson, M. Revel and Y. Groner, *Virology* **112**, 109 (1981).
34. S. E. Grossberg and J. J. Holland, *J. Immunol.* **88**, 708 (1962).
35. M. Ho, *PSEBM* **107**, 639 (1961).
36. G. Sahni and C. E. Samuel, *JBC* **261**, 16764 (1986).
37. M. N. Oxman, S. Baron, P. H. Black, K. K. Takemoto, K. Habel and W. P. Rowe, *Virology* **32**, 122 (1967).
38. L. W. Mozes and V. Defendi, *Virology* **93**, 558 (1979).
39. J. A. Robb and R. G. Martin, *J. Virol.* **9**, 956 (1972).
40. J. Y. Chou and R. G. Martin, *J. Virol.* **15**, 145 (1975).
41. J. Tooze, "Molecular Biology of Tumor Viruses: DNA Tumor Viruses," 2nd ed. Cold Spring Harbor Laboratory, Cold Spring Harbor, New York, 1981.
42. J. Avila, R. Saral, R. G. Martin and G. Khoury, *Virology* **73**, 89 (1976).
43. S. Subramanian, R. A. Bhat, M. K. Rundell and B. Thimmappaya, *J. Virol.* **60**, 363 (1986).

44. J. Kitajewski, R. J. Schneider, B. Safer, S. M. Munemitsu, C. E. Samuel, B. Thimmappaya and T. Shenk, *Cell* **45**, 195 (1986).
45. M. E. Wiebe and W. K. Joklik, *Virology* **66**, 229 (1975).
46. R. L. Galster and P. Lengyel, *NARes* **3**, 581 (1976).
47. W. E. Magee, S. Levine, O. V. Miller and R. D. Hamilton, *Virology* **35**, 505 (1968).
48. M. Esteban, *Virology* **133**, 220 (1984).
49. T. Meyer and M. A. Horisberger, *J. Virol.* **49**, 709 (1984).
50. V. Mayer, F. Sokol and J. Vilcek, *Virology* **16**, 359 (1962).
51. M. J. Morgan, C. Colby and J. D. N. Hulse, *J. Gen. Virol.* **20**, 377 (1973).
52. A. P. Jarvis and C. Colby, *Cell* **14**, 355 (1978).
53. P. A. Whitaker-Dowling, D. K. Wilcox, C. C. Widnell and J. S. Youngner, *PNAS* **80**, 1083 (1983).
54. D. K. Wilcox, P. A. Whitaker-Dowling, J. S. Youngner and C. C. Widnell, *MCBiol* **3**, 1533 (1983).
55. B. N. Fields (ed.-in-chief), "Virology." Raven Press, New York, 1985.
56. D. Baltimore, *Bacteriol. Rev.* **35**, 235 (1971).
57. N. Kitamura, B. Semler, P. G. Rothberg, G. R. Larsen, C. J. Adler, A. J. Dorner, E. A. Emilio, R. Hanecak, J. J. Lee, S. van der Werf, C. W. Anderson and E. Wimmer, *Nature* **291**, 547 (1981).
58. H. Toyoda, M. Kohara, Y. Kataoka, T. Suganuma, T. Omata, N. Imura and A. Nomoto, *JMB* **174**, 561 (1984).
59. H. B. Levy and W. A. Carter, *JMB* **31**, 561 (1968).
60. N. Miner, W. J. Ray and E. M. Simon, *BBRC* **24**, 264 (1966).
61. P. M. P. Yau, T. Godefroy-Colburn, C. H. Birge, T. V. Ramabhadran and R. E. Thach, *J. Virol.* **27**, 648 (1978).
62. G. Jen, C. H. Birge and R. E. Thach, *J. Virol.* **27**, 640 (1978).
63. B. R. G. Williams, R. R. Golgher, R. E. Brown, C. S. Gilbert and I. M. Kerr, *Nature* **282**, 582 (1979).
64. M. Knight, P. J. Cayley, R. H. Silverman, D. H. Wreschner, C. S. Gilbert, R. E. Brown and I. M. Kerr, *Nature* **288**, 189 (1980).
65. R. H. Silverman, J. J. Skehel, T. C. James, D. H. Wreschner and I. M. Kerr, *J. Virol.* **46**, 1051 (1983).
66. D. H. Wreschner, T. C. James, R. H. Silverman and I. M. Kerr, *NARes* **9**, 1571 (1981).
67. A. De Benedetti, B. A. Pytel and C. Baglioni, *PNAS* **84**, 658 (1987).
68. C. Baglioni, P. A. Maroney and D. K. West, *Bchem* **18**, 1765 (1979).
69. T. W. Nilsen, D. L. Wood and C. Baglioni, *Nature* **286**, 178 (1980).
70. S. L. Gupta, S. L. Holmes and L. L. Mehra, *Virology* **120**, 495 (1982).
71. C. W. Czarniecki, T. Sreevalsan, R. M. Friedman and A. Panet, *J. Virol.* **37**, 827 (1981).
72. A. Panet, C. W. Czarniecki, H. Falk and R. M. Friedman, *Virology* **114**, 567 (1981).
73. R. H. Silverman, P. J. Cayley, M. Knight, C. S. Gilbert and I. M. Kerr, *EJB* **124**, 131 (1982).
74. A. P. Rice and I. M. Kerr, *J. Virol.* **50**, 229 (1984).
75. P. Whitaker-Dowling and J. S. Youngner, *Virology* **152**, 50 (1986).
76. A. Zerial, A. G. Hovanessian, S. Stefanos, K. Huygen, G. H. Werner and E. Falcoff, *Antiviral Res.* **2**, 227 (1982).
77. W. G. Hearl and M. I. Johnston, *J. Virol.* **61**, 1586 (1987).
78. R. R. Wagner (ed.), "The Viruses: The Rhabdoviruses." Plenum, New York, 1987.
79. J. A. Atwater and C. E. Samuel, *Virology* **123**, 206 (1982).

80. J. Schneck, B. Rager-Zisman, O. Rosen and B. R. Bloom, *PNAS* **79**, 1879 (1982).
81. D. K. Banerjee, K. Baksi and M. M. Gottesman, *Virology* **129**, 230 (1983).
82. L. S. Belkowski and G. C. Sen, *J. Virol.* **61**, 653 (1987).
83. X. X. Zhang and C. E. Samuel, *J. Biol. Regul. Homeost. Agents* **1**, 157 (1987).
84. E. K. Manders, J. G. Tilles and A. S. Huang, *Virology* **49**, 573 (1972).
85. P. I. Marcus and M. J. Sekellick, *J. Gen. Virol.* **38**, 391 (1978).
86. F. De Ferra and C. Baglioni, *Virology* **112**, 426 (1981).
87. P. Repik, A. Flamand and D. H. L. Bishop, *J. Virol.* **14**, 1169 (1974).
88. B. Baxt, J. A. Sonnabend and R. Bablanian, *J. Gen. Virol.* **35**, 325 (1977).
89. L. A. Ball and C. N. White, *Virology* **84**, 496 (1978).
90. R. K. Maheshwari, A. E. Demsey, S. B. Mohanty and R. M. Friedman, *PNAS* **77**, 2284 (1980).
91. R. K. Maheshwari and R. M. Friedman, *Virology* **101**, 399 (1980).
92. R. K. Maheshwari, D. K. Banerjee, C. J. Waechter, K. Olden and R. M. Friedman, *Nature* **287**, 454 (1980).
93. M. Simili, F. De Ferra and C. Baglioni, *J. Gen. Virol.* **47**, 373 (1980).
94. R. M. Friedman, *Bacteriol. Rev.* **41**, 543 (1977).
95. C. E. Samuel, G. S. Knutson and P. S. Masters, *J. Interferon Res.* **2**, 563 (1982).
96. C. E. Samuel, in "The Interferon System to 1987" (S. Baron, F. Dianzani, G. Stanton and W. Fleischmann, eds.), p. 373. Univ. of Texas Press, Austin, 1987.
97. L. A. Ball, in "The Enzymes" (P. D. Boyer, ed.), 3rd ed., Vol. 15, p. 281. Academic Press, New York, 1982.
98. J. S. Youngner, H. R. Thacore and M. E. Kelly, *J. Virol.* **10**, 171 (1972).
99. H. R. Thacore and J. S. Youngner, *Virology* **56**, 505 (1973).
100. P. Whitaker-Dowling and J. S. Youngner, *Virology* **131**, 128 (1983).
101. R. A. Lamb and P. W. Choppin, *ARB* **52**, 467 (1983).
102. K. P. Anderson and E. H. Fennie, *J. Virol.* **61**, 787 (1987).
103. S. M. Munemitsu, M. J. Berry, J. Kitajewski, T. Shenk and C. E. Samuel, in "Interferons as Cell Growth Inhibitors and Antitumor Factors" (R. M. Friedman, T. Merigan and T. Sreevalsan, eds.), pp. 87–100. Liss, New York, 1986.
104. P. Lengyel, *ARB* **51**, 251 (1982).
105. F. De Ferra and C. Baglioni, *JBC* **258**, 2118 (1983).
106. A. K. Banerjee, *Microbiol. Rev.* **44**, 175 (1980).
107. A. J. Shatkin, *Cell* **9**, 645 (1976).
108. J. K. Rose and H. F. Lodish, *Nature* **262**, 32 (1976).
109. K. H. Levin and C. E. Samuel, *Virology* **77**, 245 (1977).
110. O. Haller, H. Arnheiter, J. Lindenmann and I. Gresser, *Nature* **283**, 660 (1980).
111. P. Staeheli and O. Haller, in "Interferon 8" (I. Gresser, ed.), Vol. 8, pp. 13–35. Academic Press, New York, 1987.
112. P. Dreiding, P. Staeheli and O. Haller, *Virology* **140**, 192 (1985).
113. J. Lindenmann, C. A. Lane and D. Hobson, *J. Immunol.* **90**, 942 (1963).
114. P. Staeheli, O. Haller, W. Boll, J. Lindenmann and C. Weissmann, *Cell* **44**, 147 (1986).
115. H. Arnheiter and O. Haller, *J. Virol.* **47**, 626 (1983).
116. M. A. Horisberger, O. Haller and H. Arnheiter, *J. Gen. Virol.* **50**, 205 (1980).
117. T. Meyer and M. A. Horisberger, *J. Virol.* **49**, 709 (1984).
118. R. M. Krug, M. Shaw, B. Broni, G. Shapiro and O. Haller, *J. Virol.* **56**, 201 (1985).
119. R. M. Ransohoff, P. A. Maroney, D. P. Nayak, T. M. Chambers and T. W. Nilsen, *J. Virol.* **56**, 1049 (1985).
120. W. J. Bean and R. W. Simpson, *Virology* **56**, 646 (1973).

121. M. A. Horisberger and K. de Staritzky, *FEMS Microbiol. Lett.* **29**, 207 (1985).
122. P. Staeheli, M. A. Horisberger and O. Haller, *Virology* **132**, 456 (1984).
123. P. Staeheli and O. Haller, *MCBiol* **5**, 2150 (1985).
124. J. M. Bishop, *ARB* **52**, 301 (1983).
125. P. Staeheli, D. Pravtcheva, L.-G. Lundin, M. Acklin, F. Ruddle, J. Lindenmann and O. Haller, *J. Virol.* **58**, 967 (1986).
126. W. K. Joklik (ed.), "The Viruses: The Reoviridae." Plenum, New York, 1983.
127. S. L. Gupta, W. D. Graziadi, H. Weideli, M. Sopori and P. Lengyel, *Virology* **57**, 49 (1974).
128. C. E. Samuel and G. S. Knutson, *JBC* **257**, 11791 (1982).
129. C. E. Samuel, S. M. Kingsman, R. W. Melamed, D. Farris, M. D. Smith, N. G. Miyamoto, S. R. Lasky and G. S. Knutson, *Ann. N.Y. Acad. Sci.* **350**, 473 (1980).
130. A. De Benedetti, G. J. Williams, L. Comeau and C. Baglioni, *J. Virol.* **55**, 588 (1985).
131. J. A. Atwater, S. M. Munemitsu and C. E. Samuel, *Virology* **159**, 350 (1987).
132. C. E. Samuel and G. S. Knutson, *Virology* **114**, 302 (1981).
133. B. Y. Rubin and S. L. Gupta, *PNAS* **77**, 5928 (1980).
134. A. Munoz and L. Carrasco, *J. Gen. Virol.* **65**, 377 (1984).
135. T. W. Nilsen, P. A. Maroney and C. Baglioni, *J. Virol.* **42**, 1039 (1982).
136. N. G. Miyamoto and C. E. Samuel, *Virology* **107**, 461 (1980).
137. R. C. Desrosiers and P. Lengyel, *BBA* **562**, 471 (1979).
138. P. Lengyel, R. Desrosiers, R. Broeze, E. Slattery, H. Taira, J. Dougherty, H. Samanta, J. Pichon, P. Farrell, L. Ratner and G. Sen, *in* "Microbiology 1980" (D. Schlessinger, ed.), pp. 219–226. Am. Soc. Microbiol., Washington, D.C., 1980.
139. C. E. Samuel, *PNAS* **76**, 600 (1979).
140. T. W. Nilsen, P. A. Maroney and C. Baglioni, *JBC* **257**, 14593 (1982).
141. C. E. Samuel, R. Duncan, G. S. Knutson and J. W. B. Hershey, *JBC* **259**, 13451 (1984).
142. C. E. Samuel, D. A. Farris and K. H. Levin, *Virology* **81**, 476 (1977).
143. D. Skup, H. Zarbl and S. Millward, *JMB* **151**, 35 (1981).
144. J. A. Grifo, S. M. Tahara, J. P. Leis, M. A. Morgan, A. J. Shatkin and W. C. Merrick, *JBC* **257**, 5246 (1982).
145. C. Baglioni, A. De Benedetti and G. J. Williams, *J. Virol.* **52**, 865 (1984).
146. W. K. Joklik and T. C. Merigan, *PNAS* **56**, 558 (1966).
147. C. Baglioni, *Cell* **17**, 255 (1979).
148. C. E. Samuel and G. S. Knutson, *JBC* **257**, 11796 (1982).
149. C. E. Samuel, N. Ulker, G. S. Knutson, X. Zhang and P. S. Masters, *in* "The Biology of the Interferon System 1984" (H. Kirchner and H. Schellekens, eds.), pp. 131–140. Elsevier, Amsterdam, 1985.
150. B. L. Jacobs, J. A. Atwater, S. M. Munemitsu and C. E. Samuel, *Virology* **147**, 9 (1985).
151. B. Moss, *in* "Virology" (B. Fields, ed.), p. 685. Raven Press, New York, 1985.
152. D. H. Metz, *Cell* **6**, 429 (1975).
153. D. H. Metz and M. Esteban, *Nature* **238**, 385 (1972).
154. D. H. Metz, M. Esteban and G. Danielescu, *J. Gen. Virol.* **27**, 197 (1975).
155. J. Rosel and C. Jungwirth, *EJB* **132**, 361 (1983).
156. C. Jungwirth, I. Horak, G. Bodo, J. Lindner and B. Schultze, *Virology* **48**, 59 (1972).
157. J. Grün, E. Kroon, B. Zöller, U. Krempien and C. Jungwirth, *Virology* **158**, 28 (1987).

158. J. Benavente, E. Paez and M. Esteban, *J. Virol.* **51**, 866 (1984).
159. M. Esteban, J. Benavente and E. Paez, *Virology* **134**, 40 (1984).
160. E. Paez and M. Esteban, *Virology* **134**, 12 (1984).
161. M. Esteban, J. Benavente and E. Paez, *J. Gen. Virol.* **67**, 801 (1986).
162. B. A. B. Martin, H. Kroath, C. Jungwirth, P. H. Hofschneider, G. Bodo and G. Wengler, *Exp. Cell Biol.* **48**, 31 (1980).
163. A. P. Rice, W. K. Roberts and I. M. Kerr, *J. Virol.* **50**, 220 (1984).
164. B. B. Goswami and O. K. Sharma, *JBC* **259**, 1371 (1984).
165. A. P. Rice, S. M. Kerr, W. K. Roberts, R. E. Brown and I. M. Kerr, *J. Virol.* **56**, 1041 (1985).
166. E. Paez and M. Esteban, *Virology* **134**, 29 (1984).
167. H. S. Ginsberg (ed.), "The Viruses, The Adenoviruses." Plenu, New York, 1984.
168. P. Whitaker-Dowling and J. S. Youngner, *Virology* **137**, 171 (1984).
169. M. G. Katze, D. DeCorato, B. Safer, J. Galabru and A. G. Hovanessian, *EMBO J.* **6**, 689 (1987).
170. M. I. Toth, B. Arya, R. Pusztai, K. Shiroki and I. Beladi, *J. Virol.* **61**, 2326 (1987).
171. N. Klesel, N. Wolf, G. Heller, C. Jungwirth and G. Bodo, *Virology* **57**, 570 (1974).
172. H. Kroath, H. G. Janda, G. Hiller, E. Kuhn, C. Jungwirth, H. J. Gross and G. Bodo, *Virology* **92**, 572 (1979).
173. H. Kroath, H. J. Gross, C. Jungwirth and G. Bodo, *NARes* **5**, 2441 (1978).
174. S. Muthukrishnan, B. Moss, J. A. Cooper and E. S. Maxwell, *JBC* **253**, 1710 (1978).
175. I. Domke-Opitz, P. Robershin, S. Mittnacht and H. Kirchner, *Virology* **159**, 306 (1987).
176. M. Esteban, *J. Interferon Res.* **4**, 179 (1984).
177. B. Thimmappaya, C. Weinberger, R. J. Schneider and T. Shenk, *Cell* **31**, 543 (1982).
178. R. J. Schneider, C. Weinberger and T. Shenk, *Cell* **37**, 291 (1984).
179. R. J. Schneider, B. Safer, S. M. Munemitsu, C. E. Samuel and T. Shenk, *PNAS* **82**, 4321 (1985).
180. J. Siekierka, T. M. Mariano, P. A. Reichel and M. B. Mathews, *PNAS* **82**, 1959 (1985).
181. P. A. Reichel, W. C. Merrick, J. Siekierka and M. B. Mathews, *Nature* **313**, 196 (1985).
182. J. Kitajewski, R. J. Schneider, B. Safer and T. Shenk, *MCBiol* **6**, 4493 (1986).
183. H. Hayashi, K. Tanaka, F. Jay, G. Khoury and G. Jay, *Cell* **43**, 263 (1985).
184. R. H. Schwartz, *ARI* **3**, 237 (1985).
185. L. Hood, M. Steinmetz and B. Malissen, *ARI* **1**, 529 (1983).
186. M. Andersson, S. Paabo, T. Nilsson and P. A. Peterson, *Cell* **43**, 215 (1985).
187. H.-G. Burgert and S. Kvist, *Cell* **41**, 987 (1985).
188. B. Roizman (ed.), "The Viruses: The Herpesviruses." Plenum, New York, 1982.
189. I. Domke-Opitz, P. Straub and H. Kirchner, *J. Virol.* **60**, 37 (1986).
190. P. Straub, I. Domke, H. Kirchner, H. Jacobsen and A. Panet, *Virology* **150**, 411 (1986).
191. I. Domke, P. Straub, H. Jacobsen, H. Kirchner and A. Panet, *J. Gen. Virol.* **66**, 2231 (1985).
192. A. Panet and H. Falk, *J. Gen. Virol.* **64**, 1999 (1983).
193. I. Gloger and A. Panet, *J. Gen. Virol.* **65**, 1107 (1984).
194. P. J. Cayley, J. A. Davies, K. G. McCullagh and I. M. Kerr, *EJB* **143**, 165 (1984).
195. M. Lipp and G. Brandner, *J. Gen. Virol.* **47**, 97 (1980).
196. S. Chatterjee, A. D. Lakeman, R. J. Whitley and E. Hunter, *Virus Res.* **1**, 81 (1984).

197. S. Chatterjee, E. Hunter and R. Whitley, *J. Virol.* **56**, 419 (1985).
198. A. Munoz and L. Carrasco, *J. Gen. Virol.* **65**, 1069 (1984).
199. K. Linnavuori and T. Hovi, *Virology* **130**, 1 (1983).
200. B. Wigdahl, C. A. Smith, H. M. Traglia and F. Rapp, *PNAS* **81**, 6217 (1984).
201. E. B. Fraser-Smith, D. A. Eppstein, Y. V. Marsh and T. R. Matthews, *Antimicrob. Agents Chemother.* **26**, 937 (1984).
202. E. B. Fraser-Smith, D. A. Eppstein, Y. V. Marsh and T. R. Matthews, *Antimicrob. Agents Chemother.* **25**, 563 (1984).
203. D. M. Moran, E. R. Kern and J. C. Overall, Jr., *J. Infect. Dis.* **151**, 1116 (1985).
204. A. Billiau, *Tex. Rep. Biol. Med.* **35**, 406 (1977).
205. P. M. Pitha, *Ann. N.Y. Acad. Sci.* **350**, 301 (1980).
206. A. Billiau, V. G. Edy, H. Sobis and P. DeSomer, *Int. J. Cancer* **14**, 335 (1974).
207. R. M. Friedman and J. M. Ramseur, *PNAS* **71**, 3542 (1974).
208. A. Billiau, V. G. Edy, E. DeClercq, H. Hermans and P. DeSomer, *Int. J. Cancer* **15**, 947 (1975).
209. R. M. Friedman, E. H. Chang, J. M. Ramseur and M. W. Myers, *J. Virol.* **16**, 569 (1975).
210. P. M. Pitha, W. P. Rowe and M. N. Oxman, *Virology* **70**, 324 (1976).
211. J. A. Bilello, N. A. Wivel and P. M. Pitha, *J. Virol.* **43**, 213 (1982).
212. R. E. Ziegler and W. K. Joklik, *J. Interferon Res.* **1**, 521 (1981).
213. S. Salzberg, A. Heller, M. Aboud, D. Gurari-Rotman and M. Revel, *Virology* **93**, 209 (1979).
214. G. C. Sen and N. H. Sarkar, *Virology* **102**, 431 (1980).
215. D. Chalbos, M. Crepin and B. Leblue, *J. Gen. Virol.* **62**, 65 (1982).
216. S. Chatterjee and E. Hunter, *Virology* **157**, 548 (1987).
217. A. G. Morris and D. C. Burke, *J. Gen. Virol.* **43**, 173 (1979).
218. M. Aboud, D. Moldovan-Levin and S. Salzberg, *J. Virol.* **37**, 836 (1981).
219. M. Huleihel and M. Aboud, *J. Virol.* **48**, 120 (1983).
220. W. Strube, M. Strube, H. Kroath, C. Jungwirth, G. Bodo and T. Graf, *J. Interferon Res.* **2**, 37 (1982).
221. W. Strube and C. Jungwirth, *Eur. J. Cell Biol.* **39**, 232 (1985).
222. W. Strube, C. Jungwirth, A. Ziemiecki and B. M. Jockusch, *Eur. J. Cell Biol.* **38**, 226 (1985).
223. A. G. Morris and C. Clegg, *Virology* **88**, 400 (1978).
224. R. J. Avery, J. D. Norton, J. S. Jones, D. C. Burke and A. G. Morris, *Nature* **288**, 93 (1980).
225. C. H. Riggin and P. M. Pitha, *Virology* **118**, 202 (1982).
226. C. Dani, N. Mechti, M. Piechaczyk, B. Lebleu, P. Jeanteur and J. M. Blanchard, *PNAS* **82**, 4896 (1985).
227. M. McMahon, G. R. Stark and I. M. Kerr, *J. Virol.* **57**, 362 (1986).
228. D. Levy, A. Larner, A. Chaudhuri, L. E. Babiss and J. E. Darnell, Jr., *PNAS* **83**, 8929 (1986).
229. M. Einat, D. Resnitzky and A. Kimchi, *Nature* **313**, 597 (1985).
230. G. J. Jonak and E. Knight, *PNAS* **81**, 1747 (1984).
231. E. Knight, E. D. Anton, D. Fahey, B. K. Friedland and G. J. Jonak, *PNAS* **82**, 1151 (1985).
232. C. Samid, E. H. Cheng and R. M. Friedman, *BBRC* **119**, 21 (1984).
233. G. Soslau, A. R. Bogucki, D. Gillespie and H. R. Hubbell, *BBRC* **119**, 941 (1984).
234. M. Einat, D. Resnitzky and A. Kimchi, *PNAS* **82**, 7608 (1985).
235. M. Perucho and M. Esteban, *J. Virol.* **54**, 229 (1985).

236. M. F. Dubois, M. Vignal, M. LeCunff and C. Chany, *Nature* **303**, 433 (1982).
237. H. Fan and P. MacIsaac, *J. Virol.* **27**, 449 (1978).
238. M. Aboud, R. Kimchi, M. Bakhanashvili and S. Salzberg, *J. Virol.* **40**, 830 (1981).
239. P. M. Pitha, S. P. Stall, D. P. Bolognesi, T. P. Denny and W. P. Rowe, *Virology* **79**, 1 (1977).
240. S. Z. Shapiro, M. Strand, and A. Billiau, *Infect. Immun.* **16**, 742 (1977).
241. E. H. Chang, S. J. Mims, T. J. Triche and R. M. Friedman, *J. Gen. Virol.* **34**, 363 (1977).
242. P. K. Y. Wong, P. H. Yuen, R. MacLeod, E. H. Chang, M. W. Myers and R. M. Friedman, *Cell* **10**, 245 (1977).
243. E. H. Chang, M. W. Myers, P. K. Y. Wong and R. M. Friedman, *Virology* **77**, 625 (1977).
244. E. H. Chang and R. M. Friedman, *BBRC* **77**, 392 (1977).
245. P. M. Pitha, B. Fernie, F. Maldarelli, T. Hattman and N. A. Wivel, *J. Gen. Virol.* **46**, 97 (1980).
246. G. C. Sen and A. Pinter, *Virology* **126**, 403 (1983).
247. S. Chatterjee, H. C. Cheung and E. Hunter, *PNAS* **79**, 835 (1982).
248. Y. Tomita, J. Nishimaki, F. Takahashi and T. Kuwata, *Virology* **120**, 258 (1982).
249. S. Chatterjee and E. Hunter, *Virology* **104**, 487 (1980).
250. S. Chatterjee and E. Hunter, *Virology* **95**, 421 (1979).
251. G. C. Sen, R. Herz, V. Davatelis and S. Pestka, *J. Virol.* **50**, 445 (1984).
252. D. D. Ho, K. L. Hartshorn, T. R. Rota, C. A. Andrews, J. C. Kaplan, R. T. Schooley and M. S. Hirsch, *Lancet* **1**, 602 (1985).
253. S. M. Hammer, J. M. Gillis, J. E. Groopman and R. M. Rose, *PNAS* **83**, 8734 (1986).
254. J. L. Moore, B. J. Poiesz, K. W. Zamkoff, S. A. Merl, S. Hanna, A. F. Gazdar and R. L. Comis, *J. Virol.* **53**, 440 (1985).
255. R. K. Maheshwari, F. T. Jay and R. M. Friedman, *Science* **207**, 540 (1980).
256. F. T. Jay, M. R. Dawood and R. M. Friedman, *J. Gen. Virol.* **64**, 707 (1983).
257. R. K. Maheshwari, A. E. Demsey, S. B. Mohanty and R. M. Friedman, *PNAS* **77**, 2284 (1980).
258. R. K. Maheshwari and R. M. Friedman, *J. Gen. Virol.* **44**, 261 (1979).
259. R. K. Maheshwari, M. M. Husain and R. M. Friedman, *BBRC* **117**, 161 (1983).
260. J. Lenard and R. W. Compans, *BBA* **344**, 51 (1974).
261. B. Moss, in "The Molecular Biology of Animal Viruses" (D. P. Nayak, ed.), Vol. 2, p. 849. Marcel Dekker, New York, 1979.
262. C. R. Faltynek and C. Baglioni, *Virology* **127**, 225 (1983).
263. K. Olden, B. A. Bernard, W. Turner and S. L. White, *Nature* **300**, 290 (1982).
264. D. H. L. Bishop, P. Repik, J. F. Obijeski, N. F. Moore and R. R. Wagner, *J. Virol.* **16**, 75 (1975).
265. R. Gibson, S. Schlesinger and S. Kornfeld, *JBC* **254**, 3600 (1979).
266. R. Gibson, R. Leavitt, S. Kornfeld and S. Schlesinger, *Cell* **13**, 671 (1978).
267. M. S. Kang and A. D. Elbein, *J. Virol.* **46**, 60 (1983).
268. B. Cartwright and F. Brown, *J. Gen. Virol.* **35**, 197 (1977).
269. R. M. Friedman, in "Interferon 1979" (I. Gresser, ed.), Vol. 1, p. 53. Academic Press, New York, 1979.
270. B. R. G. Williams and R. H. Silverman (eds.), "The 2-5A System." Liss, New York, 1985.
271. I. M. Kerr and R. E. Brown, *PNAS* **75**, 256 (1978).
272. H. Jacobsen, C. W. Czarniecki, D. Krause, R. M. Friedman and R. H. Silverman, *Virology* **125**, 496 (1983).

273. A. Schmidt, Y. Chernajovsky, L. Shulman, P. Federman, H. Berissi and M. Revel, *PNAS* **76**, 4788 (1979).
274. I. Heron, M. Hokland and K. Berg, *PNAS* **75**, 6215 (1978).
275. T. Y. Basham, M. F. Bourgeade, A. A. Creasey and T. C. Merigan, *PNAS* **79**, 3265 (1982).
276. M. Fellous, U. Nir, D. Wallach, G. Merlin, M. Rubinstein and M. Revel, *PNAS* **79**, 3082 (1982).
277. O. Yoshie, H. Schmidt, E. S. P. Reddy, S. Weissman and P. Lengyel, *JBC* **257**, 13169 (1982).
278. G. Trinchieri and B. Perussia, *Immunol. Today* **6**, 131 (1985).
279. T. Collins, A. J. Korman, C. T. Wake, J. M. Boss, D. J. Kappes, W. Fiers, K. A. Ault, M. A. Gimbrone, J. L. Strominger and J. S. Pober, *PNAS* **81**, 4917 (1984).
280. G. H. W. Wong, P. F. Bartlett, I. Clark-Lewis, F. Battye and J. W. Schrader, *Nature* **310**, 688 (1984).
281. H. P. Koeffler, J. Ranyard, L. Yelton, R. Billing and R. Bohman, *PNAS* **81**, 4080 (1980).
282. R. C. Strunk, F. S. Cole, D. H. Perimutter and H. R. Colten, *JBC* **260**, 15280 (1985).
283. Y.-S. Cheng, R. J. Colonno and F. Yin, *JBC* **258**, 7746 (1983).
284. P. Chezzi, M. Bianchi, A. Mantovani, F. Spreafico and M. Salmona, *BBRC* **119**, 144 (1984).
285. L. Delria, V. Abbott, N. Goderham and G. J. Mannering, *BBRC* **131**, 109 (1985).
286. R. Yoshida, J. Imanishi, T. Oku, T. Kishida and O. Hayaishi, *PNAS* **78**, 129 (1981).
287. E. R. Pferrferkorn, S. Rebhun and M. Eckel, *J. Interferon Res.* **6**, 267 (1986).
288. R. I. Friedman, S. P. Manly, M. McMahon, I. M. Kerr and G. R. Stark, *Cell* **38**, 745 (1984).
289. M. Tsujimoto, Y. K. Yip and J. Vilcek, *J. Immunol.* **136**, 2441 (1986).
290. M. Tsujimoto and J. Vilcek, *JBC* **261**, 5384 (1986).
291. B. B. Aggarwal, T. E. Eessalu and P. E. Hass, *Nature* **318**, 665 (1985).
292. M. B. Goldring, L. J. Sandell, M. L. Stephenson and S. M. Krane, *JBC* **261**, 9049 (1986).
293. J. Rosenbloom, G. Feldman, B. Freundlich and S. A. Jimenez, *BBRC* **123**, 365 (1984).
294. K. C. Zoon, Y. Karasaki, D. L. ZurNedden, R. Hu and H. Arneiter, *PNAS* **83**, 8226 (1986).
295. F. Besancon, M. Bourgeade and U. Testa, *JBC* **260**, 13074 (1985).
296. D. J. Adams, F. R. Balkwill, D. B. Griffin, J. D. Hayes, A. D. Lewis and C. R. Wolf, *JBC* **262**, 4888 (1987).
297. J. F. Bukowski and R. M. Welsh, *J. Virol.* **59**, 735 (1986).
298. M. A. N Wabuke-Bunoti, J. R. Bennink and S. A. Plotkin, *J. Virol.* **60**, 1062 (1986).
299. M. J. Blackman and A. G. Morris, *Immunology* **56**, 451 (1985).
300. R. Feinman, D. S. Siegel, J. Le and J. Vilcek, *Cell. Immunol.* **99**, 287 (1986).
301. A. DeBenedetti, B. A. Pytel and C. Baglioni, *PNAS* **84**, 6740 (1987).
302. N. Ulker, X. Zhang and C. E. Samuel, *JBC* **262**, 16798 (1987).
303. N. Ulker and C. E. Samuel, *JBC* **262**, 16804 (1987).
304. O. Takikawa, T. Kuroiwa, F. Yamazaki and R. Kido, *JBC* **263**, 2041 (1988).
305. J. Chebath, P. Benech, M. Revel and M. Vigneron, *Nature* **330**, 587 (1987).

Modulation of Cellular Genes
by Oncogenes

RUSSELL M. LEBOVITZ AND
MICHAEL W. LIEBERMAN

Department of Pathology
Fox Chase Cancer Center
Philadelphia, Pennsylvania 19111

Few recent developments in the biological sciences have had more far-reaching implications than the discovery of oncogenes. Originally identified as transforming retroviral genes (v-*onc*), they were soon found to have cellular counterparts (c-*onc*), and this discovery led to the realization that these genes probably have functions beyond their transforming potential. At the same time, analysis of the DNA tumor viruses led to the identification of a second set of transforming genes, without obvious cellular homologs, that appeared to be powerful modulators of cell function. Initially the RNA tumor-virus-related genes and the DNA tumor-virus genes were studied by different groups with different interests; however, as more was learned about both the structure and function(s) of these genes, it became clear that all oncogenes, regardless of origin, are best considered together. Therefore, we have included examples of all three types (c-*onc*, v-*onc*, and DNA tumor-virus genes) in this review of the modulation of gene expression by oncogenes.

This review has a particular focus. The fact that many reviews of oncogene structure and function have appeared in the last few years reflects recognition of the importance of the field as well as its breadth (e.g., *1–9*). It is also, however, a measure of change. Early investigations dealt primarily with the cloning and sequencing of oncogenes

73

and analysis of their transformation potential. More recently, studies have focused on the role of protooncogenes (cellular sequences from which oncogenes are derived) in normal cellular function and regulation of differentiation and development. While this area of research has proved more complex than the initial investigations and will continue to require extensive effort, new approaches are being developed to understand how oncogenes modulate gene expression. In this respect, most of the progress to date has been made in systems utilizing DNA-virus-derived genes (e.g., 2). Recently, however, workers have begun to investigate the modulation of gene expression by retroviral and cellular oncogenes. In this review we emphasize the commonality of approach of the two groups, and that different oncogenes may have remarkably similar (supplementary) effects as well as complementary effects. By focusing directly on what is known about how oncogenes modulate the expression of cellular genes, we hope to stimulate more investigation in this important area of research. As examples we have chosen a cytoplasmic oncogene (*ras*), a nuclear oncogene (*fos*), and a nuclear oncogene derived from a DNA virus (adenovirus E1A). [*ras:* an oncogene originally isolated from Harvey (H) and Kirsten (K) murine sarcoma viruses; *fos:* an oncogene originally isolated from Finkel-Biskis-Jinkins murine osteosarcoma virus; N-*ras,* R-*ras:* neuroblastoma-associated and *ras*-related *ras* genes, respectively; p21 *ras:* a 21,000-Da protein, product of the *ras* gene; E1A: an adenovirus locus that codes for a regulatory protein.]

I. The *ras* Gene Family

Three mammalian *ras* protooncogenes (H-*ras*, K-*ras*, and N-*ras*) (e.g., *10–14*) and a related gene R-*ras* (*15*) have been identified. The three protooncogenes are highly homologous (~95% amino-acid conservation), share a common intron/exon motif, encode similar 21-kDa proteins (p21), and probably evolved from a common ancestor. R-*ras* protein is predicted to be ~55% homologous to H-*ras* p21 and to contain 236 amino acids (compared to 189); the intron/exon organization of R-*ras* also differs from other members of the *ras* family. (Hereafter, for lack of information, we do not consider R-*ras* unless specifically mentioned.)

Most efforts to understand the function of the *ras* genes have centered on their effects on membrane-related functions and intermediary metabolism. Over the past few years progress has been rapid, and these genes or their mutated (activated) cellular or viral counterparts (9) have been shown to be involved in GTP binding and hydrolysis,

(16–18), diacylglycerol and phosphatidylinositol metabolism (19), and membrane ruffling (20). Microinjection of *ras* proteins also induces DNA synthesis (21, 22). In spite of this progress, it is clear that we do not understand how *ras* genes regulate cellular behavior. It seems unlikely that all of the effects of *ras* are mediated locally via standard biochemical pathways, and yet relatively little is known about the role of *ras* in altered gene expression. We still have no fundamental understanding of how *ras*-induced events at the cell membrane are communicated to the nucleus and effect changes in gene expression.

On the other hand, recent studies indicate that major changes in gene expression occur following the introduction of *ras* genes into cells (see below). While these findings are not surprising in view of the profound changes in morphology and behavior induced by the *ras* oncogenes, they are intriguing since they offer a molecular approach to understanding an important set of problems in cell and tumor biology.

Given the remarkable preservation of sequence among the protooncogenes, the question of how or if their functions vary naturally arises. Investigators have approached this problem in several ways. Studies of *ras* expression during development and in adult tissues have evaluated levels of p21*ras* and steady-state mRNA levels of H-*ras*, K-*ras*, and N-*ras* (23–25). In adult tissues, with only a few exceptions, RNA levels for the three genes parallel one another; further, there was no tissue in which expression was undetectable. Similar results were obtained in a survey of pre- and postnatal development. Even given the severe limitations of this type of study (e.g., the mixture of cell types in tissues and different states of cellular proliferation), the result is a little disappointing in that cell function does not appear to segregate strongly with expression of different *ras* genes.

Clues to differential function might also reside in sequence homologies (12). Although the amino-acid sequence of the genes is in general highly conserved, there is far greater diversity near the carboxyl terminus (residues 171–185). This region is directly adjacent to and potentially overlaps a block of amino acids related to lipid binding and membrane localization (26). It is therefore possible that differences in function might reside, not in the "active" domains, but in conformational or positional differences near or within the plasma membrane. Certainly the immunoglobulins provide a precedent for this conjecture (e.g., 27). Parenthetically, it is also of interest that R-*ras* retains a Cys residue at a position analogous to the Cys of position 186 in the three protooncogenes; site-directed mutagenesis suggests that this residue may be crucial for membrane localization and function (26).

One of the potentially important advances in the analysis of oncogene function is the identification of different functional domains as in the case of the E1A gene (see Section IV,A). Similar studies have been done with the H-v-*ras* (viral Harvey *ras*) gene (28, 29). While both studies reveal that certain regions in *ras* must be retained for transformation and GTP/GDP binding, Willumsen and collaborators have identified mutants that do not transform but bind GDP normally (positions 22–29), one that transforms cells but does not bind GDP (positions 124–131), and mutants that do not localize to the membrane and do not transform (positions 186–189) (29). Thus, while transformation appears to require membrane localization, it may be possible under some conditions to separate guanylate binding from transforming potential. Clearly, however, this area requires a more detailed analysis, including the relation between GTP/GDP binding and GTP hydrolysis and other effects on intermediary metabolism.

Although p21*ras* is associated with the cell membrane, and the local biochemical effects of *ras* have been most extensively studied, the postulated role of protooncogenes in differentiation and development (e.g., 5, 6) and the many changes in gene expression characteristically seen in neoplastic transformation both *in vivo* and *in vitro* have stimulated investigators to examine the role of *ras* genes in the control of gene expression. This proposed role is not as yet extensively documented and is almost certainly indirect or at least removed by one or several steps from the *ras* gene product. However, evidence linking *ras* to the regulation of gene expression is rapidly accumulating (Table I).

It has been known for many years that tumor cells take up glucose at elevated rates compared to untransformed cells. Recently one group demonstrated that transfection of Fisher rat 3T3 cells with an activated H-c-*ras* gene markedly increases steady-state levels of glucose transport protein RNA and the protein itself (30). Interestingly, the effect was also seen with v-*src* and FSV (Fujinani sarcoma virus carrying a *gag/fps* fusion gene), but not with *myc* (30, 31). In experiments with FSV, a 3-fold increase in transcription rates accompanied the increased RNA levels (31).

Recently, a secreted protease gene ("transin") has been cloned and sequenced (32, 33). In Fisher rat 3T3 cells and Rat-1 cells transformed with the activated H-c-*ras* oncogene (T24/EJ)—H-c-*ras* gene with a mutation in codon 12—steady-state levels of transin RNA were greatly increased while RNA levels of four glycolytic enzymes re-

TABLE I

Modulation of Gene Expression by *ras* Genes

Target	Effector	Result	Cells examined	Reference
Glucose transport protein	Human H-c-*ras* T24/EJ	Increased steady-state levels of RNA; increased protein	FR 3T3 fibroblasts	30
Transin	Human H-c-*ras* T24/EJ	Increased steady-state levels of RNA	FR 3T3 and Rat-1 fibroblasts	32, 33
γ-Glutamyltransferase	Human H-c-*ras* T24/EJ	Increased steady-state levels of RNA; increased protein	Rat liver epithelial cells; no effect in Rat-1 fibroblasts	34
Glutathione transferase (placental)	Human H-c-*ras* T24/EJ	Increased steady-state levels of RNA; increased protein	Rat liver epithelial cells; no effect in Rat-1 fibroblasts	34, 38
Polyoma virus enhancer	Human H-c-*ras* T24/EJ; human H-*ras* protooncogenes (lesser effect)	Activates polyoma enhancer	Myeloma cells, NIH 3T3 fibroblasts, and F9 embryonal carcinoma cells; no effect in LMTK⁻ fibroblasts	39
β-Globin promoter	Human H-c-*ras* T24/EJ	Increases transcription from β-globin promoter	Myeloma cells	39
Sensitivity to natural killer cytolysis	Human H-c-*ras* T24/EJ	Increased sensitivity to lysis by NK cells	C3H 10T½ fibroblasts	45
c-*fos*	MSV H-*ras* protein (p21*ras*)	c-*fos* protein accumulation	NIH 3T3 cells	40
Transforming growth factor β	H-v-*ras*	Increased TGF-β protein	NIH 3T3 fibroblasts	47

mained unchanged. The effect is not *ras*-specific as cells transformed with polyoma virus, polyoma middle-t antigen, and Rous sarcoma virus and cells treated with epidermal growth factor also accumulated transin RNA. The sequence of the promoter region and the genomic structure of this interesting gene have not been reported. The interplay of its regulation by oncogenes and its biological role as an extracellular protease will be interesting to follow.

Other groups have looked at the effect of the activated H-c-*ras* gene on γ-glutamyltransferase (EC 2.3.2.2) and placental glutathione transferase (EC 2.5.1.18) expression in rat liver epithelial cells (*34, 38, 137*). These genes are of interest as increased levels of their expression in liver are among the earliest changes seen when chemical carcinogens are administered to animals (*35–37*). Steady-state mRNA levels of these genes were 5–50 times higher in liver epithelial cells transformed with metallothionein-activated *ras* (T24) constructions than in control cells. There is at least some specificity in the phenomenon since α-tubulin expression was unchanged. There also appears to be some cellular specificity as well, since *ras*-transformed Rat-1 (a rat fibroblast line) cells show the same steady-state RNA levels as untransformed controls. The relative contributions of mRNA stability and increased or decreased rates of transcription to any of these changes are unknown, but these studies along with investigations of altered glucose transport protein gene and transin expression clearly document the role of *ras* in the modulation of gene expression.

Investigators have also looked at the effect of *ras* expression on other oncogenes. In transient expression assays, activated H-c-*ras* and to a lesser extent the H-c-*ras* protooncogene activate the polyoma virus enhancer (*39*) as much as 50-fold in a myeloma cell line and in NIH 3T3 (a mouse fibroblast line) cells, but no effect was observed in fibroblasts. In F9 (mouse) teratocarcinoma cells, an activated H-c-*ras* gene stimulates polyoma enhancer activity more efficiently in undifferentiated cells than in retinoic-acid-differentiated cells. In myeloma cells, the β-globin promoter is also stimulated, but the effect is not as large as that seen with the polyoma enhancer, and required higher levels of H-c-*ras* DNA. Another group looked at the effect of *ras* expression on c-*fos* expression by microinjecting H-v-*ras* protein into cells and examining expression by immunocytochemistry (*40*). This procedure resulted in large increases in c-*fos* protein in NIH 3T3 cells, but in lines permanently transformed with H-v-*ras*, levels of c-*fos* were similar to control cells, indicating that other factors prevent sustained high levels of c-*fos* in response to *ras* expression.

Other observations also suggest that *ras* expression has important effects on the expression of other genes. In PC12 (pheochromocy-toma) cells, infection with K-MSV (i.e., K-v-*ras*) or H-MSV (i.e., H-v-*ras*) mimicked nerve growth factor (NGF) in inducing differentiation in these cells (*41*). The effect was also achieved by microinjection of *ras* protein (*42*) and blocked by the injection of anti-*ras* antibodies (*43*); v-*src* and to a lesser extent v-*mos* also mimicked the effects of NGF in PC12 cells (*41, 44*). Transformation of cells of the mouse fibroblast line C3H 10T½ with an activated H-c-*ras* gene increased the sensitivity of these cells to natural killer cell activity; these findings suggest that *ras*-induced transformation, like other types of transfor-mation, may induce changes in membrane proteins (*45*). As early as 1978, experiments suggested that Moloney murine sarcoma virus (i.e., v-*mos*) transformed cells synthesize epidermal growth factor-like (TGF-α-like) activity (*46*). More recent studies have found that trans-formation of newborn rat kidney fibroblasts (NRK) cells with Harvey or Moloney sarcoma virus (i.e., H-v-*ras* or v-*mos*) results in a 40-fold increase in TGF-β protein and a fall in TGF-β receptors (*47*). Trans-formation of cells with a variety of oncogenes and oncogenic viruses including K-v-*ras* and *H*-c-*ras* T24 results in a decrease in available platelet-derived growth factor receptors and the synthesis of a protein that competes with platelet-derived growth factor (PDGF) in binding assays (*48*).

What conclusions may be drawn about the role of *ras* genes in the regulation of gene expression? First, since it appears that *ras* genes do not act proximally, they probably share final common pathways with other oncogenes and mediators of gene expression. That both *ras* and *src* and perhaps *mos* genes can stimulate neurite outgrowth in PC12 cells, that both *ras* and *src* as well as Fujinani sarcoma virus (FSV) infection result in increased levels of glucose transport protein RNA, and that the *ras*T24 oncogene results in increased expression of genes that are expressed in chemical-carcinogen-treated rat liver, all support this formulation. Similarly, the effects of *ras, src,* and polyoma se-quences on transin expression are in agreement with the idea of com-mon pathways of oncogene action.

The extent to which *ras* modulates the expression of other on-cogenes (e.g., *fos*) remains to be investigated. However, extensive work on growth factors indicates that this stimulation is not a unique effect of *ras*. Rather, the pressing questions are how important is the role of *ras* in the regulation of *fos* and what is the role of increased *fos* expression in cell regulation? And more generally, what pathways are involved in *ras*-initiated alterations in gene expression? Simulation of the Ela enhancer by *ras* is an intriguing finding and probably is only the first of a number of such findings to be reported. While all of these interrelationships seem complicated, complexity should not surprise us in view of what we have learned in the last 30 years about metabolic regulation—especially since *ras* and other oncogenes represent important regulatory molecules, which themselves must be carefully regulated.

II. The Role of *fos* in Differentiation, Development, and Altered Gene Expression

Interest in *fos* has been stimulated by the realization that the *fos* protein is localized in the nucleus, probably complexed to at least one other protein (p39) and perhaps DNA (49–52). Many external signals stimulate a transient burst of *fos* mRNA synthesis; epidermal growth factor, nerve growth factor, or platelet-derived growth factor, cAMP, TPA (the phorbol ester), vitamin D$_3$, *ras* protein, and thyrotropin all stimulate *fos* expression in different cell types (40, 53–60). The general responsiveness of *fos* may be related to its role in "competence" (i.e., "preparedness" for entry into the cell cycle) and seems in part, at least, to be mediated through protein kinase C (EC 2.7.1.37) (61, 62). Investigators have begun to examine the mechanism of this responsiveness and have found an enhancer element as well as a serum-responsive element that displays dyad symmetry and is located between −200 and −400 of the c-*fos* transcription start (63–66). A binding site for an EGF-induced protein has also been identified in this region (67). While the exact relationship among these sites remains to be established, it seems that at least some of the pathways by which external events stimulate *fos* transcription will soon be known. What is less accessible is the role of *fos* in modulating the expression of other genes (Table II).

Because of its responsiveness to exogenous signals and its localization in the nucleus, investigations have focused on the role of *fos* in development and differentiation. An initial study revealed that c-*fos* was expressed early in embryonic development and only at low levels after day 9 (68). However, samples from early times contained extra-embryonic tissue, and subsequent analysis suggests that these tissues account for much of the signal (57, 68, 69). During early postnatal development, c-*fos* was expressed in most tissues examined but appeared especially high in bone (68). Subsequently it was recognized that much of the expression resulted from contaminating hemopoietic cells (57, 69, 70). The story is further complicated by findings in transgenic mice carrying metallothionein (MT)-c-*fos* genes with a 3'

TABLE II

MODULATION OF GENE EXPRESSION BY *fos* GENES

Target	Effector	Result	Cells examined	Reference
α_1 (III) Collagen	v-*fos*	Transactivation in CAT assay	NIH 3T3 cells	78
RSV LTR	v-*fos*	Transactivation in CAT assay	NIH 3T3 cells	78
Glutathione transferase (placental)	Metallothionein–c-*fos* with 3′ deletion	Increased steady-state levels of RNA	Rat liver epithelial cells	R. Lebovitz and M. Lieberman (unpublished)
aP2	c-*fos*	Inhibition of aP2 expression binding to a 5′ regulatory element	3T3-F442A preadipocytes	80
aP2	c-*fos*	Binding to a 5′ regulatory element	3T3-F442A adipocytes	80

deletion (which enhances expression) (71). Although MT-c-*fos* RNA was detected in many tissues, a careful histopathologic study revealed changes only in osseus tissues. These tissues expressed MT-c-*fos* while bone marrow cells did not, suggesting that the effects were direct effects of *fos* expression and not a trophic effect from neighboring cells stimulated by *fos*. It is also of interest to remember that FBJ virus was originally isolated from an osteosarcoma. While the role of c-*fos* expression in the regulation of specific genes in osseous tissue has not yet been evaluated, other workers have demonstrated that c-*fos* expression stimulates transcription of at least one collagen gene (see following paragraphs).

Other investigations of the role of c-*fos* expression in differentiation reveal a complicated picture. Initial observations indicated that induction of monocyte (but no granulocyte) differentiation is accompanied by rapid induction of c-*fos* expression (72). More recent findings, however, suggest that c-*fos* expression and monocyte differentiation can be dissociated (61, 73). Transfection of F9 teratocarcinoma cells with c-*fos* yielded differentiated colonies that appeared to make characteristic intermediate filaments as well as fibronectin and type-IV collagen (74). In a subsequent analysis, it appeared that low levels of *fos* expression are necessary for differentiation but high levels of *fos* expression do not further alter the process or recruit additional cells (75); it seems that expression of *fos* in this system is necessary for differentiation, but that other events actually trigger the changes. In PC12 neuroblastoma cells, differentiation induced by nerve growth factor is accompanied by increases in *fos* expression, but evidence that increased *fos* expression is essential has not been obtained (76). Thus the role of *fos* in differentiation has been tantalizingly elusive, perhaps because so many stimuli in so many different systems enhance *fos* expression (see above).

One other aspect of cellular regulation by *fos* deserves comment. There has been partial success in dissociating the immortalization function of v-*fos* from its transforming function (77). Mutation of a single amino acid in the center portion of the protein greatly increases its immortalizing potential without altering its transforming potential (77). Because both these functions probably rely on alterations in the expression of cellular genes or sets of genes, this study provides a valuable model for analyzing how *fos* modulates the expression of genes known to be susceptible to regulation by it (see following).

Less is known about how *fos* regulates the expression of individual genes. In part this gap results from preoccupation with how *fos* itself is regulated, but it also stems from the inability until recently to identify suitable target genes. One group looked at the effect of v-*fos* synthesis on the expression of four genes in a transient expression system with NIH 3T3 cells (78). They found that expression from an α_1 (III) collagen/CAT gene and an RSV LTR/CAT gene was enhanced 5- to 10-fold and ~3 fold, respectively, by cotransfection of v-*fos* [LTR = long terminal repeat; CAT = chloramphenicol acetyltransferase (EC 2.3.1.28)]. No effect was found when the SV40 early-region promoter or the chicken β-actin promoter was used. Competition experiments suggested that a trans-acting factor is involved in the stimulation. Since β-actin RNA levels rise rapidly along with *fos* RNA in stimulated cells (53), the data on collagen and RSV regulation (78) suggest that *fos* expression does not stimulate β-actin expression directly, and raise the possibility of coregulation. The finding that the human c-*fos* and *Xenopus* cytoskeletal actin promoter share a conserved protein-binding site offers an opportunity to investigate this possibility (79).

R. Lebovitz and M. Lieberman (unpublished) used a metallothionein–c-*fos* fusion gene in which the 3′ end was truncated to investigate changes in gene expression (75). In rat liver epithelial cells stably transformed with this construction, steady-state levels of the placental glutathione transferase were increased as much as 3-fold in response to 5 μM CdSO$_4$.

A negative regulatory element (FSE2) that inhibits the expression of the aP2 gene in preadipocytes has been characterized (80). (FSE = fat-specific element; aP2 = adipocyte gene probably coding for a 13-kDa lipid-binding protein.) *Fos* protein appears to bind to the element as part of a transregulatory complex. In adipocytes, *fos* protein also binds to the element with other proteins, but no evidence for regulatory behavior was obtained. This novel observation should provide an opportunity to study how *fos* protein interacts with regulatory factors that are more limited in their cell and gene specificity.

One is struck by the parallels in cellular responses to *ras* and *fos* expression. The similar behavior of the placental glutathione transferase in liver epithelial cells carrying H-c-*ras* and c-*fos* constructions suggests either that one gene may act through the other or that both induce a common state in the cell. However, the observation that the *ras* construction is transforming while the *fos* construction is not indicates that the effects are not equivalent. Since effects may have different thresholds, the possibility remains that the differences between lines carrying *ras* and those carrying *fos* are largely quantitative.

III. Modulation of Cellular Gene Expression by the Adenovirus E1A Products

The adenovirus-early-region-1A (E1A) gene products are the first viral products expressed after adenovirus infection and are required for the transcriptional activation (transactivation) of other viral early genes (81, 82). At the same time, the E1A products suppress transcription from host promoters that are enhancer-driven; these apparently include some of the most abundantly expressed cellular products, such as immunoglobulins in B-lymphocytes and preproinsulin in pancreatic islet cells (83, 84). The net effect of E1A expression is therefore to shift a significant portion of the cellular transcription machinery toward viral gene expression, and in this role the E1A products have provided an extremely useful and accessible model in which to study the regulation of transcription (85).

Studies using cloned, mutated E1A products demonstrate that in addition to direct effects on transcription, constitutive expression of E1A products in a variety of cell types results in altered patterns of cellular growth, differentiation, and senescence (86). These alterations include immortalization, induction of DNA synthesis in otherwise quiescent cells, and tumorigenic transformation of primary cells in cooperation with other oncogenes. In these latter functions, E1A resembles many of the nuclear oncogenes, such as *myc*, *myb*, and *fos* (87, 88).

In this section, we review briefly the evidence for selective regulation of transcription by E1A products as well as any models that link the modulation of cellular transcription to the transforming properties of these proteins. A detailed discussion of adenovirus transcription and its regulation in permissive and semipermissive cells is beyond the scope of this manuscript; excellent reviews have been published elsewhere (85, 89, 90).

A. Structure of the E1A Products

The two early E1A products, 289 and 243 amino-acid residues in length, are translated in the same reading frame from 13-S and 12-S transcripts, respectively; they differ only by an internal stretch of 46 residues which is unique to the 289-residue product (residues 140–185). A comparison of E1A products among different adenovirus serotypes has identified three conserved domains, each of which exhibits at least 40% amino-acid-sequence homology. Two of the three conserved domains are present in both the 289- and 243-residue products, while the third consists primarily of the region unique to the 289-residue product (90).

As previously discussed, the E1A region encodes several different activities involved with the regulation of viral and host transcription and cell growth. Studies utilizing numerous E1A point mutations indicate that each of the major E1A-associated activities (transcriptional activation, transcriptional repression, stimulation of host DNA synthesis) is located in one of the three conserved domains. Furthermore, each of the conserved domains appears to function independently of the others, since point mutations within a given conserved domain inactivate a unique subset of E1A activities. For example, point mutations in conserved domain III (residues 140–188 and unique to the 289-residue product) block transactivation of viral and host promoters, but are fully competent for suppression of transcription and induction of host DNA synthesis (91, 92). Conversely, point mutations in conserved domain II (residues 121–140) no longer effectively suppress transcription, but transactivation and induction of DNA synthesis remain intact. Other E1A functions, including induction of host DNA synthesis, appear to reside in conserved domain I (residues 40–80).

At least two different models can account for the multiple, independent activities of the E1A products. The first predicts that each of the conserved domains is able to function as a completely autonomous unit, and that interactions between distant amino acids, if they occur at all, are of little significance compared to interactions within a single conserved domain. A second possibility is that the E1A products fold into several alternative three-dimensional structures, each with a different activity, and that this folding is directed primarily by sequences within the conserved domains. Mutations within each conserved domain would thus eliminate both a single folded structure and its corresponding activity. In either case, it is remarkable that so many different activities could coexist independently within such relatively small polypeptides.

B. Transactivation of Nonchromosomal Genes by E1A

Mutations within conserved domain III of the E1A gene, a region expressed only in the 289-residue product, prevent transactivation of the other adenovirus early promoters and block viral replication. Cells that express an intact E1A gene (e.g., 293 cells) can overcome this block (93). Several lines of evidence, however, argue convincingly against direct binding of any E1A product to the other early promoters; these include the following: (1) the 5' promoter regions of the adenovirus early (E) promoters (E1B, E2, E3, E4) exhibit minimal sequence homology, and there is no evidence of a consensus sequence for binding a common E1A-encoded transcription factor (94);

(2) both the pseudorabies virus (a herpesvirus) immediately early gene (95) and the HTLV-II (a lymphotropic retrovirus) X gene (96) can transactivate the adenovirus early promoters; it is highly unlikely that such evolutionarily divergent viruses would retain identical DNA-binding sites; (3) the 289-residue E1A product also stimulates transcription from RNA polymerase III promoters, which have no homology with any of the adenovirus early promoters (97); and (4) DNA-binding assays showing a high degree of sensitivity and specificity in other systems fail to demonstrate specific interactions between E1A products and any of the adenovirus early promoters (98). These observations are consistent with a model in which the 289-residue E1A product modifies the activity of multiple transcription factors, which then bind directly to the adenovirus early promoters (see following paragraphs).

More recent studies demonstrate that in addition to transactivation of adenovirus early promoters, the 289-residue E1A product stimulates transcription from a large number of eukaryotic promoters present (on viruses or plasmids) as episomal DNA. These include the human α- and β-globin promoters (99), the rat preproinsulin promoter (100), and the SV40 early promoter (101). Progressive deletions of the 5' regions can be used to identify those promoter sequences necessary for E1A transactivation; in the case of the human β-globin (99) and adenovirus E1B promoters (102), only the TATA box is required. These experiments suggest that transactivation of promoters on non-chromosomal DNA is due, at least in part, to the activation by E1A of relatively nonspecific (with respect to any particular promoter) transcription factors such as the TATA-binding factor (103, 104), or in the case of RNA polymerase III-associated transcription factor C, TF111C (105). This activation may involve posttranslational modification, increased abundance (106), or both.

In addition to the (promoter) nonspecific transactivation discussed above, stimulation of the E2, E1A, and possibly the other adenovirus early promoters by the 289-residue E1A product involves a second, more selective mechanism. Nevins and co-workers (107) identified a protein in adenovirus-infected HeLa cell nuclei, the E2 promoter-binding factor (E2F), that binds specifically to a nucleotide sequence lying upstream of both the E2 and E1A genes (107). This common sequence consists of the octanucleotide, TTTCGCGS,* that appears twice within the 5' upstream sequence of each gene. The other

---

* S = G or C (NC-IUB Recommendation; see *EJB* **150**, 1, 1985) [Eds.].

adenovirus early promoters (E1B, E3, E4) and the major late promoter do not contain this octanucleotide, and accordingly, they do not compete with E2 in binding to E2F *in vitro* (*108*).

Although maximal E2F-binding activity is dependent on expression of E1A products, at least two independent lines of evidence indicate that E2F is a cellular transcription factor. First, very low levels of an E2 promoter-binding activity with specificity identical to that of E2F can be detected in extracts from uninfected HeLa cell nuclei after exonuclease III digestion (*109*). Interestingly, a second factor, the EIIA-E [early promoter of adenovirus EII] binding factor, which binds specifically to the adenovirus E1A, E2, and E4 promoters, has also been identified in uninfected HeLa cell nuclei (*110*). However, this second factor does not appear to be E1A-dependent and its significance in the activation of the adenovirus early promoters is not yet clear (see below).

Studies using undifferentiated murine embryomal carcinoma (EC) cells provide a second line of evidence for the cellular origin of E2F. These cells are able to complement replication of the adenovirus E1A deletion mutant dl312 (*111*) by virtue of a cellular, E1A-like activity that disappears upon differentiation *in vitro* (*112*). Gel retardation assays reveal the presence in undifferentiated F9 EC cells of an E2 promoter-binding factor with the specificity of E2F (*113*).

E2F, therefore, appears to be a host-encoded, sequence-specific transcription factor whose activity can be regulated by either the 289-residue E1A product or by an E1A-like activity in undifferentiated EC cells. When activated by either the viral or cellular E1A, E2F binds specifically to its octanucleotide recognition sequence and stimulates transcription from adjacent promoters. The effect of ligating a single octanucleotide-binding site to a heterologous promoter is dramatic. E1A products stimulate transcription from a transfected β-globin promoter 3-fold in the absence of the E2F-binding site; however, upstream ligation of a single E2F-binding site (derived from the E1A enhancer) results in a 24-fold stimulation by E1A products (*108*).

The mechanism of E2F activation by E1A gene products is unclear at present, but apparently involves an increase in the rate of initiation at the E2 promoter. At least four possibilities are evident: (1) E1A increases the specific affinity of E2F for its binding site by covalent modification; (2) E1A increases the steady-state levels of E2F; (3) E1A facilitates the assembly of E2F and promoter DNA into active transcription complexes (*113a*), possibly by binding to and altering the conformation of E2F; and (4) E1A decreases the affinity of negative regulatory factors for the E2 promoter (*114*), allowing E2F access to its binding site; the EIIA-E-binding protein may represent such a negative regulatory protein (*110* and above).

E1A products transactivate all of the adenovirus early promoters in a coordinated and coincident manner. Since E2F does not recognize the regions of E1B, E3, and E4, it is likely that (an) additional E1A-dependent transcription factor(s) specific for these early promoters will be found.

C. Transactivation of Chromosomal Genes by E1A

In contrast with the very general, nonspecific activation by E1A products of promoters on virus and plasmid DNA, E1A-dependent activation of endogenous cellular promoters occurs very infrequently. Many constitutively expressed cellular genes are transcribed at comparable rates in the presence and absence of E1A products (*115*). Similarly, endogenous β-globin and preproinsulin genes, which are not expressed in uninfected HeLa cells, remain silent after infection with wild-type adenovirus (*100, 116*). These conflicting results can be reconciled by the observation that viral or plasmid DNA is usually present, at least initially, as "naked" DNA and is accessible to both E1A products and E1A-dependent transcription factors. In addition, exogenous DNA is usually introduced at high copy number relative to endogenous genes. Endogenous chromosomal DNA, in contrast, is associated with a variety of nuclear proteins as either stable transcription complexes (*117*) or DNase-I-insensitive chromatin (*118*); in either case, the endogenous promoter is relatively inaccessible to E1A-dependent factors.

Although the general pattern of cellular transcription is unchanged after either adenovirus infection or transfection with E1A-containing plasmids, several chromosomal genes appear to be activated selectively by E1A products. These include β-tubulin (*116*), the major 70-kDa heat-shock protein (hsp70) (*119*), and thymidylate synthetase (*92*). The evidence for E1A-specific transactivation of these genes is 2-fold. First, the temporal pattern of expression for these cellular genes parallels precisely that observed for E1A. In hydroxyurea-treated HeLa cells, which are unable to replicate viral DNA, transcription of E1A, E3, and β-tubulin is first detected 2 hours postinfection, peaks at 6 hours postinfection, and falls to approximately 25% of peak levels by 8 hours postinfection. Similar results have been observed for hsp70 and thymidylate synthetase.

Additional supporting evidence is provided by adenovirus E1A mutants, such as dl312, which fail to induce β-tubulin even at high multiplicities of infection. Under these conditions the transcription of the other adenovirus early genes approaches wild-type levels (*114*), most likely because the high concentration of viral DNA drives transcription factors into active complexes despite the absence of E1A products.

Although enhanced transcription in HeLa cells of the aforementioned cellular genes is E1A-dependent, it is unclear whether this represents promoter-specific interactions with E1A-dependent factors such as E2F, or merely reflects increased accessibility of these genes in HeLa cells. Several additional observations suggest that both accessibility and promoter-specific interactions may be important. Cell lines containing transfected, stably integrated adenovirus early genes demonstrate that the chromosomal forms of these genes retain their E1A dependence (*120, 121*). However, in at least one of these studies, transactivation by E1A is at least partly nonspecific with respect to the promoter, since deletion of the integrated E2 promoter to within 18 nucleotides of the cap-site (−18) does not eliminate E1A dependence (*120*).

D. Suppression of Enhancer-Driven Transcription by E1A

Enhancers are cis-acting DNA elements that activate transcription from adjacent promoters in an orientation-independent manner (reviewed in *122*). In addition, some enhancers appear to activate transcription at distances greater than 2 kilobases. General or nonspecific enhancers have been identified within the genomes of many DNA and RNA viruses (e.g., SV40, MSV, polyoma, adenovirus) and can activate transcription in a variety of cell types. A second class of enhancers, including those associated with the immunoglobulin heavy and light chain genes (*123, 124*), the insulin gene (*125*), and the albumin gene (*126*), can activate transcription in a limited number of different cell types; this class of enhancer is usually found adjacent to genes expressed at very high levels in a single, or at most a few, differentiated tissues.

Most of the enhancer sequences identified thus far, including both general and cell-type specific, contain a consensus or core sequence related to GTGGWWW (W = A or T)*; however, additional sequences are required for both enhancer activity (*127*) and cell-type specificity (*128*). Competition experiments between different enhancer-containing fragments indicate that sequence-specific binding of one or more trans-acting factors is required for enhancer activity (*129*), and that the

* NC-IUB Recommendations (see *EJB* **150**, 1, 1985) [Eds.].

core sequence constitutes at least part of an essential binding site; there is substantial evidence for the existence of both positive and negative regulation by enhancer-binding factors (130–132).

Transcription experiments *in vitro* suggest that, in order to be effective, these trans-acting, enhancer-binding factors must act prior to the formation of stable transcription complexes. Enhancer-containing DNA fragments compete effectively for enhancer-binding factors and reduce transcription from an enhancer-linked test gene (129). However, when the test gene and nuclear extract are incubated for as little as 1 minute prior to the addition of competitive fragments, full enhancer activity is observed, and this activity is resistant to further addition of competitor. These results indicate that, in the presence of appropriate binding factors, enhancer sequences mediate the formation of stable complexes with enhanced (positive control) or reduced (negative control) transcriptional activity.

The expression of E1A gene products blocks the activity of both general and cell-type specific enhancers, and reduces transcription to levels observed in the absence of enhancer sequences (83, 84, 133, 134). By analogy with E1A transactivation (see Section III,B), it is reasonable to postulate that E1A suppresses enhancer activity by inactivating one or more cell-encoded, enhancer-specific transcription factors. However, experiments involving E1A-dependent regulation of the immunoglobulin heavy chain (IgH) enhancer are inconsistent with this simple model. The IgH enhancer is active almost exclusively in lymphoid cells, and its activity is suppressed by E1A products (133). In contrast, this enhancer is minimally active in fibroblasts, but its activity is stimulated 20- to 50-fold by E1A (135). A negative regulatory factor that binds specifically to the IgH enhancer has been identified in fibroblasts, but appears to be absent in lymphoid cells (132). E1A may be able to regulate the activity of this factor; if so, it will be interesting to discover whether activation of the IgH enhancer in fibroblasts requires the 289-residual (13-S mRNA) transactivating E1A product.

E. Role of E1A in Cell Transformation

The evidence available at present suggests that the transformation-related activities of E1A, namely the induction of host cell division, immortalization, and cooperation with *ras* and E1B in tumorigenic transformation, are linked to transcriptional repression rather than to transactivation (91, 92). Working from this simple premise, it may be possible to identify one or more cellular products, down-regulated by E1A, whose inactivation results in immortalization or other growth alterations; the antioncogenes may represent such an E1A-regulated target (*136*).

It is also possible that other E1A activities, more difficult to assay, play a larger role in E1A-dependent immortalization and transformation. Mutations in E1A conserved domain II specifically block induction of mitosis, even in the presence of normal levels of DNA synthesis (*92*). It is conceivable that E1A, by stimulating cell division, increases the likelihood of subsequent transformation by E1B or *ras*.

Finally, the net effect of E1A activity in permissive cells is to shift a portion of the host cell transcriptional program toward the expression of viral genes; enhancer-driven cellular genes such as the immunoglobulin genes, which utilize a disproportionate share of the transcription apparatus but are not essential for cell survival, are preferentially suppressed. If shifting between transcriptional programs is indeed an overall result of E1A activities, E1A or cellular E1A-like activity, in the appropriate context, could play an important role in shifting a cell from one developmental program to another. It is interesting to note in this respect the substantial change in E1A-like activity that accompanies the differentiation of EC cells (*112*). It is also possible that E1A, in the context of activated *ras* or E1B expression, could initiate a shift to a transcriptional program leading to tumorigenic transformation.

ACKNOWLEDGMENTS

Work from this laboratory cited in this review was supported by NIH Grants CA 39392 and CA 40263.

REFERENCES

1. J. M. Bishop, *Cell* **42**, 23 (1985).
2. R. E. Kingston, A. S. Baldwin and P. A. Sharp, *Cell* **41**, 3 (1985).
3. R. A. Weinberg, *Science* **230**, 770 (1985).
4. K. Bister and H. W. Jansen, *Adv. Cancer Res.* **47**, 99 (1986).
5. R. Müller, *TIBS* **11**, 129 (1986).
6. E. D. Adamson, *Development* **99**, 449 (1987).
7. A. Berk, *ARGen* **20**, 45 (1986).
8. J. M. Bishop, *Science* **235**, 305 (1987).
9. H. E. Varmus, *ARGen* **18**, 553 (1984).
10. R. Dahr, R. W. Ellis, T. Y. Shih, S. Oroszlan, B. Shapiro, J. Maizel, D. Lowry and E. Scolnick, *Science* **217**, 934 (1982).
11. N. Tsuchida, T. Ryder and E. Ohtsubo, *Science* **217**, 937 (1982).
12. E. Taparowsky, K. Shimizu, M. Goldfarb and M. Wigler, *Cell* **34**, 581 (1983).
13. D. Capon, Y. Ellson, A. Levinson, P. Seeburg and D. Goeddel, *Nature* **302**, 33 (1983).

14. J. P. McGrath, D. J. Capon, D. H. Smith, E. Y. Chen, P. H. Seeburg, D. V. Goeddel and A. D. Levinson, *Nature* **304**, 501 (1983).
15. D. G. Lowe, D. J. Capon, E. Deliwart, A. Y. Sakaguchi, S. L. Naylor and D. V. Goeddel, *Cell* **48**, 137 (1987).
16. T. Finkle, C. J. Der and G. M. Cooper, *Cell* **37**, 151 (1984).
17. G. L. Temeles, J. B. Gibbs, J. S. D'Alonzo, I. S. Sigal and E. M. Scolnick, *Nature* **313**, 700 (1985).
18. F. Tamanoi, M. Walsh, T. Kataoka and M. Wigler, *PNAS* **81**, 6924 (1984).
19. L. F. Fleischman, S. B. Chahwala and L. Cantley, *Science* **231**, 407 (1986).
20. D. Bar-Sagi and J. R. Feramisco, *Science* **233**, 1061 (1986).
21. J. R. Feramisco, M. Gross, T. Kamata, M. Rosenberg and R. W. Sweet, *Cell* **38**, 109 (1984).
22. J. C. Lacal, S. K. Srivistava, P. S. Anderson and S. A. Aaronson, *Cell* **44**, 609 (1986).
23. D. J. Slamon and M. J. Cline, *PNAS* **81**, 7141 (1984).
24. M. E. Furth, T. H. Aldrich and C. Cordon-Cardo, *Oncogene* **1**, 47 (1987).
25. J. Leon, I. Guerrero and A. Pellicer, *MCBiol* **7**, 1535 (1987).
26. B. M. Willumsen, K. Norris, A. G. Papageorge, N. L. Hubbert and D. R. Lowy, *EMBO J.* **3**, 2581 (1984).
27. L. E. Hood, I. L. Weissman, W. B. Wood and J. H. Wilson, "Immunology," 2nd ed. Benjamin/Cummings, Menlo Park, California, 1984.
28. J. C. Lacal, P. S. Anderson and S. A. Aaronson, *EMBO J.* **5**, 679 (1986).
29. B. M. Willumsen, A. G. Papageorge, H.-F. Kung, E. Bekesi, T. Robins, M. Johnson, W. C. Vass and D. R. Lowy, *MCBiol* **6**, 2646 (1986).
30. J. S. Flier, M. M. Mueckler, P. Usher and H. F. Lodish, *Science* **235**, 1492 (1987).
31. M. J. Birnbaum, H. C. Haspel and O. M. Rosen, *Science* **235**, 1495 (1987).
32. L. M. Matrisian, N. Glaichenhaus, M.-C. Gensel and R. Breathnach, *EMBO J.* **4**, 1435 (1985).
33. L. M. Matrisian, G. T. Bowden, P. Krieg, G. Fürstenberger, J.-P. Briano, P. Leroy and R. Breathnach, *PNAS* **83**, 9413 (1986).
34. Y. Li, T. Seyama, A. K. Godwin, T. S. Winokur, R. M. Lebovitz and M. W. Lieberman, *PNAS* **85**, 344 (1988).
35. M. H. Hanigan and H. C. Pitot, *Carcinogenesis* **6**, 165 (1985).
36. K. Satoh, A. Kitahara, Y. Soma, Y. Inba, I. Hatayama and K. Sato, *PNAS* **82**, 3964 (1985).
37. M. Tatematsu, Y. Mera, N. Ito, K. Satoh and K. Sato, *Carcinogenesis* **6**, 1621 (1985).
38. C. Power, S. Sinha, C. Webber, M. M. Manson and G. E. Neal, *Carcinogenesis* **8**, 797 (1987).
39. C. Wasylyk, J. L. Imler, J. Perez-Mutul and B. Wasylyk, *Cell* **48**, 525 (1987).
40. D. W. Stacey, T. Watson, H.-F. Kung and T. Curran, *MCBiol* **7**, 523 (1987).
41. M. Noda, M. Ko, A. Ogura, D. Liu, T. Amano, T. Takano and Y. Ikawa, *Nature* **318**, 73 (1985).
42. D. Bar-Sagi and J. Feramisco, *Cell* **42**, 841 (1985).
43. N. Hagag, S. Halegoua and M. Viola, *Nature* **319**, 680 (1982).
44. S. Alima, P. Casabore, E. Agostini and F. Tato, *Nature* **316**, 557 (1985).
45. W. S. Trimble, P. W. Johnson, N. Hozumi and J. C. Roder, *Nature* **321**, 782 (1986).
46. J. E. DeLarco and G. J. Todaro, *PNAS* **75**, 4001 (1978).
47. D. M. A. Anzano, A. B. Roberts, J. E. DeLarco, L. M. Wakefield, R. K. Assoian, N. S. Roche, J. M. Smith, J. E. Lazarus and M. B. Sponr, *MCBiol* **5**, 242 (1985).
48. D. F. Bowen-Pope, A. Vogel and R. Ross, *PNAS* **81**, 2396 (1984).
49. T. Curran, A. D. Miller, L. Zokas and I. M. Verma, *Cell* **36**, 259 (1984).

50. T. Curran, C. Van Beveran, N. Ling and I. M. Verma, *MCBiol* **5**, 167 (1985).
51. R. A. Weinberg, *Science* **230**, 770 (1985).
52. L. C. Sambucetti and T. Curran, *Science* **234**, 1417 (1986).
53. M. E. Greenberg and E. B. Ziff, *Nature* **311**, 433 (1984).
54. W. Kruijer, J. A. Cooper, T. Hunter and I. M. Verma, *Nature* **312**, 711 (1984).
55. R. Müller, R. Bravo, J. Burckhardt and T. Curran, *Nature* **312**, 716 (1984).
56. R. Bravo, J. Burckhardt, T. Curran and R. Müller, *EMBO J.* **4**, 1193 (1985).
57. J. Deschamps, R. L. Mitchell, F. Meijlink, W. Kruijer, D. Schubert and I. M. Verma, *CSHSQB* **50**, 733 (1985).
58. R. Bravo, J. Burckhardt, T. Curran and R. Müller, *EMBO J.* **5**, 695 (1986).
59. G. Colletta, A. M. Cirafici and G. Vecchio, *Science* **233**, 458 (1986).
60. R. Bravo, M. Neuberg, J. Burckhardt, J. Almendral, R. Wallich and R. Müller, *Cell* **48**, 251 (1987).
61. B. Calabretta, *MCBiol* **7**, 769 (1987).
62. D. Radzioch, B. Bottazzi and L. Varesio, *MCBiol* **7**, 595 (1987).
63. R. Treisman, *Cell* **42**, 889 (1985).
64. J. Deschamps, F. Meijlink and I. M. Verma, *Science* **230**, 1174 (1985).
65. R. Treisman, *Cell* **46**, 567 (1986).
66. M. E. Greenberg, Z. Siegfried and E. B. Ziff, *MCBiol* **7**, 1217 (1987).
67. R. Prywes and R. G. Roeder, *Cell* **47**, 777 (1986).
68. R. Müller, D. J. Slamon, J. M. Tremblay, M. J. Cline and I. M. Verma, *Nature* **299**, 640 (1982).
69. R. Müller and I. M. Verma, *Curr. Top. Microbiol. Immunol.* **112**, 73 (1984).
70. R. Müller, D. Müller and L. Guilbert, *EMBO J.* **3**, 1887 (1984).
71. U. Rüther, C. Garber, D. Komitowski, R. Müller and E. F. Wagner, *Nature* **325**, 412 (1987).
72. R. L. Mitchell, L. Zokas, R. D. Schreibler and I. M. Verma, *Cell* **40**, 209 (1985).
73. R. L. Mitchell, C. Henning-Chubb, E. Huberman and I. M. Verma, *Cell* **45**, 497 (1986).
74. R. Müller and E. F. Wagner, *Nature* **311**, 438 (1984).
75. U. Rüther, E. F. Wagner and R. Müller, *EMBO J.* **4**, 1175 (1985).
76. W. Kruijer, D. Schubert and I. M. Verma, *PNAS* **82**, 7330 (1985).
77. T. Jenuwein and R. Müller, *Cell* **48**, 647 (1987).
78. C. Setoyama, R. Frunzio, G. Liau, M. Mudryj and B. De Crombrugghe, *PNAS* **83**, 3213 (1986).
79. T. Mohun, N. Garett and R. Treisman, *EMBO J.* **6**, 667 (1987).
80. R. J. Distel, H-S Ro, B. S. Rosen, D. L. Groves and B. M. Spiegelman, *Cell* **49**, 835 (1987).
81. A. J. Berk, F. Lee, T. Harison, J. Williams and P. A. Sharp, *Cell* **17**, 935 (1979).
82. N. Jones and T. Shenk, *Cell* **27**, 683 (1979).
83. E. Borrelli, R. Hen and P. Chambon, *Nature* **312**, 608 (1984).
84. R. Stein and E. B. Ziff, *MCBiol* **7**, 1164 (1987).
85. A. J. Berk, *AR Gen* **20**, 45 (1986).
86. H. E. Ruley, *Nature* **304**, 602 (1983).
87. H. E. Barmus, *AR Gen* **18**, 553 (1984).
88. R. E. Kingston, A. S. Baldwin and P. A. Sharp, *Cell* **41**, 3 (1985).
89. H. S. Ginsberg, "The Adenoviruses." Plenu, New York, 1984.
90. E. Moran and M. B. Mathews, *Cell* **48**, 177 (1987).
91. J. W. Lillie, M. Green and M. R. Green, *Cell* **46**, 1043 (1986).
92. B. Zerler, R. J. Roberts, M. B. Mathews and E. Moran, *MCBiol* **7**, 821 (1987).

93. F. L. Graham, J. Smiley, W. C. Russell and R. Nairn, *J. Gen. Virol.* **36**, 59 (1977).
94. C. C. Baker and E. B. Ziff, *JMB* **149**, 189 (1981).
95. L. T. Feldman, M. F. Imperiale and J. R. Nevins, *PNAS* **79**, 4952 (1982).
96. I. S. Y. Chen, A. J. Cann, N. P. Shah and R. B. Gaynor, *Science* **230**, 570 (1985).
97. W. K. Hoeffler and R. G. Roeder, *Cell* **41**, 955 (1985).
98. B. Ferguson, B. Krippl, O. Andrisani, N. Jones, H. Westphal and M. Rosenberg, *MCBiol* **5**, 2653 (1985).
99. M. R. Green, R. Treisman and T. Maniatis, *Cell* **35**, 137 (1983).
100. R. B. Gaynor, D. Hillman and A. J. Berk, *PNAS* **81**, 1193 (1984).
101. R. Treisman, M. R. Green and T. Maniatis, *PNAS* **80**, 7428 (1983).
102. L. Wu, D. S. E. Rosser, M. C. Schmidt and A. Berk, *Nature* **326**, 512 (1987).
103. C. S. Parker and J. Topol, *Cell* **36**, 357 (1984).
104. M. Sawadogo and R. G. Roeder, *Cell* **43**, 165 (1985).
105. J. Segall, T. Matsui and R. G. Roeder, *JBC* **255**, 11986 (1980).
106. S. Yoshinaga, N. Dean, M. Han and A. J. Berk, *EMBO J.* **5**, 343 (1986).
107. I. Kovesdi, R. Reichel and J. R. Nevins, *Science* **231**, 719 (1986).
108. I. Kovesdi, R. Reichel and J. R. Nevins, *PNAS* **84**, 2180 (1987).
109. I. Kovesdi, R. Reichel and J. R. Nevins, *Cell* **45**, 219 (1986).
110. L. SivaRaman, S. Subramanian and B. Thimmappaya, *PNAS* **83**, 5914 (1986).
111. N. Jones and T. Shenk, *Cell* **27**, 683 (1979).
112. R. Reichel, I. Kovesdi and J. R. Nevins, *Cell* **48**, 501 (1987).
113. N. B. La Thangue and P. W. J. Rigby, *Cell* **49**, 507 (1987).
113a. K. Leong and A. J. Berk, *PNAS* **83**, 5844 (1986).
114. J. R. Nevins, *Cell* **26**, 213 (1981).
115. A. Babich, L. T. Feldman, J. R. Nevins, J. E. Darnell and C. Weinberger, *MCBiol* **3**, 213 (1983).
116. R. Stein and E. B. Ziff, *MCBiol* **4**, 2792 (1984).
117. M. S. Schlissel and D. D. Brown, *Cell* **37**, 903 (1984).
118. B. M. Emerson and G. Felsenfeld, *PNAS* **81**, 95 (1984).
119. H.-T. Kao and J. R. Nevins, *MCBiol* **3**, 2058 (1983).
120. R. E. Kingston, R. J. Kaufman and P. A. Sharp, *MCBiol* **4**, 1970 (1984).
121. G. Curtois and A. Berk, *EMBO J.* **3**, 1145 (1984).
122. G. Khoury and P. Gruss, *Cell* **33**, 313 (1983).
123. J. Banerji, L. Olson and W. Schaffner, *Cell* **33**, 729 (1983).
124. D. Picard and W. Schaffner, *Nature* **307**, 80 (1984).
125. T. Edlund, M. D. Walker, P. J. Barr and W. Rutter, *Science* **230**, 912 (1985).
126. K. Gorski, M. Carneiro and U. Schibler, *Cell* **47**, 767 (1986).
127. U. Schlokat, D. Bohmann, H. Schöler and P. Gruss, *EMBO J.* **5**, 3251 (1986).
128. C. Wasylyk and B. Wasylyk, *EMBO J.* **5**, 553 (1986).
129. P. Sassone-Corsi, A. Wildeman and P. Chambon, *Nature* **313**, 458 (1985).
130. S. Goodbourn, H. Burstein and T. Maniatis, *Cell* **45**, 601 (1986).
131. P. Augerau and P. Chambon, *EMBO J.* **5**, 1791 (1986).
132. H. Schöler and P. Gruss, *EMBO J.* **5**, 3005 (1985).
133. R. Hen, E. Borrelli and P. Chambon, *Science* **230**, 1391 (1985).
134. A. Velcich and E. Ziff, *Cell* **40**, 705 (1985).
135. E. Borrelli, R. Hen, C. Wasylyk, B. Wasylyk and P. Chambon, *PNAS* **83**, 2846 (1986).
136. A. G. Knudson, *AR Gen* **20**, 231 (1986).
137. L. Braun, M. Goyette, P. Yaswen, N. L. Thompson and N. Fausto, *Cancer Res.* **47**, 4116 (1987).

DNA Damage Produced by Ionizing Radiation in Mammalian Cells: Identities, Mechanisms of Formation, and Reparability

J. F. WARD

Radiation Biology Division
Department of Radiology
School of Medicine
University of California at
San Diego
La Jolla, California 92093

The effects of ionizing radiation on DNA have been studied for many years (*1–5*). Such studies are justified by the central role DNA plays as the major cellular "target." Cell killing, mutagenesis, and transformation are caused by damage to this molecule. The purpose of this review is to provide a framewᴏrk for understanding how permanent heritable damage in cellular DNA results from exposure to ionizing radiation. If the processes that occur in the time between the initial radiation energy deposition and the formation of such damage can be described, then rationales can be developed for the modulation of radiation damage: e.g., it may be possible to (1) devise a means of differentially modulating the amounts of radiation damage, for

95

instance in tumor versus normal tissue in radiotherapy (6), or (2) predict the effects of variations of several parameters (dose rate, dose fractionation, linear energy transfer,* sensitizer, or protector) on the biological consequences of a radiation dose.

The types of information that would be useful in this regard are as follows:

1. Structures of radiation-induced lesions.
2. Yields of the various lesions.
3. Identities of lesions that might be expected to be biologically significant.
4. Chemical mechanisms by which these lesions are produced.
5. Identities of stages in the mechanisms of production of this damage at which the yields or types of damage could be modulated.
6. Descriptions of the cell's response to such lesions: How are they repaired, and with what efficiency and accuracy? Are some lesions more significant than others (i.e., less reparable)?

I. Energy Deposition Mechanisms

Ionizing radiation produces changes in the material through which it passes via intermediary radical ions, free radicals, and excited states. In general, these species are very reactive. They have high second-order rate constants for reaction and hence have very short half-lives within a mammalian cell where high concentrations of molecules are present. In order to describe the types of damage to be expected in cellular DNA, it is necessary to identify not only the radicals involved and their reactions, but also, since they will react

---

* Glossary:

Linear Energy Transfer (LET): A quantity to express radiation quality for radiobiological purposes; defined ("Quantitative Concepts and Dosimetry in Radiobiology," Report No. 30. International Commission on Radiation Units and Measurements, Washington D.C., 1979) as the quotient of dE by dl, where dl is the distance traversed by a particle and dE is the average energy loss due to collisions. The units are usually $keV/\mu m$.

Relative Biological Effectiveness (RBE): The ratio of the absorbed dose of reference radiation to the absorbed dose of a test radiation to produce the same biological effect. ("Quantitative Concepts and Dosimetry in Radiobiology," Report No. 30. International Commission on Radiation Units and Measurements, Washington D.C., 1979).

Gray: A measure of the absorbed dose of radiation; the amount of energy deposited per unit mass. One Gray corresponds to the deposition of 1 Joule/kg.

G (value): The yield of a particular radiation-induced reaction; the number of molecules changed per 100 eV absorbed.

close to their position of formation, their initial spacing relative to each other.

A detailed description of energy deposition mechanisms is beyond the scope of this review; the reader interested in more information is referred to any of several excellent basic radiation physics texts. Many types of ionizing radiation have been described and can generally be classified as particulate or electromagnetic in nature. The interaction mechanisms of the former are collisional ionizations, and of the latter, energy absorption events (photoelectric effect, Compton effect, or pair production). All of these processes result in ionizations and consequent release of energetic electrons. In the initial interaction of both particulate and electromagnetic radiations, a single positively charged ion is produced, and most of the energy transferred is carried away as kinetic energy by the secondary electrons. The energy losses of these secondary electrons, then, are the processes by which most of the energy of any radiation type is transferred to the medium.

Different radiation types deposit their energy in the medium through which they pass at different rates. The rate is characterized as the linear energy transfer (LET) of the radiation. The differences in the relative biological effectiveness (RBE) of radiations of differing LET is not inherent in the differences in the *nature* of the initial individual events; the RBE is dependent on the *spacing* of these events within the biological structures.

The description of the quality of radiation in terms of LET provides an average of the rate of energy deposition at the micron level. However, energy deposition events occur in molecular systems at the nanometer level by processes not completely understood even in homogeneous media. The molecular and atomic heterogeneity of biological systems adds an extra dimension of complexity.

To achieve the goal of determining the molecular mechanisms of damage production (at the nanometer level), a concept devised by radiation chemists is used here. Their model was developed to explain the yields of radiation-induced chemical products in simple chemical systems, both aqueous (7) and nonaqueous (8).

For aqueous systems, the energy deposition events have been divided into three types: spurs, blobs, and short tracks (7). This classification is made in terms of energy deposited per event. A "spur" is about 4 nm in diameter and has less than 100 eV deposited. The "blob" is larger, 7 nm with between 100 and 500 eV deposited. "Short tracks" are self-descriptive and involve amounts of energy greater than 500 eV. Descriptions of these various events are presented in Table I. For comparison, the sizes of DNA and of the nucleosomes in

TABLE I
ENERGY DEPOSITION EVENTS FOR LOW LET RADIATION

Entity	Energy deposited	Size	Number of water molecules per event	Energy (%)	Events (%)
Spur	<100 eV	4 nm (diam.)	1100	~80	95
Blob	<500 eV	7 nm (diam.)	6000	~20	5
Short track	500–5000 eV	a			
DNA		2 nm (diam.)			
Nucleosome disc		Thickness 5.7 nm, radius of 5.5 nm			

a Electrons with sufficient energy to form short tracks will also produce spurs and blobs.

which the DNA is packaged are also presented. It is evident that the sizes of these energy deposition events are on a scale in the same range as the sizes of DNA secondary structure and of the nucleosome.

Although the spurs include 80% of the energy deposited, they represent, by virtue of their smaller energy content, 95% of the actual events. Hence in a typical cell volume (1.5 pl) a dose of 1 Gray will produce 75,000 spurs and 4,000 blobs. These events will be distributed among all molecules present, the amount in any one molecular species being directly proportional to the mass of the species present. For high energy electrons (or γ rays) these energy deposition events occur well separated [400 nm apart on the track of an energetic electron (9)]. Thus the localities of events within a cell from such irradiation are completely independent of each other.

The energy deposited in these events is sufficient to cause several ionizations. It has been suggested (10) that the requirement in water is 20 eV for the production of 1 ion-pair. Hence a 100-eV spur could contain 5 positive ions and 5 electrons ejected. The ionization process in water is generally written

$$H_2O \longrightarrow H_2O^+ + e \tag{1}$$

The ionized water molecule reacts at the first collision with another water molecule to produce the OH radical

$$H_2O^+ + H_2O \longrightarrow {}^\cdot OH + H_3O^+ \tag{2}$$

and the electron loses energy and becomes hydrated

$$e + n\ H_2O \longrightarrow e_{aq} \tag{3}$$

Immediately after their formation, the radicals begin to interact (5 ion-pairs in a spur is equivalent to a molarity of 0.5 of radicals within that volume). The radicals react at every collision with each other, so that at these high initial concentrations, back reactions occur producing hydrogen molecules, hydrogen peroxide, and water.

$$e_{aq} + e_{aq} \, (2 \, H_2O) \longrightarrow H_2 + 2 \, OH^- \tag{4}$$

$$\cdot OH + \cdot OH \longrightarrow H_2O_2 \tag{5}$$

$$e + \cdot OH \longrightarrow OH^- \tag{6}$$

Thus the initial species produced on water radiolysis are generally written as (7)

$$\begin{array}{c} H_2O \rightsquigarrow \cdot OH, \, e_{aq}, \, H^{\cdot}, \, H_2O_2, \, H_2 \\ G \text{ value (in dilute solution)} \quad 2.4, \; 2.8, \, 0.4, \, 0.8, \quad 0.4 \end{array} \tag{7}$$

In the absence of high concentrations of reactive solutes, these event sizes increase with time after formation, and the initial yields of radicals are decreased as a consequence of the back reactions to molecular products. The yields of the various entities measured in dilute solution (i.e., at microsecond times after spur expansion has occurred) are indicated underneath Eq. (7) in terms of G values. The yields of hydrogen and hydrogen peroxide are called the molecular yields, to distinguish these yields from the total yield of these molecules. (Hydrogen and hydrogen peroxide can also be produced by reactions of the free radicals with molecular solutes.)

Turner *et al.* (*11*) presented a computer-generated representation of the change in the initial distribution of radical species with time (Fig. 1). They simulated the distribution of the reactive entities present 10 psec after the deposition of energy from the short track of a 5-keV electron, originating at the origin of Fig. 1. At this short time, the track shape is still evident, and 1174 reactive chemical species (*N*) were present in spurs and blobs. With time, some of the reactive species disappear by intereaction [forming molecular products—Eqs. (4, 5, and 6)] and the free radicals that escape this recombination diffuse, causing spreading of the track. After 280 nsec the residual reactive species, about one-third of the original number, are almost homogeneously distributed.

If a solute is present with which the radicals can react, the half-life of such a reaction will be

$$= \ln 2/(k[S])$$

where k is the rate constant for reaction of species S with the radical of interest. Consequently, assuming a typical rate constant (k) for a radi-

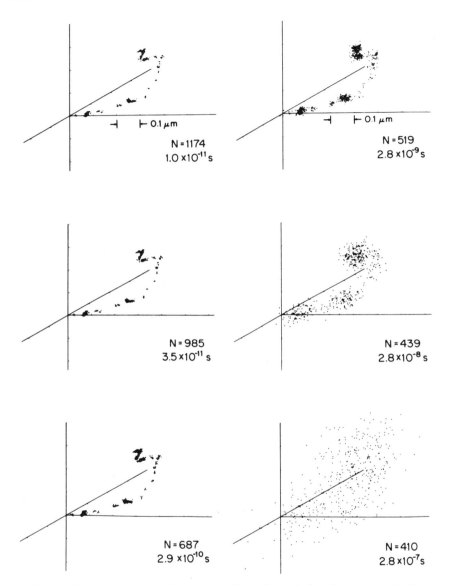

FIG. 1. Progression of reactive intermediates formed after deposition of radiation energy. Changes in location and yields as a function of time. Each dot represents the location of a reactive species, and N is the number present at each time. [Reproduced with permission from J. E. Turner, J. L. Magee, H. A. Wright, A. Chatterjee, R. N. Hamm and R. H. Ritchie, *Radiat. Res.* **96**, 437 (1983).]

cal reaction of 10^9 M^{-1} sec^{-1}, at 2.5 mM S the half-life of the reaction will be 2.8×10^{-7} seconds.

If the energy is deposited in the presence of a high concentration of a reactive species, the reaction will occur correspondingly more quickly. This means that radical recombination reactions will be scavenged (reducing the molecular yields of hydrogen and hydrogen peroxide and increasing the number of radicals reacting with solute) and that radicals will react at sites closer to their initial position of formation.

Schwarz (12) has collated data from studies of the molecular yields of water radiolysis showing that at high concentrations of scavengers the molecular yields can be reduced and hence intraspur reactions can be scavenged. For instance the yield of hydrogen peroxide for low LET radiation is 0.8 molecules per 100 eV of energy absorbed (G value). This is equivalent to 0.08 μM per Gray. The OH radicals within a spur are presumably precursors of this molecular yield of hydrogen peroxide. Therefore if a species that can react with the OH radical is present at sufficiently high concentration, the molecular yield of hydrogen peroxide would be reduced. The data quoted (12) show that, in the presence of high concentrations of bromide ion, the molecular yield of hydrogen peroxide is reduced. As the concentration of bromide ion rises above 1 mM, the yield of hydrogen peroxide decreases reaching 50% at about 0.3 M bromide ion. (At this concentration, the OH radicals have a half-life of 2.1×10^{-9} seconds, i.e., the distribution of energy deposition events would still exist at this time; see Fig. 1.)

In other work (13, 14), pulse radiolysis indicates that at very early times after the irradiation energy has been deposited, the yields of the reactive radicals are much higher than the dilute solution values quoted above. For OH radicals, the G value 2×10^{-10} seconds after the energy is deposited is 5.9 ± 0.2 (13), and for electrons $G = 4.6 \pm 0.2$ at the same time (14).

If the radiation chemical picture described above is to be translated to DNA in the intracellular situation, consideration must be given to the following:

1. The spatial distribution of the radicals at the time they react with the macromolecule.

2. The yield(s) of the reactive species at the time they react—has intraspur recombination taken place?—i.e., What fraction of the total initial yield of radicals reacts with the target molecule?

For Chinese Hamster cells, the protective ability of four different OH scavengers indicates that the half-life of the OH radical in these cells was 10^{-9} seconds (15). In Fig. 1 it can be seen that, at this time after the initial energy deposition event, little change in the spatial distribution of the OH radicals will have occurred. Indeed, using a diffusion constant for OH radicals equal to that of water molecules $(2 \times 10^{-5} \ cm^2 \ sec^{-1})$, the diffusion distance of these radicals in 10^{-9} seconds is 3.2 nm. It is not clear why these data for Chinese Hamster cells are a factor of 3 different from those found for mouse L 5178Y cells (16), since one would not expect the intracellular scavenging capacity in the neighborhood of the target DNA to be a third that of the mouse cells.

While the spur picture of energy deposition is generally accepted for energy deposited in water, it is not clear that the situation will be similar when other molecules are involved in the energy deposition volume: Are similar volumes of high-energy deposition formed when systems involving molecules other than water are irradiated? The production of molecular yields of products from spur reactions in the radiolysis of organic liquids appears to be a general phenomenon (8). No such information is available for irradiated DNA—most studies of pure DNA have examined (by electron paramagnetic resonance) the free radicals produced by irradiation, i.e., the species that remain after any intraspur reactions have occurred. Since the interaction of the fast electrons through which ionizing radiation deposits its energy is with the electrons of the material through which they pass, it might be expected that volumes of high-energy deposition would occur within DNA.

Cation radicals formed on DNA by such processes in spur-like volumes (3–4 per 4-nm-diameter sphere) may be unable to interact to form molecular products. In dry DNA, they may be unable to diffuse together and recombine (in the manner of OH radicals forming hydrogen peroxide) since they would be held immobilized in the polymer molecule at distances beyond their interaction distance. Of course, recombination of cation with the electron (hydrated or otherwise) could occur. In addition, when the DNA is irradiated in the presence of other species that can form diffusible radicals, recombination between DNA radicals and these mobile reactive species could occur when the reactants originate in the same spur.

Within the cellular environment, the structures at nanometer dimensions present a complexity of atoms with which the radiation-induced secondary electrons will interact at random. It is not possible to predict how this complexity will affect the energy-deposition mechanisms. The subsequent reactions of the free radicals to form products cannot be determined a priori. In order to achieve a description of the damage induced in DNA irradiated intracellulary, it is necessary to hypothesize the types of damage that would be formed, and then devise assays to detect and quantitate them. With the availability of the techniques of molecular biology, and with care in choosing the system to investigate, such information should be forthcoming.

Most of the studies of DNA damage have been carried out in model systems in which the various steps in the mechanisms of damage production are known and controlled. The types of damage that will be produced intracellularly can be predicted from the information available from these model systems and from what is known of the environment of DNA within a cell.

II. Amount of Damage Produced in DNA *in Vivo*

To derive an approximation of the yields of damage which may be expected in the various moieties of DNA within an irradiated cell, consideration must be given to the damage produced from direct deposition of energy in the DNA and that produced by energy deposition in other molecules. The amounts of energy deposited in the various moieties of a cell can be derived in terms of the definition of a Gray. Assuming the amount of DNA in a cell to be 6 pg the amounts of energy deposited in each moiety of DNA for a dose of 1 Gray are summarized in Table II. The number of 60-eV events is quoted as this is generally agreed to be the average amount of energy deposited per event.

Table II does not consider the manner in which this energy is deposited in individual events involving spurs, etc. or the spread of these spurs among or over the DNA and its neighboring molecules. If the G value for DNA damage formation from direct ionization is

TABLE II
AMOUNTS OF ENERGY DEPOSITED IN DNA PER CELL PER GRAY

Constituent	Mass per cell (pg)	eV deposited	Number of 60-eV events
Deoxyribose	2.3	14,000	235
Bases	2.4	14,700	245
Phosphate	1.2	7,300	120
Bound water	3.1	19,000	315
Inner hydration shell	4.2	25,000	415

TABLE III
Measured Numbers of Damaged Sites per Cell per Gray

Type	Yield	Reference
Single-strand breaks	1000	17
8-Hydroxyadenine	700	18
T* (thymine damage)	250	19
Double-strand breaks	40	17
DNA–protein cross-links	150	20

assumed to be 2, and G (product) for indirect effect is assumed to be 5, yields of damage from this energy deposition could be predicted (if it is known what fraction of the OH radicals produced in the hydration shells reacts with DNA). Approximate yields would be 100–1000 damaged moieties per Gray per cell. To attempt to validate this picture of mechanisms of damage production, the yields of the various types of damage that have been found in irradiated cells are indicated in Table III.

If it is assumed that single-stranded breaks (ssB) are produced solely from energy deposited in the deoxyribose moieties (14,000 eV per Gray) then the number of such breaks produced would be expected to be 280. This assumes a G value of 2 for the production of direct effect damage and it assumes that every deoxyribose cation radical gives rise to an ssB. It is clear that sources of ssB other than energy deposition in deoxyribose must exist. The uncertainties in the fractions of OH radicals that react with the various moieties limit this approach; however, direct ionization of DNA cannot explain the total yields of products.

III. Direct and Indirect Effects

The damage to DNA in mammalian cells is generally considered to arise from two sources, the direct effect and the indirect effect. Direct-effect damage originates from energy deposited in the DNA molecule; indirect-effect damage arises following attack on the DNA of reactive species produced by ionizations in other molecules. The major source of the indirect effect is the free radicals produced from water. Within the cell are two classes of water to consider: bound water and solvent water. Ionization of all water molecules forms H_2O^+; however, such a species produced from a bound water molecule may react with the molecule to which it is bound before it can undergo the conversion to an OH radical via reaction (2)—the reaction of solvent water cation radicals. The reaction of a cation water radical with DNA could produce a cation DNA radical and it is possible that this could result in a different radiation product, although as argued in Section IV it is also possible that products from cationic species and OH radicals are the same.

A second consideration of the reactions of radicals formed from bound water is that it may not be possible to prevent them from reacting with the DNA by the use of scavengers. By this criterion, damage produced by reactions of radicals from bound water would not be described as being caused by the indirect effect (21).

Studies of the importance of water in biological radiation damage were begun by Powers in 1957 (22). He showed that water could markedly increase in the radiation response of living systems. Using the bacterial spore as a model, he took advantage of its resistance to relatively harsh treatment, such as complete drying. In a comprehensive series of papers, Powers and his co-workers showed that there are three water compartments that are significant in the radiosensitivity of the spore (summarized in 23). These compartments interreact with oxygen and with other sensitizers and protectors. In this system (in which the various components can easily be manipulated), the contributions of water to radiosensitivity are found to be complex; hence the situation could be expected to be even more complex in mammalian cells because of the manner in which DNA is packaged.

Attempts to define the fraction of damage produced by free radicals produced from water radiolysis in other cell systems have utilized the abilities of solute molecules to scavenge the free radicals produced from water efficiently. The pioneering work of Johansen and Howard-Flanders (24) showed that scavengers of the OH radicals produced by water radiolysis can reduce the radiosensitivity of bacteria by a factor of 3 if the scavenger is present at molar concentrations at the time of radiation. These authors also showed that the ability of the scavenger to protect is directly related to its second-order rate constant for reaction with the radicals. Studies using free-radical scavengers (ethylene glycol, methanol, dimethyl sulfoxide, etc.) have been extended to mammalian cell survival (15, 16), DNA single-strand breaks (25), DNA double-strand breaks (26), and chromosomal aberrations (27, 28) (all using low LET radiation). In all instances, the effects of the scavengers were to reduce the effectiveness of the radiation by a factor of 3. The only exception is that Sasaki and Matsubara (27) [in contrast to Littlefield et al. (28)], found that one class of chromosomal aberrations (terminal deletions) was not protected.

To achieve maximum radioprotection from OH radicals, high

concentrations of scavenger (up to 2 M) have been required. It has been pointed out (21) that at this concentration, the scavenger, if evenly distributed within the cell, would be 10% of the mass and could affect the immediate molecular environment of the DNA. The effects of high concentrations of dimethyl sulfoxide (Me_2SO) on water content and cell size have been observed (29). At the concentrations used for radioprotection, Me_2SO, being freely diffusible, has no effect on the cell volume, but does have a marked effect on the water proton-spin lattice-relaxation time, T1, probably caused by changes in the hydration shell of macromolecules. This same T1 can be modulated by changing ionic strength, but when the T1 is changed by ionic strength there is no accompanying change in radiosensitivity in a manner consistent with what would be predicted from the effects of Me_2SO on T1 and radiosensitivity. Hence, although high concentrations of Me_2SO, etc. may have effects on intracellular structures, these changes alone do not explain their ability to radioprotect. It is more likely that the radioprotection is due to their ability to react with OH radicals. Radioprotective OH scavengers have been reviewed by Okada (30), who reached the conclusion that the maximum radioprotection factor in oxygenated systems is 3.0 in almost all cases.

Radioprotection in one-tenth the concentration range is achieved with thiol compounds, as might be expected from their 10-fold higher rate constants for reactions with OH radicals. At the lower concentrations, they would be expected to have lesser effects on intracellular structures than the molar concentrations of other compounds. However, these compounds have an additional property that can increase their protective action. They can chemically repair a radiation-damaged molecule by donating a hydrogen atom to a radical produced by H-atom abstraction (31).

From this discussion it is evident that, in a description of radiation damage to intracellular DNA, the radiation damage produced both from the water free-radicals and from direct ionization must be considered. Reactions of radicals from species other than water could be important; however, little is known about these.

IV. Reaction Mechanisms

The mechanisms by which the various individual moieties of DNA are damaged by either OH free-radicals or by direct ionization have been discussed in several earlier reviews (32–34). These reviews also describe the alterations produced by these radical mechanisms. These topics are not considered in detail here, but are only generally discussed.

The initial damage produced by either direct ionization or by free-radical attack is randomly distributed among the DNA bases and the deoxyribose moieties. In a previous review (32), it was suggested that the ion radicals produced by direct ionization of DNA moieties may react further to produce radicals equivalent to those formed by OH-radical attack on the DNA. It was suggested that a cation radical formed in a saturated moiety of DNA could deprotonate, forming the same radical that would have been formed by H-atom abstraction by an OH radical. Similarly, a cation radical formed at an unsaturated center could react with a hydroxyl ion to form the same species as would be produced by addition of an OH radical to the same site. Consequently, the same products might be expected from both direct ionization and from OH-radical reaction. The products arising from the base radical cations are qualitatively similar to those formed as a consequence of OH radical attack (35).

V. Sites of Attack

The enzymatic repair mechanisms acting on base damage and on sugar damage differ; therefore, it is of interest to determine the relative amounts of these two types of damage.

The determination of the ratio of base damage to sugar damage in DNA irradiated in a cellular environment is not straightforward. Such measurements have not yet been made. One approach to this ratio is to calculate the contributions of the two different mechanisms of damage (direct or indirect) and use this to calculate the value.

For the direct ionization of DNA, there are no data available; however, since the ratio of the mass of bases to deoxyribose is about 1.2 (Table II) the amounts of energy deposited in each will be in the same ratio. Hence, to a first approximation the ratio of the yields of base damage to sugar damage produced by direct ionization can be assumed to be about 1.2.

The contributions of OH radical damage to base versus sugar can be estimated from experimental data from dilute aqueous solution. For measurement of total base damage, since it is not feasible to measure the yield of every type of altered base, the total change in ultraviolet absorbance could be used (most base-damaged products have little absorption at 260 nm). However, the production of sufficient damage to enable changes in UV absorption to be detected requires that the DNA be denatured to a large extent during the damage production (32). Therefore such yields of damage will not reflect those occurring in double-stranded DNA. In single-stranded DNA, the relative amounts of OH radical reacting with base and with sugar are readily measured so that, in this instance, the ratio is known to be between 7 and 10 (36). Since the bases in double-stranded DNA are more protected from diffusing OH radicals (37), the yield of sugar damage (as measured by strand-break yield) is increased by a factor of 2.5 (36). Hence the ratio of base damage to sugar damage from diffusing OH radicals in double-strand DNA is between 2.8 and 4.

If we assume that in a cell 65% of the damage is caused by OH radicals and 35% by direct ionization (15), summing the two effects gives the ratio for base damage to sugar damage in the cell of 2.7 (38).

Recent work has investigated the reactions of OH radicals with DNA when the macromolecule is present in the "Z" conformation (39). It was thought that the structure of this DNA would change the ratio of base damage to sugar damage, as in this form the bases are more exposed to the aqueous solution. However, measurement of strand breaks (in terms of release of free bases) indicates that any change in the specificity of the site of OH radical attack is minimal.

The damage produced in DNA should be considered in terms of the abilities of cells to repair that damage. Studies with other damaging agents have established mechanisms by which base damage can be repaired (40). In most cases, the types of base damage produced by ionizing radiation would be expected to be repaired by a simple mechanism involving glycosylase and apurinic endonuclease. In contrast to base-damage repair, there is little published on the mechanisms by which sugar damage may be repaired.

VI. Sugar Damage

Most radiation damage to the sugar moieties of DNA results in strand breaks. Several studies of the terminal groups remaining as a result of a strand breakage have been made (41–43). Earlier work (41) indicated that in most cases the termini are monophosphate groups, both 3′ and 5′. Later it was determined (42) that all of the 5′ ends were monophosphates while 70% of the 3′ were also monophosphates and 30% had glycolate groups attached.

Von Sonntag (44) has reviewed the types of lesions resulting from hydrogen atom abstraction from the various deoxyribose carbon atoms. He shows that some products that result from abstraction from the 1′, 2′, and 3′ positions could result in damage that would not yield an immediate strand break. He points out that some base damage results in cleavage of the glycosylic bond, again not producing a strand break but rather an apyrimidinic or apurinic (AP) site.

An additional type of sugar damage that would not result in strand breakage is that constituting the precursor of malondialdehyde. Several groups (32, 45–47) have observed a radiation product formed from the 1', 2', and 3' carbon atoms that reacts as malondialdehyde. This activity is only released from DNA upon heating (46), and it precipitates with DNA (32). It seems therefore that the reacting group is present after irradiation, but is not found at a strand-break terminus; consequently, the sugar damage is present but does not appear as a strand break. In one schema [presented by Janicek *et al.* (43)], the DNA backbone is held together by an ester linkage that would be expected to be both acid- and alkali-labile; it is suggested that this type of damage is initiated by hydrogen abstraction from the 4' position of the deoxyribose. The data from all sources do not indicate whether the base moiety remains attached to the damaged sugar in the final product.

VII. Base Damage

In general, all the bases within the DNA structure seem to be equally sensitive to OH radical attack, but there is some specificity in the sites of the intermediate radical ions observed after direct ionization of the DNA (48).

It is clear from the studies of model systems that a large array of damaged base products form upon irradiation of DNA (32, 33, 49). While their identification, characterization, and quantitation in model systems have become relatively straightforward, there remain problems in assaying them in the DNA of mammalian cells at reasonable radiation doses. The major problems in detecting such damage in irradiated cells are those of sensitivity and selectivity. Yields of damage measured in irradiated mammalian cells are shown in Table III. The mechanisms proposed for their formation indicate that other damaged bases would be formed in similar yields. Thus the amounts produced at a biologically significant dose (1 Gray) using an easily handled number of cells (10^7) can be calculated. For 8-hydroxyadenine, for instance, 700 moieties per cell per Gray are produced, this is equivalent to 1.1×10^{-14} mol in 10^7 cells. Thus any procedure to detect this damage must be sensitive enough to quantitate 10 fmol, and selective enough to discriminate at a level of one altered base in the presence of 2×10^7 undamaged bases. If repair of the damage is to be monitored after this dose of radiation, the sensitivity must be further increased: e.g., if repair down to 10% of residual lesions is to be followed, the specificity and selectivity must be increased further by a factor of 10.

Additional problems in the development of valid assays are associated with quantitative extraction and processing of the DNA from the cells.

Detection and assay of damaged bases are currently performed by several techniques, including specific antibodies (50–54), production of fluorescent products (55), gas chromatography/mass spectrometry (56, 57), and damage-specific endonucleases (58–60). The sensitivity of the assays, as tested in model systems, is approaching that required for biological studies and may soon be sufficient. However, because of the findings described in the next section, our work on the development of sensitive serological assays of base damage (50–52) was discontinued and our efforts have since been concentrated on the studies of lesions that we believe to be more biologically significant.

VIII. Singly Damaged Sites

When a moiety of the DNA is damaged in isolation, i.e., without damage to neighboring groups, we term this a "singly damaged site." Such a site would be expected to be produced by a reaction of a single radical or reactive molecule. It is clear that repair of singly damaged sites has the potential to be carried out efficiently and accurately using the complementary undamaged strand as template. Because of the varieties of damage identities, a variety of enzyme activities can be expected to be involved in this repair. The types of damage can be classified in terms of repair-enzyme requirements. From the descriptions of the types of damage (produced by OH radicals) presented above, such a classification is possible. A different initial enzyme reaction is potentially required for each of the following types of radiation damage:

1. Single-strand break with 3'- and 5'-phosphate end-groups and loss of a deoxynucleoside: this would require dephosphorylation of the 3' end (phosphatase) as an initial action forming a 3' hydroxyl prior to repair synthesis.

2. Single-strand break with 3' phosphoglycolate and 5'-phosphate end-groups and loss of a base+sugar fragment: again the 3' end would require "clean-up" (61) before a polymerase could initiate its action.

3. Sugar damage that does not result in a break (malonaldehyde

precursor): repair can possibly be initiated by AP endonuclease [deoxyribonuclease (apurinic or apyrimidinic), EC 3.1.25.2]; Goldberg (62) has observed repair of such damage after bleomycin* damage to sugars—excess AP endonuclease is required.

4. AP site: AP endonuclease.

5. Damaged bases: base-damage-specific glycosylase or endonuclease.

6. Base damage involving an 8,5' cyclization with the deoxyribose (63): this cannot be removed by simple glycosylase action since the damaged base remains connected to the sugar by the additional 8-5' bond; repair could be initiated by an endonuclease.

Thus, even though a variety of damaged sites is produced, it is possible to propose mechanisms for their successful repair using known enzymatic functions (40). The results from the hydrogen peroxide experiments (64—see next section) indicate that efficient repair of such damage can and does take place.

IX. Significance of Singly Damaged Sites

We have previously questioned (64) the biological significance of single-damage lesions in DNA produced by ionizing radiation. In studies using hydrogen peroxide as a source of OH free radicals (64) we found that this agent (at 0°C) is proficient in producing single-strand breaks (ssB) in the DNA of mammalian cells (Chinese hamster fibroblasts). However, with others (65, 66), we showed that hydrogen peroxide is inefficient in producing double-strand breaks (dsB) in DNA *in vivo*. We could show that ssBs are produced by OH radicals formed close to the DNA, and hypothesized that a Fenton reaction,

$$M^{n+} + H_2O_2 \longrightarrow M^{(n+1)+} + OH^- + \,^{\cdot}OH \tag{8}$$

between the peroxide and an adventitious, oxidizable metal ion bound to DNA was the mode of production. Cell killing by hydrogen peroxide at 0°C was, by contrast, inefficient—if there is a linear dependence of ssB on hydrogen peroxide concentration, about 2.6 million ssB are necessary, on the average, to kill a cell. This is in comparison to the number of ssB present in cellular DNA at a lethal dose of ionizing radiation—1000 (17).

The range of damage classes (strand breaks, cross-links, etc.) produced by hydrogen peroxide treatment of DNA is the same as the

* The action of bleomycin is discussed by W. E. G. Müller and R. K. Zahn in Vol. 20 (1977) of this series [Eds.].

damage produced by ionizing radiation (reviewed in 67). The actual range of base damage identities is almost exactly the same as that produced by radiation (68). While the measurements of intracellular damage produced by hydrogen peroxide are limited to ssB, there is evidence that this damage is produced through the intermediation of OH radicals. Consequently, it would be expected that the range of damage identities is the same in cells as it is in DNA in aqueous solution.

The ability of a lesion to kill a cell can be measured as the absolute number of lesions necessary to kill 63% of the cells at risk. (At this fraction of cells killed, it can be shown that, on average, each cell has sustained one lethal event.) In Table IV the number of damaged sites present in cellular DNA when 63% of the cells is killed is listed.

We have pointed out that other agents that cause DNA alterations in the form of singly damaged sites by the formation of adducts, alkylated sites, etc. in DNA require many more of these lesions to kill cells than the number of ionizing radiation-induced lesions. The data previously collated with the help of J. J. McCormick are reproduced in Table IV.

The distinction between ionizing radiation (and bleomycin) from the other agents must lie in the types of DNA damage produced. We have shown above that the single-damage lesions induced by OH radicals are not the reason for the high efficiency with which DNA damage induced by ionizing radiation kills cells. We suggest that the efficiency of ionizing radiation (and bleomycin) in killing cells while producing relatively low levels of DNA damage lies in its ability to produce damage in which more than one moiety in a localized region of the DNA is damaged. We have called these lesions "locally multiply damaged sites" (LMDS). Their mechanisms of production and the characteristics that would make them lethal are described below.

The data summarized in Table IV emphasize the problems in studying ionizing radiation damage at the molecular level in cells. Very few such lesions are required to kill a cell, in contrast to the other agents listed. To be able to describe the response of viable cells to damage, the assays for radiation damage must be much more sensitive than those for damage produced by agents that produce singly damaged sites. This task is further complicated by the large variety of lesions produced by ionizing radiation.

One peculiarity of damage induced by hydrogen peroxide should be mentioned. While it is apparent that single-damage lesions produced by hydrogen peroxide are not normally lethal, they can become lethal lesions by posttreatment with 3-aminobenzamide. The addition

TABLE IV
YIELDS OF DNA DAMAGE NECESSARY TO KILL 63% OF THE CELLS EXPOSED[a]

Agent	DNA lesion	Number of lesions per cell per D_{37}[b]	Reference
Ionizing	ssB	1000	17
radiation	dsB	40	17
	Total LMDS[c]	440	68
	DPC[d]	150	20
Bleomycin A2	ssB	150	69, 70
	dsB	30	
UV light	T<>T dimer	400,000	71–73
	ssB	100	
Hydrogen peroxide			
0°C	ssB	<2,600,000	64
37°C	?		
Benzo[a]pyrene 4,5-oxide	Adduct	100,000	74
Aflatoxin	Adduct	10,000	75
1-Nitropyrene	Adduct	400,000	76
Methylnitrosourea	7-Methylguanine	800,000[e]	77
	O^6-Methylguanine	130,000[e]	
	3-Methyladenine	30,000[e]	
2-(N-Acetoxy-N-acetyl)amino-			
fluorene	Adduct	700,000	74
Other similar aromatic amides produce about the same number of adducts per lethal event			

[a] This table is reproduced with permission from J. F. Ward, C. L. Limoli, P. Calabro-Jones and J. W. Evans, Radiation vs. chemical damage to DNA. In "Anticarcinogenesis and Radiation Protection" (O. F. Nygaard and P. Cerutti, eds.). Plenum, New York (1988).

[b] D_{37} = dose of agent required to reduce survival of cells to 37% of the number exposed.

[c] Calculated; LMDS = locally multiply damaged sites (see below).

[d] DPC = DNA–protein cross-links.

[e] D_{37} calculated from individual exposures; no survival curves available.

of 3-aminobenzamide to hydrogen peroxide-treated cells causes a synergistic increase in cell kill (78). This compound is an inhibitor of poly(ADP-ribose) synthetase* (as well as having other effects) (79). Also, treatment with 3-benzamide of cells that had incorporated 5-hydroxymethyldeoxyuridine (which is also a minor radiation product of thymidine) into their DNA was lethal (in its absence, the cells were viable) (80). It appears that 3-aminobenzamide exerts its sensitizing effect after treatments that produce single-damage sites in DNA. Therefore, it is not surprising that its ability to sensitize irradiated cells is not marked, since radiation produces lesions (LMDS) that are more effective in killing than the singly damaged sites plus 3-amino-benzamide.

* NAD+ ADP-ribosyltransferase [also poly(ADP-ribose) polymerase] EC 2.4.2.30 [Eds.].

X. Cellular Environment of DNA

From the arguments presented above, it is clear that the free radicals that react within a cell will do so at short distances (nanometers) from their site of origin. Therefore, in attempting to describe the nature of damage produced by ionizing radiation in the DNA in mammalian cells, the spatial distribution of the species produced within the spurs, blobs, and short tracks must be considered in conjunction with the structures in which the DNA is packaged. In particular, the OH scavenging capacity of the milieu should be taken into account. Thus the DNA packaging at the 10-nm scale is of consequence for low LET radiation, as in this instance the events in which the energy is deposited have the dimensions of 4–50 nm.

DNA is known to be packaged within the cell nucleus in a hierarchy of structures—nucleosomes, 10 nm fibers, 30 nm fibers, etc. (81). At the lowest order of organization, DNA is coiled around histones into nucleosomes. These structures are disk-like with a thickness of 5.7 nm and a radius of 5.5 nm, two coils of DNA wrapped around each circumference 2.7 nm apart (82). The nucleosome core is made up of histone proteins, but is not tightly packed. The DNA and proteins contain hydration (bound) water (0.3 g/g) (83). (This corresponds to five water molecules per nucleotide.) Also, 60% of the particle volume is water. Hence, the core particle structure is a relatively loose complex of components, and the solvent spaces are accessible to smaller molecules such as sucrose or glycerol (0.3 nm in diameter), but not to larger molecules such as cyclodextrin (1.6 nm in diameter). Pores exist into which the smaller molecules can enter and these pores have a diameter between 0.3 and 1.6 nm. Small molecules, even though they enter the structure, do not exchange with the water of hydration, and apparently cause no change in the structure of the nucleosome up to a concentration of 10 M (sucrose) (84).

These studies clear up the doubt regarding the importance of indirect effects of ionizing radiation damage to intracellular DNA. It has been suggested that most intracellular DNA damage is caused by direct ionization, and that water and free radicals originating from water do not have access to the macromolecule. From the studies described above, it is clear that water molecules, both of hydration and as free solvent, have significant access to the DNA molecule, and that the volume of water in the nucleosome is at least equal to the volume of DNA. The OH radicals produced by ionizations within this volume therefore have easy access to the DNA molecule. [It is unclear whether ionization of water of hydration will lead to OH reactions with the DNA since the water cation radical (reaction 1) may react as such before reacting with another water molecule (reaction 2).]

Another often-posed criticism of the evidence for OH radical damage to cellular DNA is also answered by these studies. It has been suggested that the compounds used to scavenge OH free radicals (see Section III) do not have access to the DNA within the cell and may have their effect by modifying the packaging of the DNA. The presence of pores clearly shows that the molecules used for OH scavenging have easy access and are not restricted by the structures involved. In addition, the absence of effects of high concentrations of small uncharged molecules on nucleosome structures would argue that the molecules used as OH scavengers would be unlikely to have an effect on the DNA packaging.

Other work provides details of the DNA and its immediate neighboring groups within the nucleosome. Structures down to 0.7 nm resolution have been published (85). This work shows that, in a nucleosome, no histone protein density extends around the outside of the DNA and none is observed between the turns of the DNA helix. Thus, in addition to the access of water and hence OH radicals to the DNA structure within the nucleosomal structure (see above), the greater part of the DNA surface on the outside of the nucleosomal coils is also exposed to an aqueous environment.

The relationship between the DNA double-strand and the proteins within the nucleosome is not close; contact between the molecules is made only about once in every turn around the core (1 contact per 80 base pairs). In Fig. 2 (from 85) is reproduced on the same scale the size of an average energy deposition event. Again it appears that, at the distances of interest for consideration of radiation energy deposition, the DNA within the fundamental structural unit is accessible on all sides to water molecules.

We conclude, from a consideration of the structures in which DNA is packaged, that the surface of the molecule has ready access to the aqueous environment. Thus we consider that the conclusions reached by earlier authors from OH scavenging studies are valid, i.e., that OH radicals are responsible for 65% of the strand breaks (single and double), 65% of cell killing, and 65% of chromosomal aberrations produced by low LET ionizing radiation.

XI. Interaction of Energy Deposition Events with Nucleosomal Structures

The most important consequence of the relationship between DNA packaging structures and energy deposition events is that the free radicals produced in the vicinity of the DNA will react close to their point of origin. The high local concentration of solute ensures that reactions will occur within short times (nanoseconds) after the energy deposition event and therefore at distances approximating the original spatial distribution of the events.

Since the energy deposition events, in general, contain more than one reactive species, it is probable that a significant number of the damaged sites on the DNA will contain more than one damaged moiety in a local region (LMDS). These sites should not be considered rare; at each position at which a single radical is produced on the DNA, it is implicit, from the size of the energy deposition event (see Fig. 2), that other radicals will be present in the vicinity. Singly damaged sites would be produced from spurs containing only one radical, or from spurs containing multiple radicals, where all but one radical is scavenged by a different molecule or by another radical. Because of the molecular heterogeneity present in the local volumes in which the energy is deposited there will be a mixture of direct ionizations and OH radicals as originators of this damage.

The individual lesions within the LMDS will be separated on the DNA molecule: since 4 nm is the average spur diameter and since 1 nsec is the average half-life of an OH radical reacting with DNA, separation of the individual damages within the LMDS can be greater than 6.8 nm. The separation of the damages in the LMDS produced solely by direct ionization would be smaller than those that involve OH radical attack, and would be more representative of the spacing of the events immediately after energy deposition.

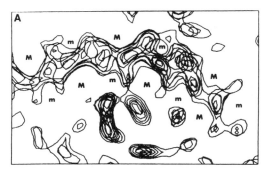
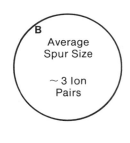

FIG. 2. (A) Electron density of an arc of the DNA superhelix, showing two turns of the double helix. Alternating major (M) and minor (m) grooves are indicated. The density shown below the arc is part of histone 2B. [Reproduced with permission from T. J. Richmond, J. T. Finch, B. Rushton, D. Rhodes and A. Klug, *Nature* **311**, 532 (1984).] (B) The size of the average energy deposition event (60 eV) on the same scale as A. In this spur volume, ~3 ion-pairs are produced.

XII. Locally Multiply Damaged Sites

These types of damage in cellular DNA can be of many types (see next section). To point out their potential significance relative to singly damaged sites, it is useful to consider the type of this damage most commonly measured, the DNA double-strand breaks (dsB). Such damage obviously consists of two single-strand breaks (ssBs) produced in opposite strands by either OH radical reactions with, or direct ionization of, the deoxyribose moieties. From model studies (see above) it is clear that a base moiety is lost from the DNA at the site of every ssB.

The overall structures of possible dsBs are shown schematically in Fig. 3. In the case where the individual ssBs of a dsB are directly opposite each other (Fig. 3A), a base moiety is lost from each strand—this constitutes a loss of base-sequence information from the DNA, which can only be replaced either fortuitously by repair synthesis or

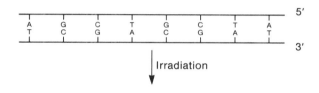

A. Directly Opposed Single Strand Breaks

B. Offset Single Strand Breaks (5' offset)

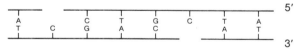

C. Offset Single Strand Breaks (3' offset)

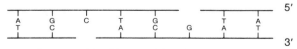

FIG. 3. Schematic diagram of double-strand breaks. Three possibilities are shown. (A) The constituent breaks are directly opposed. (B) The breaks are offset 5'. (C) The breaks are offset 3'.

by recombinational repair [if such repair occurs in mammalian cells (86, 87)].

If the constituent ssBs of a dsB are offset from one another on opposite strands (Fig. 3B and C), accurate repair is possible; no loss of base-sequence information has occurred. However, during repair of DNA damage, a patch of deoxynucleotides is inserted into the DNA. It is generally considered that the size of the patch inserted after ionizing radiation is two to three deoxynucleotides.* If the insertion of such a patch (in a 3' → 5' direction) forces synthesis past the site on the opposite strand at which a base has been deleted at an ssB, then again loss of base sequence information would occur. If repair is initiated at the 3' phosphate (phosphoglycolate) terminus of each ssB, then up to half of the dsB that comprises offset damage could potentially lead to loss of base sequence information. The other 50% would be accurately repaired, as repair synthesis would take place in the direction away from the opposing ssB (Fig. 3B).

Obviously if the two ssBs are sufficiently separated, they can be repaired as if they were singly damaged sites. In fact, in all of the assays for dsBs, there is no discrimination between closely opposed ssBs and those far apart. Thus the measured yields of dsBs will include those existing inside the cell as such and those revealed during the assay procedure by the breaking of the hydrogen bonding between the oligonucleotides in the overlap region between the two ssBs. In the observation of dsB repair, it is not surprising that part of the observed yield is repaired rapidly at a rate similar to that of ssB repair (90), i.e., where the separation of the individual ssBs is sufficient for them to be repaired independently.

* Note on patch size determination. In the determination of the patch size of deoxynucleotides inserted at each damaged site after treatment of cells with an agent, the total number of deoxynucleotides incorporated per cell is divided by the number of damaged sites. The application of these assays to ionizing radiation damage (88, 89) deserves consideration because of the following:

  1. The number of ssBs present after irradiation in the past has been taken as the total number of lesions being repaired. Now it is known that high yields of other types of damage are present—repair of all types of damage will involve insertion of a patch of deoxynucleotides.

  2. The repair of ssBs following ionizing radiation is a relatively fast process (90) with a half-life of 4 minutes even at room temperature. It is not clear in previous assays that (a) the cells were irradiated at 0°C to inhibit such repair, or (b) the marker deoxynucleoside was added to the cells sufficiently early to be present in the deoxynucleotide pools at the beginning of the rapid repair process.

  3. The assay only measures those patches in which thymidine is inserted.

XIII. Types of Locally Multiply Damaged Sites (LMDS)

A large variety of these types of damage is possible, the following being some of the possible variations:

A. Different Distributions among Strands

Multiple damages can be produced in opposite strands or in the same strand. The presence of more than one damage locally in the same strand would not be expected to be biologically significant, since the complementary strand would be undamaged and would remain as a template for repair synthesis. Lesions of this type may have already been measured. When DNA is irradiated in situations in which high radical scavenging is present (in yeast or in phage), sites are produced that are sensitive to single-strand-specific nuclease (91, 92). Irradiation *in vitro* (where singly damaged sites predominate) does not produce such sites (92). It was hypothesized (92) that these observations indicate that lesions are produced in clusters in the protected DNA, and that these distort the helix so that the opposite strand appears single-stranded and is acted upon by single-strand-specific nucleases. An alternate interpretation of such data is that the single-stranded regions arise from an LMDS in which two ssBs occur in the same strand and hence cause the deletion of an oligonucleotide, revealing a single-stranded region, which is susceptible to single-strand-specific nucleases. The yield of these lesions is approximately equal to the yield of dsBs and is therefore in keeping with the latter mechanism.

As discussed above, the presence of multiple damages in opposing DNA strands would be expected to be more significant biologically. The example presented above in Fig. 3 is for two ssBs in opposite strands. The presence of other types of damage or of greater numbers of damage sites in the LMDS is discussed below.

Yet another type of LMDS is possible, one that spans the two turns the DNA makes around a nucleosome. The separation of the two DNA strand wraps on a nucleosome is 2.7 nm (82), well within the range of the separation of the two events of an LMDS. Again these could be in the same strand or in opposite strands. These damages would occur about 80 base-pairs apart and would not be expected to be inherently biologically significant (i.e., unless damage on one wrap were already an LMDS itself). It is unclear whether two ssBs in opposite strands so far apart (80 base-pairs) would result in a dsB even under dsB assay conditions. They would be expected to be innocuous to a cell and be expected to be repaired as individual ssBs. Again, if the two lesions on adjacent wraps are on the same strand it is unclear whether an oligonucleotide would be released.

B. Numbers of Lesions per Site

Since energy deposition events can contain several ion pairs (see above), it is possible that more than two damaged moieties per LMDS could occur. From the problems inherent in repairing even simple LMDS (on opposite strands), it can be seen that the more individual lesions per LMDS (if both strands are damaged) the greater the difficulty the cell will have in carrying out accurate repair. Thus, although the spurs containing 2 to 3 ion-pairs are the predominant energy deposition events (see Table I), blobs in which a greater number of ion-pairs are present could be more significant biologically, producing LMDS, which are more difficult to repair.

It is clear that as the linear energy transfer of the radiation increases (i.e., in energetic ion beams, etc.) and the local concentration of radicals increases, more LMDS involving more than two lesions will be produced. As the density of local damage to the DNA increases, so does the relative biological effectiveness of the radiation increase.

C. Identities of Individual Damage Types

The LMDS comprise mixtures of all the singly damaged types produced in sugars and bases by either direct ionization or by OH radicals. It might be expected that the enzymes that initiate the repair of each separate lesion of an LMDS would be the same as those required for the repair of the same damage when it exists as a singly damaged site (see Section VIII). If the individual lesions of an LMDS are sufficiently separated on the opposite strands, they would be expected to be repaired as singly damaged sites. However, as described above, the repair of multiple lesions close together presents problems for the repair systems. It is unlikely that two lesions of an LMDS would be acted on simultaneously by repair enzymes (unless recombinational repair takes place); sequential repair is more probable. There may be priorities in the sequence of action of initial repair enzymes. Base-damage-specific glycosylases (apart from uracil glycosylase) do not act on single-stranded DNA, hence base damage in DNA opposite a single-strand break would not be expected to be acted upon by a glycosylase since it exists in a single-stranded region. Thus the specificities of the repair enzymes may lead to a defined sequence of the repair processes acting on the individual constituent damages in an LMDS.

XIV. Locally Multiply Damaged Sites (LMDS) as Lethal Lesions

The manner in which LMDS in the form of dsBs constitute sites at which loss of base-sequence information in DNA can occur has been pointed out above. A similar rationale can be applied to LMDS containing other individual damage types. A scenario similar to that of Fig. 3 can be drawn for base damage. If damaged bases existed at the sites of the strand breaks, the damage in Fig. 3A would represent damaged bases opposite each other, and it is not clear what base would be inserted opposite the damaged base in the opposite strand. If the base damages are offset, a similar rationale to that for the strand-break damage in Fig. 3B and C can be applied. Again, repair on a damaged template, depending on patch size and direction of patch insertion, could force synthesis on a damaged template. In the situation where a damaged base occurs on one strand and an ssB is present on the other strand, the ssB would be repaired first (base-damage glycosylase will not act on single-stranded regions).

It is clear that the number of deoxynucleotides added in the patch inserted is significant in determining the outcome of offset damages. If the patch size is short (2 to 3 moieties) then only those LMDS with damages within 2 to 3 base-pairs would be a hazard. If the patch size is longer, then LMDS with greater separations between the damages would be affected. It is possible that the patch sizes for the different individual damage types are different; they differ for damages produced by other agents (88). As has been mentioned, the assays of dsBs do not discriminate dsBs with regard to the distance of separation of the constituent ssBs. A consideration of the mechanisms that originate these lesions indicates that a separation distance of 10 to 20 base-pairs is possible. If the total dsBs are distributed across this size range, then the majority of them are not a hazard to the cell: the separation permits repair of constituent lesions to be effective. Hence only a fraction of the number of measured dsBs can be considered biologically significant.

XV. Conclusions

1. The types and yields of damaged moieties produced in intracellular DNA by low LET ionizing radiation are consistent with

mechanisms of production that involve both OH radical attack and direct ionization of the macromolecule.

2. At the radiation-dose levels producing one lethal lesion per cell, the amounts of damage produced by ionizing radiation (and bleomycin) are several orders of magnitude lower than the amounts of damage required for equal kill by other agents.

3. Individual damaged moieties are not biologically significant; they can easily be repaired using the undamaged DNA strand as a template.

4. The lethal lesion produced in cellular DNA is more probably a locally multiply damaged site (LMDS). Such lesions are produced as a consequence of the interaction of a small volume (3×10^{-17} ml) of high local energy deposition with DNA. This volume contains multiple radicals that cause multiple damages locally.

5. Several types of LMDS can be produced (i.e., containing different combinations of all possible singly damaged sites).

6. Current assays of DNA damage in cells do not measure LMDS; they only measure such lesions in the form of a DNA double-strand break.

7. The individual lesions making up an LMDS can be relatively widely separated on the opposite strands of the DNA (up to 70 nm). Again, assays do not distinguish between lesions close together and those distant from each other.

8. If the individual lesions of an LMDS are widely separated on opposite strands, they could be repaired as individual lesions.

9. If the damages are immediately opposite each other, irreversible loss of base sequence information may occur.

10. If the damages are within 2 to 3 base-pairs of each other, loss of base sequence information is possible during attempted excision repair, depending on the size of the patch of deoxynucleotides inserted during the resynthesis step.

ACKNOWLEDGMENTS

Work in my laboratory is supported by USPHS Grants CA26279 and CA39582 awarded by the National Cancer Institute.

I thank L. Ling and J. W. Evans for their helpful comments on the manuscript.

REFERENCES

1. B. Taylor, J. P. Greenstein and A. Hollaender, *ABB* **16**, 19 (1948).
2. G. Scholes, G. Stein and J. Weiss, *Nature* **164**, 709 (1949).
3. J. A. V. Butler and K. A. Smith, *Nature* **165**, 847 (1950).
4. E. S. G. Barron, P. Johnson and A. Coburce, *Radiat. Res.* **1**, 410 (1954).

5. G. Scholes, *Int. J. Radiat. Biol.* **3**, 312 (1959).
6. J. F. Ward, *Int. J. Radiat. Oncol. Biol. Phys.* **12**, 1027 (1987).
7. A. Mozumder and J. L. Magee, *Radiat. Res.* **28**, 203 (1966).
8. R. A. Holroyd, *in* "Fundamental Processes in Radiation Chemistry" (P. Ausloos, ed.), p. 413. Wiley (Interscience), New York, 1968.
9. A. Chatterjee and J. L. Magee, *Radiat. Prot. Dosim.* **13**, 137 (1985).
10. J. L. Magee and A. Chatterjee, *J. Phys. Chem.* **30**, 2219 (1978).
11. J. E. Turner, J. L. Magee, H. A. Wright, A. Chatterjee, R. N. Hamm and R. H. Ritchie, *Radiat. Res.* **96**, 437 (1983).
12. H. Schwarz, *JACS* **77**, 4960 (1955).
13. C. D. Jonah and J. R. Miller, *J. Phys. Chem.* **81**, 1974 (1977).
14. C. D. Jonah, M. S. Matheson, J. R. Miller and E. J. Hart, *J. Phys. Chem.* **8**, 1267 (1976).
15. A. P. Reuvers, C. L. Greenstock, J. Borsa and J. D. Chapman, *Int. J. Radiat. Biol.* **24**, 533 (1973).
16. R. Roots and S. Okada, *Radiat. Res.* **64**, 306 (1975).
17. M. M. Elkind and J. L. Redpath, *in* "Cancer: A Comprehensive Treatise" (F. F. Becker, ed.), Vol 6, p. 51. Plenum, New York, 1977.
18. J. F. Ward, I. W.-L. West and G. J. West, unpublished.
19. M. R. Mattern, P. V. Hariharan and P. A. Cerutti, *BBA* **395**, 48 (1975)
20. N. Ramakrishnan, S.-M. Chiu and N. L. Oleinick, *Cancer Res.* **47**, 2032 (1987).
21. G. E. Adams, *in* Discussion, *Radiat. Res.* **104**, S-173 (1985).
22. E. L. Powers, C. F. Ehret and A. Bannon, *Appl. Microbiol.* **5**, 61 (1957).
23. R. B. Webb and E. L. Powers, *Int. J. Radiat. Biol.* **7**, 481 (1963).
24. I. Johansen and P. Howard-Flanders, *Radiat. Res.* **24**, 184 (1965).
25. R. Roots and S. Okada, *Int. J. Radiat. Biol.* **21**, 329 (1972).
26. J. W. Evans, C. L. Limoli and J. F. Ward, *33rd Annu. Meet. Radiat. Res. Soc.*, Abstr. Cq 17 (1985).
27. M. S. Sasaki and S. Matsubara, *Int. J. Radiat. Biol.* **32**, 439 (1977).
28. L. G. Littlefield, E. E. Joiner, E. L. Frome, S. P. Colyer and A. M. Sayer, *Int. Congr. Radiat. Res., 8th*, Part 1, Abstr. C41-11P (1987).
29. G. P. Raaphorst and J. Kruuv, *in* "Contemporary Biophysics" (E. C. Pollard and A. D. Keith, eds.), Vol. 1, p. 91. Dekker, New York, 1978.
30. S. Okada, *in* "Radioprotectors and Anticarcinogens" (O. F. Nygaard and M. G. Simic, eds.), p. 339. Academic Press, New York, 1983.
31. J. F. Ward, *in* "Radioprotectors and Anticarcinogens" (O. F. Nygaard and M. G. Simic, eds.), p. 73. Academic Press, New York, 1983.
32. J. F. Ward, *Adv. Radiat. Biol.* **5**, 181 (1975).
33. F. Hutchinson, *This Series* **32**, 115 (1985).
34. W. Bernhard, *Adv. Radiat. Biol.* **9**, 199 (1981).
35. J. Cadet, *Int. Congr. Radiat. Res., 8th*, Part 1, Abstr. S30-3 (1987).
36. J. F. Ward and I. Kuo, *Radiat. Res.* **75**, 278 (1978).
37. J. F. Ward and I. Kuo, *Int. J. Radiat. Biol.* **18**, 381 (1970).
38. J. F. Ward, *Radiat. Res.* **104**, S103 (1985).
39. S. Zheng, G. L. Newton, G. Gonick, R. C. Fahey and J. F. Ward, *Radiat. Res.* **113**, (1988).
40. E. C. Friedberg, "DNA Repair." Freeman, New York, 1985.
41. J. F. Ward and I. Kuo, *Int. J. Radiat. Biol.* **23**, 543 (1973).
42. W. D. Henner, S. M. Grunbert and W. A. Hazeltine, *JBC* **258**, 4694 (1982).
43. M. F. Janicek, W. A. Hazeltine and W. D. Henner, *NARes* **13**, 9011 (1985)

124

J. F. WARD

44. C. von Sonntag, *Int. J. Radiat. Biol.* **46**, 507 (1984).
45. N. P. Krushinskya and M. I. Shal'nov, *Radiobiology* **7**, 36 (1967).
46. M. Ullrich and U. Hagen, *Int. J. Radiat. Biol.* **19**, 507 (1971).
47. J. F. Ward, *Isr. J. Chem.* **10**, 1123 (1972).
48. A. Graslund, A. Ehrenberg, A. Rupprecht and G. Strom, *BBA* **254**, 172 (1971).
49. C. von Sonntag and H. P. Schuchmann, *Int. J. Radiat. Biol.* **49**, 1 (1986).
50. G. J. West, I. W.-L. West and J. F. Ward, *Radiat. Res.* **90**, 595 (1982).
51. G. J. West, I. W.-L. West and J. F. Ward, *Int. J. Radiat. Biol.* **42**, 481 (1982).
52. H. L. Lewis, D. R. Muhleman and J. F. Ward, *Radiat. Res.* **75**, 305 (1978).
53. R. Rajagopalan, R. J. Melamede, M. F. Lapsia, B. F. Erlanger and S. S. Wallace, *Radiat. Res.* **97**, 499 (1984).
54. S. A. Leadon and P. C. Hanawalt, *Mutat. Res.* **112**, 191 (1983).
55. K. B. Lesiak and K. T. Wheeler, *35th Annu. Meet. Radiat. Res. Soc.*, Abstr. Ei2 (1987).
56. M. Dizdaroglu, *BioTechniques* **4**, 536 (1986).
57. M. Dizdaroglu and D. S. Bergtold, *Anal. Biochem.* **156**, 182 (1986).
58. M. C. Paterson, B. P. Smith and P. J. Smith, *in* "DNA Repair, A Laboratory Manual of Research Procedures," (E. C. Friedberg and P. C. Hanawalt, eds.), p. 99. Dekker, New York, 1981.
59. P. Bryant *in* "Mechanisms of DNA Damage and Repair" (M. G. Simic L. Grossman and A. C. Upton eds.), p. 171. Plenum, New York, 1986.
60. J. W. Evans, C. L. Limoli and J. F. Ward, *Int. Congr. Radiat. Res., 8th*, Abstr. C42-2V (1987).
61. D. S. Kapp and K. C. Smith, *Radiat. Res.* **42**, 34 (1970).
62. I. H. Goldberg, *in* "Mechanisms of DNA Damage and Repair" (M. G. Simic, L. Grossman and A. C. Upton eds.), p. 231. Plenum, New York, 1986.
63. J. A. Raleigh and A. F. Fuciarelli, *Radiat. Res.* **102**, 165 (1985).
64. J. F. Ward, W. F. Blakely and E. I. Joner, *Radiat. Res.* **103**, 383 (1985).
65. M. E. Hofmann, A. C. Mello-Filho and R. Meneghini, *BBA* **781**, 234 (1984).
66. M. O. Bradley and L. C. Erickson, *BBA* **654**, 135 (1981).
67. J. F. Ward, *in* "Mechanisms of DNA Damage and Repair" (M. G. Simic, L. Grossman and A. C. Upton, eds.), p. 135. Plenum, New York, 1986.
68. W. F. Blakely, D. P. Dodgen, E. Holwitt and M. Dizdaroglu, *34th Annu. Meet. Radiat. Res. Soc.*, Abstr. Ek2 (1987).
69. J. S. Lazo, I. D. Braun, B. Meandzija, K. A. Kennedy, E. T. Pham and L. F. Smaldone, *Cancer Res.* **45**, 2103 (1985).
70. M. O. Bradley and K. W. Kohn, *NARes* **7**, 793 (1979).
71. A. M. Rauth, *Curr. Top. Radiat. Res.* **6**, 195 (1970).
72. R. B. Setlow, J. D. Regan, J. German and W. L. Carrier, *PNAS* **64**, 1035 (1969).
73. J. Jagger, *in* "Photochemistry and Photobiology of Nucleic Acids" (S. Y. Wang, ed.), Vol. 2, p. 147. Academic Press, New York, 1976.
74. V. M. Maher, R. H. Heflich and J. J. McCormick, *Natl. Cancer Inst. Monogr.* **58**, 217 (1981).
75. E. M. Mahoney, J. C. Ball, D. H. Swenson, D. Richmond, V. M. Maher and J. J. McCormick. *Chem.-Biol. Interact.* **50**, 59 (1984)
76. J. D. Patton, V. H. Maher and J. J. McCormick. *Carcinogenesis* **7**, 89 (1986).
77. J. R. Connell and A. S. C. Metcalf. *in* "Sister Chromatid Exchanges" (R. R. Tice and A. Hollaender, eds.), Part A, p. 343. Plenum, New York, 1984.
78. O. Cantoni, D. Murray and R. E. Meyn, *BBA* **867**, 135 (1986).
79. K. M. Milam and J. E. Cleaver, *Science* **223**, 589 (1984).

80. R. J. Boorstein, D. D. Levy and G. W. Teebor, *Cancer Res.* **47**, 4372 (1987).
81. W. Saenger, "Principles of Nucleic Acid Structure." Springer-Verlag, Berlin and New York, 1984.
82. J. Widom and A. Klug, *Cell* **43**, 207 (1985).
83. K. O. Greulich, J. Ausio and H. Eisenberg, *JMB* **186**, 167 (1985).
84. H. Eisenberg and G. Felsenfeld, *JMB* **150**, 537 (1981).
85. T. J. Richmond, J. T. Finch, B. Rushton, D. Rhodes and A. Klug, *Nature* **311**, 532 (1984).
86. K. Fonck, R. Barthel and P. E. Bryant, *Mutat. Res.* **132**, (1984).
87. B. Rydberg, *Int. J. Radiat. Biol.* **46**, 299 (1984).
88. A. A. Francis, R. D. Snyder, W. C. Dunn and J. D. Regan, *Mutat. Res.* **83**, 158 (1981).
89. R. B. Painter and B. R. Young, *Mutat. Res.* **14**, 225 (1971).
90. W. F. Blakely, E. I. Joner and J. F. Ward, *Radiat. Res.* **91**, 387 (1982).
91. J. Andrews, H. Martin-Bertram and U. Hagen, *Int. J. Radiat. Biol.* **45**, 497 (1984).
92. H. Martin-Bertram, P. Hartl and C. Winkler, *Radiat. Environ. Biophys.* **23**, 95 (1984).

Human Ferritin Gene Expression

JAMES W. DRYSDALE

Department of Biochemistry
Tufts University School of
Medicine
Boston, Massachusetts 02111

Iron is essential for all living cells. Its ubiquitous nature finds
expression in a myriad of functions in cellular biochemistry, ranging
from heme pigments in oxygen and electron carriers to such nonheme
enzymes as ribonucleotide reductase in DNA synthesis. The need for
iron poses special problems for cells. Free ferric iron is essentially
insoluble at physiological pH, while ferrous ions generate hydroxyl
radicals from hydrogen peroxide with devastating effects on cell
function and viability. Many organisms, ranging from bacteria to
mammals, cope with the challenge of keeping iron in a nontoxic bio-
available form by synthesizing the protein apoferritin. This large
multimeric structure is ideally suited for this purpose. Its spherical
protein shell is about 12 nm in diameter, but only 2.5 nm thick, leav-
ing a spacious interior, 7 nm in diameter, which can accommodate up
to 4500 atoms of iron (reviewed in *1–4*). As a result, most ferritin
populations contain a spectrum of molecules of widely different iron
content. These molecules sediment between 20 and 250 S and have
often plagued quantitation or purification of such cellular components
as ribosomes and other ribonucleoprotein particles (*5*). An unusual
aspect of ferritin is that iron enters through pores in the shell and so
can traverse molecules without concomitant synthesis or breakdown
of the shell (*6*). Another interesting feature is that iron is not only a

127

substrate for apoferritin, but is also intimately involved in regulating its synthesis.

In addition to gathering rust, ferritin may also play more active roles. Many years ago, Samuel Granick, a pioneer in ferritin research, suggested that the proportional uptake of iron into ferritin regulates the intestinal uptake of dietary iron (1), a notion that is finding renewed interest as a possible basis for the iron-storage disease, idiopathic hemochromatosis. Intracellular concentrations of ferritin may also help regulate iron traffic in other cells. As cells absorb increasing amounts of iron, intracellular ferritin concentrations rise and the proportional uptake into ferritin increases (7). At low levels of iron, much of the incoming iron bypasses ferritin.

For reasons as yet unknown, ferritin is found in serum, and in amounts higher than expected from nonspecific tissue damage. In general, serum ferritin levels correlate with body iron stores, so that immunological assessment of serum ferritin provides a simple means for assessing iron stores (8, 9), a welcome relief from liver or marrow biopsy. The source of this ferritin is still a matter of debate, as is its physiological significance or function. Receptors for ferritin have been found in cell membranes in liver and in placenta, suggesting that serum ferritin plays a role in transporting iron between organs (10). This certainly seems the case in insects, where 40% of the total body iron in some larvae is present in the blood as ferritin (11). However, in humans the amount of iron in serum ferritin is usually less than 0.1% of total body iron. Serum ferritin has also been implicated in a variety of immunosuppressive effects involved in cellular immunity, including AIDS (12–14). A provocative finding that subpopulations of extracellular ferritin regulate myelopoiesis (15) has been disputed by some (16), while others find the effective levels nonphysiological (17).

Gross elevations in serum ferritin are associated with a number of malignant disorders, inflammatory conditions, iron overload, and liver disease (8, 9, 18). In neuroblastoma, the level of serum ferritin is useful prognostically (19). Extracellular ferritin is also both a marker and a target for some cancers. Some spectacular remissions and apparent cures for primary liver hepatoma have been achieved with radioimmunotherapy with ferritin antibodies (20).

For many years, research in ferritin was stymied by a heated controversy over the structure of the protein shell and by inconsistencies in estimating mRNA abundance by cell-free translation. Recent applications of molecular biology techniques with recombinant DNA have at last dispelled the controversies on structure and have created unique opportunities to identify critical functional domains in the protein shell. Studies with cDNA probes and cloned genes have given valuable new insights into the regulation of ferritin gene expression. This review describes some of these recent advances. Most of the emphasis is on human ferritins.

I. Isoferritins

Ferritin molecules consist of an approximately spherical shell of 24 subunits surrounding a variable core of an iron-oxide–phosphate complex (21–23). The variable iron content does not appreciably alter the surface charge of the protein. However, molecules of different surface charge, called isoferritins, are readily displayed by a variety of electrophoretic or chromatographic procedures (24, 25). These are hybrid molecules containing different proportions of two subunit types, H and L, with M_rs of about 21,000 and 19,000, respectively (26). Isoferritins differ metabolically and perhaps functionally. L-rich ferritins predominate in tissues that store substantial amounts of iron, such as liver, spleen, and bone marrow. H-rich ferritins are found in organs with no major iron storage function, such as heart, pancreas, and kidney and in rapidly proliferating tissues (26–30). Ferritin phenotypes change during development and in pathological situations such as iron overload and cancer (27, 28, 30). In lymphoid cells, isoferritin patterns vary with maturation stage, proliferative status, and anatomical location. Most of these differences appear to be caused by variations in production of H type ferritins (31). Intracellular levels of ferritin usually reflect the intracellular level of nonheme iron. However, for reasons unknown, higher levels of ferritin are found in some cancers.

In many ways, H-rich ferritins seem metabolically more active than L-rich ferritins, with respect to both their protein shells and their iron cores. H-rich ferritins take up and release iron faster than L-rich isoferritins *in vitro* (32, 33). Unfortunately, these observations are difficult to correlate with the behavior of individual isoferritins *in vivo*, as neither the natural donor of iron nor its reducing agent is yet known. The identification of the molecular donor of iron or the so-called labile iron pool would be enormously helpful in these areas and also in studies of the regulation of transcription and translation of ferritin mRNA.

In addition to metabolizing iron more actively, the protein shells of H-rich ferritins also turn over more rapidly than those of L-rich isoferritins. In rat liver, the half-life of H-rich ferritins can be less than 10% of the more stable L-rich ferritins (28, 29). Taken together, the

present data suggest that the H subunit plays a more important catalytic role in the uptake and release of iron, while the L subunit is
better suited for long-term iron storage. In this respect, the H and L
ferritins may be the structural basis for the "anabolic" and "catabolic"
ferritins postulated by Gabuzda and Pearson (34) many years ago.

II. H cDNA Clones

The controversy over the relationships, or even the existence, of
different subunit types was finally settled in 1984 and 1985 when
cDNA clones for H and L subunits for human ferritins were isolated.
Ironically, despite questions of its very existence, it was the H chain
that was first to be cloned (35, 36). Clones that proved to be H cDNAs
were isolated by screening a human lymphocyte cDNA "library" with
oligonucleotides corresponding to a peptide in a minor "contaminating" sequence from human spleen ferritin, which we guessed repre-
sented the H chain. Because of the limited sequence available and
codon degeneracy, we required a mixture of 32 tetradecamers to en-
sure that one would be correct. The identity of selected clones was
established by hybrid selection of mRNA and by sequence analysis
(35). Other clones that proved to be ferritin H cDNAs were isolated
during a search for tissue-specific mRNAs in a liver cDNA library and
were identified because of the partial homology of their deduced
amino-acid sequence with L chains. Interestingly, of about 250 randomly selected liver cDNA clones, several were identified as ferritin
H cDNAs, indicating an abundance of ferritin mRNA in liver (36).
Clones that also proved to be ferritin H cDNAs were isolated from a
human neutrophil cDNA library during a search for mRNAs that are
highly regulated during neutrophil differentiation (37). As in the liver,
ferritin mRNA is particularily abundant in neutrophils.

Initially, it appeared that there might be two sequences for human
H chains since the two reported cDNA sequences differed in coding
sequence by one base, resulting in different C-terminal regions from
the frame shift. This difference proved to be a sequencing error. At
present, despite analyses of several clones from different libraries
including liver, HeLa cells, lymphocytes, endothelial cells, and neutrophils, only one human H cDNA sequence has been found so far.
However, in view of suggestive evidence for H subunit heterogeneity
(see later), the question of the number of expressed human H chains
must remain open.

III. L cDNA Clones

cDNA clones for human ferritin L chains were also isolated by oligonucleotide probes (38), by analyses of liver and neutrophil cDNA libraries for tissue-specific RNAs (37, 39), and by immunological detection from an expression library from U937 cells (40). Again, the evidence strongly suggests that only one L sequence is expressed in several human tissues. Only one sequence has been found in L cDNAs from liver and neutrophils. A sequence differing in a single nucleotide in the coding, and substantially in the 5' noncoding region, from the U937 clone has been reported (40), but has not been confirmed by others. Primer extension analyses of mRNA from human liver, placenta, HeLa, and Daudi cell lines give one extension product, not two. Further, no hybridization was obtained with a subprobe specific for the 5' unique U937 sequence with either mRNA or genomic DNA, again suggesting that this 5' sequence is incorrect (39). We have found this sequence in plasmid sequences, and suspect a cloning or sequencing error.

IV. Evolutionary Aspects

Sequences for ferritin cDNAs from rat (41) tadpole (42), chicken (43), and mouse (M. Souroujon, C. Beaumont and J. W. Drysdale, unpublished) have also been obtained, and provide a starting point for assessing the evolutionary relationships of the H and L chains. In the human sequences, there are mutations at 27% of the replacement sites affecting amino-acid sequence and at 66% of the silent sites that do not change the protein sequence. These values for replacement and silent changes are similar to those between mammalian and avian globins, and suggested initially that the H and L sequences evolved from a common precursor about the time when birds and mammals diverged, perhaps 200 million years ago (38). Thus one might expect chicken H and L sequences to be substantially different from their human counterparts, and also to be more homologous to one another than to the human sequences. Surprisingly, the chicken H chain is 93% homologous to the human H chain. By contrast, two types of H chains in frogs are only about 70% homologous with the human H chain and about 80% with each other. The frog L chain shares even less homology (55%) with the human L chain and about 60% homology with the frog H chains. One of the frog H chains, denoted M (42), has an intermediate sequence to the frog H and L chains. This sequence may therefore be closer to the primordial sequence from which the known human H and L sequences evolved. The remarkable similarity of chicken and human H sequences suggests that the H sequence has not mutated as much as the L. Also, given the large differences in the three frog sequences, it now seems more likely that the original divergence occurred long before the development of amphibia. An analysis of fish genes, preferably bluefish or salmon, is clearly in order!

V. Heterogeneity in H and L Subunits

It is now generally agreed that most species have at least two distinct subunit types, denoted H and L. This original classification was based on electrophoretic differences (26), but, because of electrophoretic anomalies (42), it now seems preferable to classify the subunits according to their amino-acid sequence. Discussion is now focused on the question of further heterogeneity in subunit classes. For example, it is possible that some of the ferritin in serum is actively secreted and not just released from damaged cells (44, 45). Normal serum ferritin and an apparently related ferritin in milk bind to concanavalin A (44, 46), and are therefore thought to be glycosylated. Serum ferritin reacts with monoclonal antibodies to L but not H subunits, and is therefore probably related more to the L than to the H subunit (47, 48). The protein sequence for these ferritins is not yet known. While they could arise from postsynthetic modification of the intracellular L chain, it seems more likely that a secreted ferritin would be synthesized from its own mRNA with appropriate signal sequences. This mRNA could arise either from differential splicing of the known L gene or from another gene altogether.

There may also be multiple forms of the H subunit. The evidence for this notion came initially from protein analyses and is as follows: (1) Three subunit species can be separated by acid–urea gel electrophoresis or by isoelectric focusing, though only two size classes, H and L, are given by gel electrophoresis in dodecyl sulfate (26, 49). (2) Isoferritins of the same pI in liver and heart have different H/L subunit ratios (29). (3) Translation of HeLa mRNA in cell-free systems yields two isoelectric forms of human H subunits (50). (4) The immunological reactivities of isoferritins from some erythroid cells differ substantially from isoferritins of similar surface charge from liver or heart (51). Charge heterogeneity in H or L subunits, either from postsynthetic modification or from different primary structures, is thus clearly indicated.

Solid evidence for sequence heterogeneity in H chains has recently come with the discovery in tadpoles of three types of ferritin
mRNAs that are expressed in a tissue-specific manner (42). Two are
H-type and are about 80% homologous at the protein level. To complicate matters, two H subunits have been isolated by liquid chromatography from human and from pig tissues, but the partial sequences of
the pig chains are about 98% homologous (52). No sequence information is available on the two human H subunits. Since the differences
in pig do not correspond to those in the tadpole H chains, it will be
interesting to see how these sequences evolved and which type of
heterogeneity occurs in other species. The existence of more than one
functional H gene in frogs and pigs and perhaps in humans seems at
odds with indications from Southern blot analyses that chickens and
mice appear to manage perfectly well with only one H gene. However, one could argue that if, as in frogs, a second H gene in other
species is only 80% homologous, it may have escaped detection so far.

VI. Structural and Functional Relationships

A. Structural Aspects

Present knowledge of the secondary, tertiary, and quaternary
structure of ferritin comes mostly from analyses of horse spleen ferritin, the first ferritin to be isolated. It was obtained in crystalline form
by Laufberger in 1937 by a remarkably simple procedure involving
heat extraction, ammonium sulfate fractionation, and crystallization
with cadmium (53). So specific is this interaction with cadmium that
crystals can be formed even in broken cells just by adding cadmium (1).

X-Ray diffraction studies by Harrison and her colleagues, together
with amino-acid sequence data, indicate that this apoferritin contains
24 structurally equivalent subunits arranged in icosahedral symmetry
(23, 54). Each subunit consists of a bundle of four helices (A, residues
10–39; B, 45–72; C, 92–120; and D, 124–155), held together by hydrophobic interactions to form a haggis- (or sausage-)like shape
(Fig. 1). A fifth helix (E, residues 160–169) at the C-terminal region
lies acutely across this bundle to interact with the loops between
helices A and B, and between C and D. Residues 73–91 form a long
loop that lies on the outer surface. The inner face of the subunit is
hydrophilic, as might be expected for an interior containing water and
iron. The driving force for subunit aggregation and shell assembly
probably comes from interactions of two patches of hydrophobic

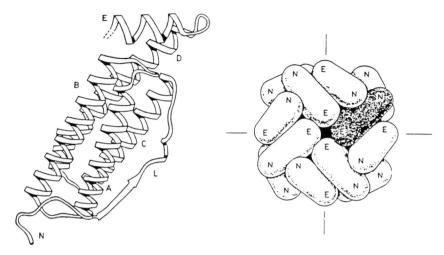

Fig. 1. Schematic drawing of a ferritin subunit. The main features are the five
helices, A to E, and the long interhelix loop, L. The loop, L, and the N-terminal
residues, N, lie on the outside of the protein shell. Helix E runs from the outside to the
inside, so that the C-terminal end of the chain is at the inside surface of the molecule.
From (23) with permission.

regions in helices A and B. In the shell, pairs of helix bundles in each
subunit lie antiparallel so that their N- and C-terminal regions are
adjacent to N- and C-terminal regions of another subunit.

Each shell has 3-fold and 4-fold axes of symmetry that form channels large enough to be penetrated by sucrose and $FMNH_2$. These
channels also allow iron to enter and leave, though through which
channel is not yet clear. Antibodies that bind to the 3-fold channel
block iron uptake, while antibodies that bind to the 4-fold channel
block iron release (55). On the other hand, mutations of amino acids in
the 4-fold channel alter iron uptake, but not iron release (56). The site
of iron oxidation is also not known, but this probably occurs near the
shell surface rather than within a channel (57). Thereafter, the ferric
iron is translocated to the interior with hydrolysis and subsequent
polymerization to iron bound to carboxylates (58).

The derivation of the fine structure of horse spleen ferritin was a
great impetus for correlations of structure and function. Oddly, however, it was a major impediment to the general acceptance of the idea
that most apoferritins are hybrid molecules, as the X-ray data indicated that all subunits are structurally equivalent. For many years
these apparently contradictory viewpoints were bandied about. The
paradox was partly resolved with the finding that cadmium crystal-

lizes only a small subpopulation of isoferritins and that these consist almost entirely of L subunits (59). The issue was finally put to rest when deductions of the secondary and tertiary structure of H subunits indicated that both subunits are structurally equivalent despite large differences in sequence (38).

In humans, the sequences of the H and L subunits as deduced from the cDNAs are about 55% homologous at the amino-acid level and 65% at the nucleotide level. The H subunit contains 182 amino acids and can be perfectly aligned with the 174 residues of the L subunit if arranged with an overlap of four amino acids at both ends (Fig. 2) (38). Since the N-terminal residue in the deduced sequence from the L cDNA corresponds to that given by protein sequencing, except for acetylation of the N-terminal serine, it seems likely that newly synthesized human L chains are incorporated as such into apo-

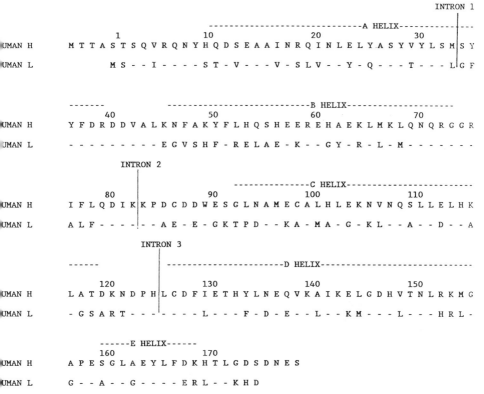

FIG. 2. Amino-acid sequence of human H and L ferritin chains. The numbering system here and in the text follows that of the L chain. From (38).

ferritin shells. Similarly, the evidence indicates that human H chains also are not processed before incorporation into shells. Other species differ. Mouse H subunits appear to be synthesized as a precursor that undergoes two processing steps before or soon after incorporation into shells (60). Plant ferritin subunits are also similarly processed (61).

Other modifications are possible. It has been claimed that subunits are cross-linked in shells through lysine or threonine residues (62), but the evidence is not compelling. Both subunits can be phosphorylated *in vitro* (63), but again it is not known whether this occurs *in vivo*. Finally, both H and L sequences have potential glycosylation sites. That on the L subunit is at residue 9 and probably lies on the exterior of the shell and so could be functional. That on the H subunit, corresponding to residue 108 in the L sequence, is buried in the subunit and therefore not likely to be glycosylated. There are no Cys residues in the L subunit, but three in the H, at residues 86, 98, and 127. Although their positions make it unlikely that these will form intrachain disulfides, the CysH at 98 lies on the exterior and could perhaps cross-link different shells. This would be in accord with our unpublished findings that ferritin aggregates can be broken down by reducing agents into monomeric shells.

Although H-rich ferritins have recently been crystallized (64), no X-ray diffraction patterns have yet been obtained. Nevertheless, predictions of secondary structure by Chou-Fasman rules indicate that the H subunit has the same distribution of α helices and of hydrophilic and hydrophobic regions as the L subunit (38). The hydrophobic intrasubunit domain in the L subunits formed by interactions of Val-20, Leu-24, Tyr-28, and Leu-31 in the A helix with Phe-78, Leu-81, and Pro-84 in the C helix is highly conserved in the H subunit. Also conserved are residues in the E helix important for assembly of dimer subunits into shells, consistent with previous findings that H and L subunits from the same or different species are interchangeable in the protein shell (65). The N- and C-terminal regions are not part of the helices. In H subunits the additional four residues at the N-terminus probably project from the surface of the shell. This projection might explain the anomalously large molecular volume of H-rich ferritins seen by gel filtration (66).

Despite variation in chain length in other species, the basic structural features of their ferritins seem to be conserved. Rat and mouse L chains contain an additional eight amino-acid residues between residues 158 and 159 (41, and M. Souroujon, I. Dugast, C. Beaumont and J. Drysdale, unpublished), but these residues lie in the loop between helices D and E and thus probably do not alter the functional domains or the overall shell conformation.

B. Functional Domains

Although differing in 74 residues, the H and L chains have several regions of extensive homology. These include residues 123–129 and 163–169 which are also conserved in all other known H and L sequences (except for two residues in frog L) and therefore probably play critical roles in structure and function. For example, in molecules consisting only of L subunits, the 4-fold axes of symmetry are lined by 12 leucines. This pore is therefore very hydrophobic and would seem an inhospitable environment for a hydrated iron atom. However, in the human H subunit, leucine-169 at the outside of the pore and on the surface of the shell is replaced by a histidine (38). Given its propensity for binding iron, this histidine residue could be critical for the passage of iron into or out of ferritin shells. One might even argue that at least one H subunit is necessary for the uptake of iron into human ferritin shells. This would explain why in iron-loaded cells, natural apoferritin, a homopolymer of L subunits (60), exists as an empty shell, when other molecules containing only a few H subunits are essentially full of iron.

The pore structure at the 3-fold axes is highly polar in human L subunits and is lined by His-114, His-124, CysH-126, Asp-127, Glu-130, and His-132. All of these residues are retained in the human H subunit, suggesting that this pore is functionally conserved in H-rich ferritins. However, the inner face to which iron binds is quite different in H and L subunits. This may account for differences in iron content in isoferritins (38). Many of these hypotheses can now be rigorously examined. Functional human ferritin H and L ferritins have now been expressed from cDNA clones and can easily be modified by site-directed mutagenesis (64).

VII. H and L Genes

The human genome contains multiple copies of H and L sequences. Southern blot analyses of genomic DNA digested with a variety of restriction enzymes and hybridized with 3' and 5' subprobes from cDNA clones for H and L chains from lymphocytes initially indicated that there were at least 10 H genes and 5 L genes (35, 67). With improved resolution, it now appears that there are probably close to 20 distinct H genes. The question therefore arises as to which of these many sequences represent functional genes. Initially, this genomic heterogeneity seemed consistent with isolated reports of sequence heterogeneity for various tissue ferritins. However, this proved not to be the case, as none of these sequences from protein analyses corresponded to the single sequence predicted so far from cDNA clones: testimony perhaps to problems of sample heterogeneity or other technicalities in protein sequencing, and to the power of the new biology.

Since only one sequence for human H or L chains has been found from cDNA clones from a variety of tissues, we expected that, at most, only a few of the H and L gene sequences would be functional. By analogy with other large gene families whose complexity is not reflected in protein heterogeneity (68), it seemed likely that many of the ferritin sequences in human DNA would be nonfunctional and probably represent processed pseudogenes. The latter are thought to arise from reverse transcripts of mRNA, and therefore contain no introns (69, 70).

To address this problem, we examined genomic clones with H or L sequences which Julian Crampton had obtained by screening a genomic library from bacteriophage λ with human H and L cDNA probes. We obtained about 20 apparently different H clones and 5 L clones. The problem then became to identify which, if any were functional. Among the options we considered were (1) transfection to show expressed RNA or protein, (2) sequencing, (3) restriction mapping, and (4) heteroduplex mapping. Transfection and sequencing give more information than restriction or heteroduplex mapping, but neither is necessarily definitive. A positive result with transfection can prove a gene is functional, but a negative result may merely reflect an inappropriate choice of cells for a gene that is expressed in a tissue-specific manner. Likewise, sequencing can indicate a viable coding region and appropriate transcriptional control sequences, but does not establish expression or functionality. Expediency prevailed, and we elected to screen by restriction mapping to identify clones with the same restriction sites as the expressed cDNAs and also to distinguish genes with introns from those without introns.

Chromosomal Localizations

While this preliminary screening of our genomic clones was in progress, the problem of identifying functional genes was greatly simplified from immunological analyses of ferritin protein expression in human–rodent hybrid cells containing different subsets of human chromosomes. Using antibodies that could distinguish between human and hamster H- and L-ferritin subunits, Seligman and his colleagues (71) showed that human L ferritin is expressed from chromosome 19. This was confirmed by Worwood et al. (72), who showed similarly that human H chains are expressed from chromosome 11.

Thus ferritin falls into the same pattern as other heteropolymers such as lactate dehydrogenase and globin whose genes are not syntenic.

This information led us to determine the chromosomal distribution of the various human ferritin genes and to correlate Southern banding patterns with chromosomal assignments. We took three different approaches: (1) Southern analyses of DNA from rodent–human hybrid cells containing different subsets of human chromosomes (73, 74), (2) dot-blot and Southern analyses of DNA from sorted human chromosomes (75), and (3) *in situ* hybridization of spread human metaphase chromosomes (74). Happily, all three approaches were mutually supportive. To our surprise we found that ferritin sequences are present on most human chromosomes. From Southern blots from hybrid cells, we were able to assign the chromosomal origins of seven different *Eco*RI fragments with H genes and three fragments with L genes. The chromosomal positions of many of these genes were determined from *in situ* hybridization studies. These assignments are supported by analyses of cells with informative chromosomal translocations. At present we have found ferritin H genes at 1p22-31, 1q32-42, 2q32-33, 3q21-23, 6p12-21.3, 11q13, 13q12, and Xq26-28, and L genes at 19q13.1-qter, 20q12-13.3, and Xp21.2-22.3 (Fig. 3). We do not yet know the position of an H gene, found from Southern analyses (74) to be on chromosome 17.

Interestingly, several genes map near known heritable fragile sites such as the H genes on chromosomes 11 and X. These may be useful markers for diseases involving chromosomal abnormalities or for mapping other genes. Some genes map near the loci of other genetic disorders. For example, an L gene lies near Xp21 and could be useful for mapping around the locus for Duchenne's muscular dystrophy, while an H gene at Xq26-28 could be a useful starting point for identifying the gene responsible for premature ovary maturation (76). The fact that one probe visualizes so much DNA is particularly appealing. Also, since most of these genes have now been cloned, unique markers for their loci can be obtained from flanking regions outside the common ferritin sequences.

The finding of ferritin sequences on many different chromosomes considerably narrowed the search for the expressed H and L genes. In view of the protein expression data, we were particularly interested in identifying the H gene from chromosome 11 and the L gene from chromosome 19. From the *in situ* evidence it appeared that the H sequences on chromosome 11 were all clustered near 11q23. How could this gene be easily identified? An important clue came from analyses of hybrid cells which indicated that this gene was contained

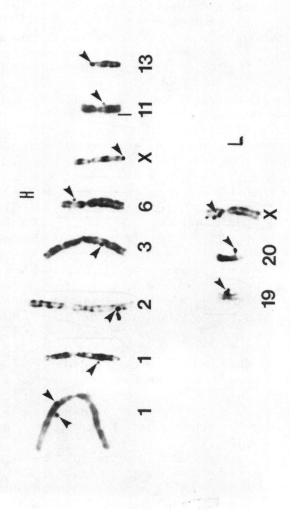

Fig. 3. Chromosomal localization of human ferritin H and L genes (courtesy of John McGill). From (74).

on a 17-kb *Eco*RI fragment. This was the only *Eco*RI band with H sequences found on chromosome 11 by this method, but it should be noted that we were able to map only nine of the human H genes because of comigrating hamster genes from the parent cell or from limitations in hybrid cell lines.

Similarly, we found that all of the L sequences on chromosome 19 appeared to be on a 6.1-kb *Eco*RI fragment. Subsequently, we found, from analyses of DNA from sorted chromosomes, that L sequences on chromosome 19 lie on two *Bgl*II fragments of about 3.8 and 9.4 kb (75). The question therefore arises as to whether these fragments contain different parts of the same gene, or two distinct genes. We do not yet know the answer, though analyses with subprobes from the L cDNA indicate that both *Bgl*II fragments contain different genes. If so, both genes may lie close to one another, possibly on the same *Eco*RI fragment. It will be interesting to know whether both are functional.

VIII. Expressed H and L Genes

A. H Gene

Unfortunately, none of our genomic clones contained the 17-kb *Eco*RI fragment mapped to chromosome 11, perhaps because they came from a library constructed from 15- to 20-kb fragments of genomic DNA cut randomly by *Hae*III. A large 17-kb *Eco*RI fragment might therefore suffer truncation during cloning and no longer be recognizable as such. Although we could not identify this gene on this basis, our preliminary screening by restriction mapping and by electron microscopy indicated that 2 of our 15 clones contained introns. Further mapping and sequence analyses from subcloned fragments showed that both clones contained the same ferritin H gene.

This gene (77, 78) contains three introns of about 1.6, 0.25, and 0.1 kb, so that the H sequence is spread over 3 kb. Intron 1 is placed between mRNA residues 331 and 332, intron 2 at residues 478 and 479, and intron 3 at 604 and 605. All intron–exon junctions have the usual AG-GT splice sites. All three introns are in the coding region at positions corresponding to amino-acid residues 33, 83, and 126 (Fig. 2). The second intron splits the coding region almost in half, but the two halves are unlikely to come from duplicated sequences. The coding region and noncoding regions are exactly as in our lymphocyte and liver H cDNA clone sequences. Interestingly, the four exons correspond closely to the α-helical regions in the protein subunit, except that helices D and E are both contained within exon 4. Conclusive evidence that this is an expressed ferritin gene was provided by transfecting this gene into mouse B6 cells and demonstrating human H mRNA transcripts by S1 nuclease mapping of mRNA (77).

The ferritin sequence in this genomic clone was contained in two *Eco*RI fragments of about 6.5 kb and 4 kb arising from an *Eco*RI site in the large intron in the 5' noncoding region. Since no such fragments had been mapped to chromosome 11, it was important to define the sizes of the original *Eco*RI fragments in genomic DNA, and also the chromosomal origin of this gene. To do this, we prepared subprobes from flanking regions of the ferritin sequence in the two *Eco*RI fragments. These subprobes did not contain ferritin sequences and so could hybridize only to ferritin genes with these flanking sequences. They also did not contain repetitive genomic sequences. These subprobes showed that the 3' ferritin sequences on the cloned 4-kb fragment were derived from a 17-kb *Eco*RI fragment in genomic DNA, which must therefore have been truncated by *Hae*III when cloned (P. Papadopoulous and J. W. Drysdale, unpublished). This was an important finding in view of previous findings that a 17-kb *Eco*RI fragment containing a ferritin H gene was derived from chromosome 11, the only chromosome shown so far to contain a functional gene.

This identification was confirmed by Southern analyses of hybrid cells. In one such analysis we were fortunate to obtain hybrid cells from Carol Jones in Denver in which the only human chromosome was chromosome 11. With these cells and the unique flanking 3' subprobe, we were able to show definitively that the 17-kb *Eco*RI fragment recognized by our subprobe was indeed derived from chromosome 11. Similarly, we showed with the 5' flanking subprobe that the ferritin sequences on the 6.5-kb *Eco*RI fragment in our genomic clone was derived from a similar sized *Eco*RI fragment in genomic DNA and therefore had been cloned intact. As expected, hybridization with the 5' flanking subprobe confirmed that this fragment also came from chromosome 11. This result is a good example of the value of unique flanking subprobes for mapping members of a multiple gene family whose members are comingled in hybrid cells with cross-hybridizing members of another related family.

B. L Gene

Because of the lower number of L genes, the identification of the functional gene was considerably simpler than for the H gene. A candidate for the expressed L gene has been cloned and sequenced (39). Its *Eco*RI fragment size corresponds to that containing the gene on chromosome 19, but its chromosomal origin has not been established, nor has it been shown to be expressed. Nevertheless, its overall similarity to the H gene in its intron–exon arrangement, and the concordance of its sequence with that of the only known L cDNA, strongly suggests it is indeed the functional L gene. Like the H gene, the exons in the L gene correspond to the regions of α-helix in the protein subunit. However, they differ in size from those in the H gene on chromosome 11. Intron 1 contains only 163 bp, intron 2 about 360 bp, and intron 3 about 170 bp.

C. Other Species

The only other functional gene to be characterized so far is that of a chicken H chain (43). Its intron–exon boundaries are similar to those in the human H gene on chromosome 11, though its second and third introns are substantially larger than their human counterparts, so that the primary transcript in chickens is about 4.6 kb as compared to 3.3 kb in humans. The chicken H chain contains 179 amino acids as against 182 in the human H. There are four differences in the two chains in exon 1, none in exon 2, four in exon 3, and seven in exon 4. Of these, only one, at residue 135, corresponds to a substitution in the human L chain. However, four differences at residues 12, 86, 91, and 161 correspond to sequences in all three frog chains, while those at 143 and 173 are only present in the two frog H genes.

IX. Other Human Genes

A. H Genes

In addition to the functional H gene on chromosome 11, several other human genes have also been cloned. Their chromosomal locations have been tentatively assigned from the sizes of their hybridizing fragments, but await confirmation from subprobes from flanking sequences outside the ferritin sequences. We have analyzed 9 different clones and find, by restriction mapping and heteroduplex mapping, that none have introns. Costanzo et al. (78), also found no introns in 15 different clones by heteroduplex mapping. They sequenced two and showed that they have all the hallmarks of processed pseudogenes. Both are colinear with the cDNA sequence, both have a poly(A) sequence at the 3' end and about 15-bp repeats at their 5' and 3' ends. Interestingly, although both have multiple mutations in coding sequence, both could potentially code for a polypeptide with the same number of residues as the functional H chain. Although they only sequenced two such genes, they concluded, perhaps prematurely, that all other ferritin H genes would similarly prove to be nonfunctional processed pseudogenes.

While processed pseudogenes seriously complicate gene analyses, they have their redeeming features. They can provide clues about the probable number of expressed genes in some species. For example, humans and hamsters appear to have at least 10 ferritin H gene sequences in at least 10 different loci (74), while mice (74) and chickens (43) appear to have only one. This suggests that the number of functional genes in humans and hamsters is likely to be small. Also, since mice and hamsters are more closely related than mice and men, the hamster's aquisition of its pseudogene family must have occurred after rodent speciation. Pseudogenes may also give other useful information on evolution. We have found large differences in sequences of some human pseudogenes indicating that their retrotranscription and insertion occurred at different points in evolution. If so, pseudogene patterns may offer a method for studying the origins and spread of human populations.

On the other hand, the different pseudogene sequences may have originated from different transcripts. This latter possibility cannot be rejected, particularly given the evidence for heterogeneity in H chains. It is known that some isoproteins are expressed from genes on different chromosomes (79). There are even examples of expression from genes which at first sight might be dismissed as processed pseudogenes. Such a case occurs with the enzyme phosphoglycerokinase. This protein is expressed in most tissues from a gene with introns, but in spermatogenesis from an intronless gene with flanking sequences characteristic of a processed pseudogene (80).

If there are two expressed H genes in humans, where is the other? We consider three to be likely candidates: (1) a second gene, which we have recently found on chromosome 11 (P. Papadopoulos, C. Jones and J. Drysdale, unpublished); (2) a gene on chromosome 3 that lies near the genes for other proteins of iron metabolism, including transferrin, lactoferrin, and transferrin receptor (74); and (3) a gene on chromosome 6 that lies near the HLA locus (74). We are particularly intrigued by the gene on chromosome 6, in view of its potential role in the pathogenesis of idiopathic hemochromatosis. This disease results in massive iron overload associated with liver cirrhosis, diabetes, and cardiomyopathy. The gene occurs with a frequency of 1 in 20 in Celtic populations and is one of the most frequent gene abnormalities in Europe and the USA. The gene maps near the HLA locus at 6p21 (81,

82). This remarkably high frequency may reflect a selective advantage for heterozygotes in absorbing dietary iron. The disease is likely to be caused by some defect in iron absorption, storage, or transport. Little is known of the molecular mechanism of iron absorption, though some think uptake is mediated by transferrin through its receptor as in other cells. However, genes for transferrin and its receptor lie on chromosome 3, and are unlikely candidates unless their action is modulated by a gene product from chromosome 6.

The ferritin H gene at 6p21, if expressed, is an attractive candidate. Many years ago, Granick postulated that incorporation of iron into intestinal mucosal ferritin regulated iron absorption by blocking further iron uptake (1). Iron in ferritin is then normally lost through migration of siderotic macrophages to the lumen. This process does not appear to occur in hemochromatosis (83). Several years ago, we found that ferritin phenotypes in tissues such as heart, pancreas, and kidney changed in hemochromatosis from their normally high proportion of acidic, H-rich ferritins to the more basic L-rich patterns of liver and spleen (27). This suggested a defect in H-chain synthesis in hemochromatosis. However, since iron loading causes a similar shift in phenotype (28), the phenotype shift could also have been a secondary effect. We have recently been examining ferritin H-gene patterns in family studies (with Jean Yves Legall and Marcel Simon in Rennes) and have found what seems to be an informative polymorphism in a ferritin gene. This polymorphism is much more frequent in hemochromatotic patients than in normals. Even more tantalizing is the finding that the polymorphic band comes from the gene in chromosome 6, which maps near the known locus of HLA-linked hemochromatosis. Although we have not characterized this gene yet, it conceivably could represent another H subunit that is functional in normal intestinal cells but defective in hemochromatosis.

B. L Genes

In addition to the presumed functional L gene, several other L genes have been isolated and are now being analyzed. Santoro et al. (39) found no evidence of introns by heteroduplex mapping in four different genomic clones. A fifth had a small loop of about 300 bp, which falls at residue 243. Sequencing showed that this loop did not have consensus splice sequences and probably represents an insertion into a sequence that in all other respects seems to be a processed pseudogene. Based on these findings, they speculate that all other L genes will similarly prove to be nonfunctional. However, if serum ferritin truly is actively secreted and is also glycosylated, it may also be wise to reserve judgment on the number of functional L genes for a later day.

X. Regulation of Expression

A. Transcriptional Controls

It seems likely that the large differences in ferritin concentrations and in the relative amounts of H and L subunits in different tissues are determined primarily by differential gene transcription. This seems the case in malignant and nonmalignant lymphocytes, where large differences in amounts of ferritin and in the relative amounts of H and L subunits correspond closely to differences in the levels of H and L mRNAs (84). Other evidence for transcriptional control comes from studies with HL60 cells, a promyelocytic leukemia cell line. When this line is induced to differentiate into neutrophils with Me_2SO, ferritin H and L mRNAs increase about 25-fold and 3-fold, respectively. When induced to differentiate to the macrophage pathway with phorbol esters, H mRNA increases 40-fold after 2 days, while the L mRNA increases 5-fold. The net result in both systems is a substantial increase in the H/L mRNA ratio (37). This finding is consistent with earlier findings of a progressive increase in H/L subunit ratio during macrophage development (85). Although the basis for the increased ferritin mRNA levels was not established in these experiments it seems likely, from studies of transcription levels in differentiating Friend cells, that the increased ferritin mRNA levels arise from increased transcription rather than decreased mRNA breakdown (60).

Iron also increases ferritin transcription, but apparently not in all cells. Iron administration causes substantial increases in H and L mRNA levels in HeLa cells (86) and in frog reticulocytes (42). Cairo *et al.* (86) showed that the increase in ferritin L mRNA in HeLa cells involves increased transcription. They did not report on transcription levels for H mRNA, perhaps because of cross-hybridization with 28-S RNA. These results contrast with those in rat liver or in rat hepatoma cells where iron has no apparent effect on total cytoplasmic levels of ferritin H or L mRNAs (87). There is no obvious explanation for these differences. Conceivably, cells that do not normally have a major iron storage function respond by increasing transcription, because their available ferritin mRNA levels cannot cope with the additional iron, whereas cells like liver that normally store large amounts of iron have adequate levels of ferritin mRNA either in polysomes or in mRNP particles and may only turn to transcription when these are insufficient (see Section X,C).

S1 analyses of DNA · RNA hybrids produced from mouse B6 cells transfected with the functional H gene indicate that the 5' noncoding region contains about 213 bp (77). A similar size was predicted from primer extension analyses (36). However, in K562 cells, two fragments differing by about 8 bp are protected (77). This result could reflect use of different initiating sites in different cells, or perhaps two different mRNA species. Similarily, S1 analyses of DNA · RNA hybrids of the functional L gene and mRNA from human liver indicate that the L mRNA initiates about 25 bp downstream from the TATA-like sequence in the L gene (39), consistent with results from primer extension indicating a noncoding region of about 200 bp. However, as with the H mRNA, two discrete fragments were protected in S1 analyses of mRNA from U937 cells, a promyelocytic human cell line (39). Again, this could be due to different initiation sites or to different mRNAs.

B. Promoter Region

Not much is yet known of functional sequences in the promoters of ferritin genes. It seems likely that both ferritin genes will have regulatory sequences for baseline expression and for induction by iron and other factors in tissues where ferritin levels vary substantially. In this regard, it is interesting to note that the ferritin H promoter has sequences that are also found in promotors of many growth-related genes and of other metal-binding proteins such as transferrin, transferrin receptor, and metallothionein.

The H gene has a conventional TATA box, 25 bp upstream from the transcription initiation site indicated by primer extension, but no CAAT sequence. The entire promoter is highly G + C-rich and contains at least four "GC boxes" that are binding sites for the transcription factor Sp1 (88). There are also similar GC boxes in the transcribed 5' noncoding region. Such sequences are found in promoter regions of SV40, herpes simplex and AIDS virus, C-*myc* and N-*myc* oncogenes, epidermal growth factor, thymidine kinase, and dihydrofolate reductase (88).

The ferritin H gene has interesting parallels with those of the metallothionein gene family, which are expressed in a tissue-specific manner. Metallothionein transcription is affected by several factors including heavy metals, glucocorticoids, epidermal growth factor, platelet-derived growth factor, interleukin-I, β-interferon, and phorbol esters (89, 90). Several of these factors also increase ferritin levels.

Many of these agents appear to act in cis through promoter sequences that have been identified and mapped. It is therefore intriguing to find similar sequences in the ferritin H promoter. For example, the H promoter has several sequences that are identical or very similar to the sequence GCGGGGCGKGTGCRRG* required for basal expression of metallothionein. It also has three sequences that are similar to the sequence TGCGCCCGSYCC* required for induction of metallothionein by cadmium. These metal-responsive elements may function similarly in the ferritin H gene since we find that ferritin H mRNA levels are also induced by cadmium (E. Zappone, M. Kirin and J. W. Drysdale, unpublished). Strangely, the promoter of another iron-binding protein, transferrin, also has these sequences (91). Since ferritin binds cadmium, it may not be unreasonable to think that it is also induced by cadmium. However, there is no such rationale for transferrin. Perhaps some of the metal-regulating elements respond to more than one heavy metal through interaction with different proteins. In the case of metallothionein, the metal-regulating sequences bind a nuclear protein that regulates transcription in the presence of cadmium (92). It will be interesting to see if the ferritin induction by cadmium involves the same sequences and the same protein.

About 250 bp upstream from the TATA box (Fig. 4), there is a 9-bp sequence corresponding to the adenovirus-Ela core-enhancer sequence and its homologues in SV40, heat-shock proteins, interferon, c-*fos*, and interleukin-2 (93). The same sequence enhances transcription of the transferrin receptor gene (94). We also find a 19-bp sequence that is highly homologous to that required for expression of c-*fos* and another 13-bp sequence in the first intron that is identical to a promoter sequence in the epidermal growth-factor receptor (95). Although ferritin H mRNA is induced by phorbol esters (37), we cannot find in its promoter region the sequences identified for phorbol induction of metallothionein genes, and assume other sequences are involved (90). Experiments in progress in several laboratories should soon improve our knowledge of ferritin H gene regulation and identify which, if any, of these putative regulatory sequences are functional.

Less is known of putative regulatory elements in the L gene, as only a short segment of sequence above the initiation site is known. However, it has a TATA-like sequence (TAAAA) 30 bp upstream from

---

* K = T or G; R = A or G; S = G or C; Y = T or C [Recommendations of the Nomenclature Committee of the International Union of Biochemistry (NC-IUB); see *EJB* **150**, 1 1985]. [Eds.].

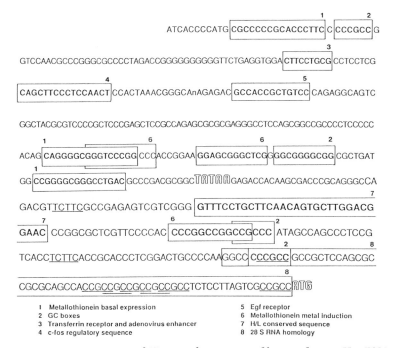

FIG. 4. Promoter region and 5′ noncoding region of human ferritin H mRNA.

the deduced initiation site, but no CAAT sequence. With a protein literature so long dominated by studies of L ferritins, it is ironic that much more is now known about H genes than L genes. No doubt the pendulum will soon swing the other way.

C. Translational Control

The mRNAs for both H and L chains have unusually long 5′ non-coding regions of about 215 bp, suggesting that they have important regulatory functions. Such functions might include regulation of the compartmentation of ferritin mRNA between functional polysomes and inactive mRNP particles and of the selection of ferritin mRNAs for translation. Elements for both processes are present in H and L mRNAs.

1. mRNA COMPARTMENTATION

This is one of the most exciting findings to come out of the explosion of information on ferritin gene regulation in the past few years. It had been suspected for many years that ferritin synthesis is under translational control by iron (6). Several studies indicated that a large proportion of ferritin mRNA in many cells is not engaged in protein synthesis, but exists in a masked form in the cytoplasm. This masked mRNA can be readily translated if first stripped of proteins (96). From estimates of mRNA levels by *in vitro* translation, it was postulated by Munro and his colleagues that increases in intracellular iron mobilize the ferritin mRNA in these particles to functional polysomes (96). This attractive model has now been confirmed by hybridization studies with cDNA probes which show that both H and L mRNAs are under this form of translational control (87, 97). Both H and L mRNAs are mobilized from mRNP particles to functional polysomes within 2 hours of iron administration to rat hepatoma cells. This movement is completely blocked by desferoxamine, a potent chelator of the labile iron pool, suggesting that this elusive component is intimately involved in the activation process (87). These studies also cast light on the mechanism of induction of ferritin synthesis by hemin in K562 cells and in Friend erythroleukemic cells. It has been suggested (7) that iron is released from hemin intracellularly and thereby increases ferritin synthesis. Since desferoxamine inhibits the increased synthesis of ferritin in hemin-treated cells (91), it appears likely that the hemin effect is largely due to increases in intracellular iron (98) with consequent derepression of ferritin mRNP particles (97).

Studies of the molecular mechanism of this fascinating system are now beginning. The noncoding regions of H and L mRNAs are substantially different. However, both contain a common sequence of 21 nucleotides close to the cap site (Fig. 4). Because this sequence is also present in all known ferritin mRNAs, including those of humans, mice, chickens, and tadpoles, it was proposed that it is the element responsible for translational control by iron. This hypothesis has recently been confirmed by fusing this sequence to the 5' noncoding region of the reporter enzyme chloramphenicol acetyltransferase. When transcribed in transfected cells, the modified transferase mRNA shows the same responsiveness to iron as the ferritin mRNA. By contrast, ferritin mRNA lacking this sequence is no longer responsive to iron (99, 100). Experiments are now underway to characterize the protein that presumably binds to this sequence, and to determine whether iron modulates its binding to the mRNA directly or through another protein.

In addition to elucidating the action of iron on ferritin synthesis, this translational control should prove of considerable general interest. For example, it should now be possible to design genes whose translation could be controlled by insertion of the iron-responsive element. Such an approach would be feasible for expression of transfected genes in cells susceptible to iron loading.

2. TRANSLATABILITY OF FERRITIN mRNA

Ferritin mRNAs are translated with remarkably high efficiency in some heterologous cell-free systems. At low input levels of unfractionated cellular mRNA in wheat germ lysates, the proportional synthesis of ferritin H and L subunits to other proteins reflects the relative abundance of ferritin H and L mRNAs in the total mRNA population. However, when the mRNA levels are increased beyond the point of maximal protein synthesis, the proportional synthesis of ferritin rises to extraordinarily high levels (50). In some cases, ferritin H and L subunits can be the major translation products even though hybridization analyses with cDNA probes indicate that their mRNAs are less than 5% of the total mRNA population. This phenomenon is not seen in retriculocyte cell-free systems where the relative synthesis of ferritin may actually be lower than the relative abundance of ferritin mRNA in the mRNA population (101). These differences may reflect the greater propensity of wheat germ lysates for translating small mRNAs like ferritin, but more likely the inhibition of ferritin mRNA translation in reticulocytes by binding of a repressor protein to the metal regulatory site.

Other factors may also contribute to the unusual translation properties of H and L mRNAs in heterologous cell-free systems. Both mRNAs contain multiple sites near their initiating AUG that are potential sites for binding ribosomes (38 and Fig. 5). In addition, as shown in Fig. 5, the human H mRNA has a massive complementarity in (G + C)-rich sequences with sequences in 28-S RNA (102). Minor variations of these sequences occur 12 times in human 28-S RNA. Similar sequences occur in other ribosomal species but show

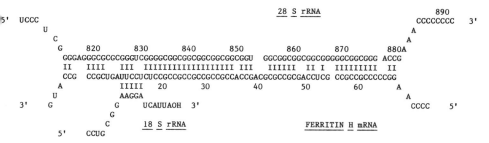

FIG. 5. Complementarity between 5' noncoding region of human ferritin H mRNA and 28-S RNA. From (101).

considerable interspecies variability. Their function in 28-S RNA is not known, but all can fold into a tight helix that lies between two conserved loop structures. Conceivably, the complementary sequences in ferritin H mRNA and 28-S RNA allow interactions that stabilize ferritin H mRNA or even improve its translatability. As more sequences become available, it will be interesting to see if similar relationships occur in ferritin mRNA and 28-S RNA in other species. If so, it seems likely that both sequences are evolving in concert for functional reasons.

In summary, the past few years have seen an explosion in our knowledge of the structure of ferritin and the regulation of ferritin phenotypes in different cells. The emerging picture is that the transcription of H and L genes is independently regulated in many cells, and that each gene responds differently to a variety of factors that affect cell differentiation and proliferation. These events may be related to different functions of isoferritins in iron metabolism and perhaps in other areas. Iron is involved at all levels including transcription, translation, shell assembly, and shell stability. It appears to affect ferritin transcription in only some cells, perhaps those where ferritin is a housekeeping protein. In cells that have a major iron storage function, translational controls seem more important, perhaps because they are more rapid and more flexible. The next few years should give insights into the molecular basis for many of these phenomena and a clearer understanding of the physiological functions of this fascinating protein.

ACKNOWLEDGMENTS

The author thanks many colleagues for communicating their most recent results before publication. He also thanks E. Zappone, P. Papadopoulos, and K. Theriault for help with the manuscript. This work was supported by NIH AM17775-15.

REFERENCES

1. S. Granick, *Physiol. Rev.* **31**, 489 (1951).
2. P. Aisen and I. Listowsky, *ARB* **49**, 357 (1981).
3. H. N. Munro and M. C. Linder, *Physiol. Rev.* **58**, 317 (1978).
4. E. C. Theil, *ARB* **56**, 289 (1987).
5. J. W. Drysdale and H. N. Munro, *BBA* **138**, 616 (1972).
6. J. W. Drysdale and H. N. Munro, *JBC* **214**, 3630 (1966).
7. E. Mattia, D. Josie, G. Ashwell, R. D. Klausner and J. van Renswoude, *JBC* **261**, 4587 (1986).
8. D. A. Lipschitz, J. D. Cook and C. A. Finch, *NEJM* **290**, 1213 (1974).
9. A. Jacobs and M. Worwood, *NEJM* **292**, 951 (1975).
10. U. Mack, L. A. Powell and J. W. Halliday, *JBC* **258**, 4672 (1983).

11. S. R. Smalley, D. J. Macey and I. C. Potter, *J. Exp. Zool.* **237**, 149 (1986).
12. Y. Matzner, C. Hershko, A. Polliack, A. M. Konijn and G. Izak, *Br. J. Haematol.* **42**, 354 (1979).
13. C. Moroz, N. Lahat, M. Biniaminov and B. Ramot, *J. Clin. Lab. Immunol.* **29**, 30 (1986).
14. S. Gupta, A. Iman and K. Licorish, *J. Clin. Lab. Immunol.* **20**, 11 (1986).
15. H. E. Broxmeyer, J. Bognacki, M. Dorner and M. de Sousa, *J. Exp. Med.* **153**, 1426 (1981).
16. G. Sala, A. Jacobs and M. Worwood, *Blood* **67**, 436 (1986).
17. L. Dezza, M. Cazzola, W. Piacibello, P. Arosio, S. Levi and M. Aglietta, *Blood* **67**, 789 (1986).
18. J. W. Drysdale, *J. Clin. Immunoassay* **6**, 234 (1983).
19. H. W. Hann, A. E. Evans, S. E. Siegel, K. Y. Wang, A. Dalton, D. Hammond and R. C. Seeger, *Cancer Res.* **45**, 2843 (1985).
20. S. E. Order, G. B. Stillwagon, J. L. Klein, P. K. Leichner, S. S. Siegelman, E. K. Fishman, D. S. Ettinger, T. Haulk, K. Kopher, K. Finney, M. Surdyhe, S. Self and S. Leibel, *J. Clin. Onc.* **3**, 1573 (1985).
21. S. H. Banyard, D. K. Stammers and P. M. Harrison, *Nature* **282** (1978).
22. W. H. Massover, *JMB* **123**, 721 (1978).
23. G. C. Ford, P. M. Harrison, D. W. Rice, J. M. A. Smith, A. Treffry, J. C. White and J. Yariv, *Philos. Trans. R. Soc. London, Ser. B* **304**, 201, 551 (1984).
24. I. Urushizaki, Y. Niitsu and K. Ishitani, *BBA* **243**, 187 (1971).
25. J. W. Drysdale, *Ciba Found. Symp.* **51**, 41 (1977).
26. P. Arosio, T. G. Adelman and J. W. Drysdale, *JBC* **253**, 4451 (1978).
27. L. W. Powell, E. Alpert, K. J. Isselbacher and J. W. Drysdale, *Nature* **250**, 333 (1974).
28. Y. Kohgo, M. Yokota and J. W. Drysdale, *JBC* **255**, 5195 (1980).
29. A. Bomford, C. Conlon-Hollingshead and H. N. Munro, *JBC* **256**, 948 (1981).
30. M. E. Alpert, R. L. Coston and J. W. Drysdale, *Nature* **242**, 194 (1973).
31. P. Vezzoni, S. Levi, E. Sabri, M. R. Pozzi, S. Spinazzi and P. Arosio, *Br. J. Haematol.* **62**, 105 (1986).
32. M. Wagstaff, M. Worwood and A. Jacobs, *BJ* **173**, 969 (1978).
33. T. Jones, R. Spencer and C. Walsh, *Bchem* **17**, 4011 (1978).
34. T. G. Gabuzda and J. Pearson, *Nature* **220**, 1234 (1968).
35. D. Boyd, S. K. Jain, J. Crampton, K. J. Barrett and J. W. Drysdale, *PNAS* **81**, 4751 (1984).
36. F. C. Costanzo, C. Santoro, V. Colantuoni, G. Bensi, G. Raugei, V. Romano and R. Cortese, *EMBO J.* **3**, 23 (1984).
37. C.-C. Chou, R. A. Gatti, M. L. Fuller, P. Concannon, A. Wong, S. Chada, R. C. Davis and W. A. Salser, *MCBiol* **6**, 566 (1986).
38. D. Boyd, C. Vecoli, D. M. Belcher, S. K. Jain and J. W. Drysdale, *JBC* **260**, 11755 (1985).
39. C. Santoro, M. Marone, M. Ferrone, F. Costanzo, M. Colombo, C. Minganti, R. Cortese and L. Silengo, *NARes* **14**, 2863 (1986).
40. M. H. Dorner, J. Salfeld, H. Will, E. A. Leibold, J. K. Vass and H. N. Munro, *PNAS* **82**, 3139 (1985).
41. E. Leibold, N. Aziz, A. J. P. Brown and H. N. Munro, *JBC* **259**, 4327 (1986).
42. L. F. Dickey, S. Sreedharen, E. C. Theil, J. R. Didsbury, Y.-H. Wang and R. E. Kaufman, *JBC* **262**, 7901 (1987).
43. P. W. Stevens, J. B. Dodgson and J. D. Engel, *MCBiol* **7**, 1751 (1987).

44. S. J. Cragg, M. Wagstaff and M. Worwood, *Clin. Sci.* **58**, 259 (1980).
45. H. W. Hann, M. W. Stahlut and I. Millman, *Cancer Res.* **44**, 3898 (1984).
46. P. Arosio, A. Pozone, R. Ferrero, I. Renoldi and S. Levi, *Clin. Chim. Acta* **161**, 201 (1986).
47. P. Santambrogio, A. Cozzi, S. Levi and P. Arosio, *Br. J. Haematol.* **65**, 235 (1987).
48. S. J. Cragg, M. Worwood and A. Jacobs, *BJ* **199**, 565 (1981).
49. T. G. Adelman, P. Arosio and J. W. Drysdale, *BBRC* **63**, 1056 (1975).
50. N. Watanabe and J. W. Drysdale, *BBRC* **98**, 507 (1981).
51. F. Wyllie, A. Jacobs, K. Waradanukul, M. Worwood and M. Wagstaff, *Leuk. Res.* **8**, 1095 (1984).
52. J. F. Collawn, L. K. Gowan, H. Crow, C. Schwabe and W. W. Fish, *ABB* **259**, 105 (1987).
53. V. Laufberger, *Bull. Soc. Chim. Biol.* **19**, 1575 (1937).
54. P. M. Harrison, *Bchem* **14**, 154 (1986).
55. A. Treffry and P. M. Harrison, *in* "Iron Storage and Transport Proteins" (P. Ponka and H. Schulman, eds.), CRC Press, Boca Raton, Florida (in press).
56. S. Levi, G. Luzzago, A. Ruggeri, S. Cozzi, P. Campanini, P. Arosio and P. Cesarini, *in* "Iron Storage and Transport Proteins" (P. Ponka and H. Schulman, eds.), CRC Press, Boca Raton, Florida (in press).
57. G. R. Bakker and R. F. Boyer, *JBC* **261**, 13182 (1986).
58. S. M. Gorun and S. J. Lippard, *Nature* **319**, 616 (1987).
59. P. Arosio, M. Yokota and J. W. Drysdale, *Br. J. Haematol.* **36**, 56 (1977).
60. C. Beaumont, S. K. Jain, M. Bogard, Y. Nordmann and J. W. Drysdale, *JBC* **262**, 10619 (1987).
61. F. von der Mark, F. Bienfair and H. von der Ende, *BBRC* **115**, 463 (1983).
62. J. R. Mertz and E. C. Theil, *JBC* **258**, 117 (1983).
63. K. Ihara, K. Maeguchi, C. T. Young and E. C. Theil, *JBC* **259**, 278 (1984).
64. S. Levi, G. Cesareni, P. Arosio, R. Lorenzetti, M. Soria, M. Sollazzo, A. Albertini and R. Cortese, *Gene* **51**, 269 (1987).
65. S. Otsuka, I. Listowsky, Y. Niitsu and I. Urushizaki, *JBC* **255**, 6234 (1980).
66. J. W. Drysdale, T. G. Adelman, P. Arosio, D. Casareale, P. Fitzpatrick, J. T. Hazard and M. Yokota, *Semin. Hematol.* **14**, 71 (1977).
67. S. K. Jain, K. J. Barrett, D. Boyd, M. F. Favreau, J. Crampton and J. W. Drysdale, *JBC* **260**, 11762 (1986).
68. S. O. Freytag, A. L. Beaudet, H. G. Bock and W. E. O'Brien, *MCBiol* **4**, 1978 (1984).
69. E. F. Vanin, *BBA* **782**, 231 (1984).
70. A. M. Weiner, P. L. Deininger and A. Efstratiadis, *ARB* **55**, 631 (1986).
71. J. H. Caskey, C. Jones, Y. E. Miller and P. A. Seligman, *PNAS* **80**, 482 (1983).
72. M. Worwood, J. D. Brook, S. J. Cragg, B. Hellkull, B. M. Jones, P. Perera, S. H. Roberts and D. J. Shaw, *Hum. Genet.* **69**, 371 (1985).
73. S. J. Cragg, J. W. Drysdale and M. Worwood, *Hum. Genet.* **71**, 108 (1985).
74. J. R. McGill, D. Boyd, K. J. Barrett, C. M. Moore and J. W. Drysdale, *Hum. Genet.* **76**, 66 (1987).
75. R. V. Lebo, Y. W. Kan, M. C. Cheung, S. K. Jain and J. W. Drysdale, *Hum. Genet.* **71**, 325 (1985).
76. V. A. McKusick, *Clin. Genet.* **29**, 545 (1986).
77. M. W. Hentze, S. Keim, P. Papadopoulos, S. O'Brien, W. Modi, J. W. Drysdale, W. J. Leonard, J. Harford and R. Klausner, *PNAS* **83**, 7226 (1986).
78. F. Costanzo, M. Colombo, S. Staempfli, C. Santoro, M. Marone, R. Frank, H. Delius and R. Cortese, *NARes* **14**, 721 (1986).

79. E. Solomon, L. R. Hiorns, N. Spurr, M. Kurkinen, D. Barlow, B. L. M. Hogan and R. P. Dalgleish, *PNAS* **82**, 3330 (1985).
80. J. R. McCarrey and K. Thomas, *Nature* **326**, 501 (1987).
81. J. P. Kushner, C. Q. Edwards, M. M. Dadove and M. H. Skolnick, *Gastroenterology* **88**, 1232 (1985).
82. M. Simon, L. Le Mignon, R. Fauchet, J. Yaouanq, V. David, G. Edan and M. Bourel, *Am. J. Hum. Genet.* **41**, 89 (1987).
83. G. Astaldi, G. Meardi and T. Lisino, *Blood* **28**, 70 (1986).
84. G. Cairo, P. Vezzoni, L. Bardella, L. Schiaffonati, E. Rappocciolo, S. Levi, P. Arosio and B. Bernelli-Zazzera, *BBRC* **139**, 652 (1986).
85. M. H. Dorner, A. Silverstone, K. Nishiya, A. deSostoa, G. Munn and M. deSousa, *Science* **209**, 1019 (1980).
86. G. Cairo, L. Bardella, L. Schiaffonati, P. Arosio, S. Levi and A. Baernelli-Zazzera, *BBRC* **133**, 314 (1985).
87. J. Rogers and H. N. Munro, *PNAS* **84**, 2277 (1987).
88. D. Gidoni, J. T. Kadonaga, H. Barrera-Saldana, K. Takahashi, P. Chambon and R. Tijian, *Science* **230**, 511 (1985).
89. U. Varshney, N. Jahroudi, R. Foster and L. Gedamu, *MCBiol* **6**, 26 (1986).
90. P. Angel, M. Imagawa, R. Chuc, B. Steen, R. J. Imbra, H. J. Rahmadorf, C. Jonat, P. Herrlich and M. Karin, *Cell* **49**, 429 (1987).
91. G. S. Adrian, B. W. Korinek, B. H. Bowman and F. Yang, *Gene* **49**, 167 (1986).
92. C. Seguin and D. H. Hamer, *Science* **235**, 1383 (1987).
93. B. J. Wu, G. T. Williams and R. I. Morimoto, *PNAS* **84**, 2203 (1987).
94. W. K. Miskimins, A. M. McClelland, M. P. Roberts and F. H. Ruddle, *J. Cell Biol.* **103**, 1781 (1986).
95. S. Ishii, Y. H. Xu, R. H. Stratton, B. A. Roe, G. T. Merlino and I. Pastan, *PNAS* **82**, 4920 (1985).
96. J. Zahringer, B. S. Baliga and H. N. Munro, *PNAS* **73**, 857 (1976).
97. N. Aziz and H. N. Munro, *NARes* **14**, 915 (1986).
98. T. Raoult, K. Rao, J. Harford, E. Mattia and R. D. Klausner, *JBC* **260**, 14862 (1985).
99. M. W. Hentze, T. A. Rouault, S. W. Caughman, A. Dancis, J. B. Harford and R. D. Klausner, *PNAS* **84**, 6730 (1987).
100. N. Aziz and H. N. Munro, *PNAS* **84**, 8478 (1987).
101. G. E. Schull and E. C. Theil, *JBC* **258**, 2921 (1983).
102. S. K. Jain, J. Crampton, I. L. Gonzalez, R. D. Schmickel and J. W. Drysdale, *BBRC* **131**, 863 (1985).

Molecular Biology of the Insulin Receptor

Robert E. Lewis and
Michael P. Czech

Department of Biochemistry
University of Massachusetts
Medical Center
Worcester, Massachusetts 01655

Considerable effort has gone into investigations of the transmembrane glycoprotein receptor that binds insulin and transduces its multiple intracellular signals (for review, see *1–3*). When insulin binds to its receptor, it initiates a series of short-term events, which are probably linked to subsequent physiological effects. Insulin binding rapidly enhances the receptor's intrinsic tyrosine kinase activity resulting in autophosphorylation on its tyrosine residues (*4, 5*). Within minutes, insulin stimulates amino acid (*6, 7*) and hexose (*8*) uptake, regulates gene expression (*9*), and initiates the redistribution of membrane proteins (*10–12*), including the internalization of the insulin receptor itself (*13*). Synthesis of proteins and the promotion of cell growth are long-term effects of insulin (*14, 15*). Though insulin's effects on these metabolic events are well known, the precise pathway leading to their initiation is not yet known. The realization that the insulin receptor encodes a tyrosine kinase (*16, 17*), similar to other growth factor receptors (*18–20*) as well as certain oncogene products (for review, see *21*), suggests that a better understanding of insulin receptor function may provide important insight into the mechanisms of normal and uncontrolled cellular growth and development.

The ability to clone large cDNA fragments has opened new avenues for determining the primary structure of membrane receptors and for exploring the regulation of their expression *in vivo*. Recent cloning of the insulin receptor (*16, 17*) has revealed its detailed molecular structure and made possible the dissection of those elements that compose the transduction mechanism. With the tyrosine kinase of

157

growth-controlling proteins prominent as a potential regulatory mechanism, site-directed mutagenesis experiments have been useful in determining the role of this activity in mediating biological actions of insulin. The purpose of this article is to document the recent molecular biological investigations into the problem of insulin action and to demonstrate how, in conjunction with biochemical approaches, they are contributing to our understanding of insulin action.

I. Cloning of the Human Insulin Receptor cDNA

A. Structure/Function Relationships

1. STRUCTURAL DOMAINS

Two nearly identical cDNAs containing the human insulin proreceptor have been characterized (16, 17). These cDNAs encode a 1370-amino-acid (16) or 1382-amino-acid (17) sequence including a 27-residue signal peptide. There are nine single-base discrepancies between the cDNAs, three of which are neutral changes. The major discrepancy between the two clones is a 36-nucleotide insertion (nucleotides 2368–2403 of Ebina et al., 17), contributing 12 additional amino acids on the C-terminal side of a putative cleavage site separating α- and β-subunits. The open reading-frame is followed by 1018 nucleotides of 3' untranslated sequence and includes an imperfect polyadenylation signal (AATATA) followed by a prolonged A-stretch (16).

The mature proreceptor has a predicted molecular weight of 152,000 to 154,000. Recent biochemical data suggest that the insulin receptor is synthesized as a disulfide-linked polypeptide dimer, which is subsequently glycated,* proteolytically processed into two subunits, and capped with terminal sugars before insertion into the plasma membrane (22). Hormone binding develops in the proreceptor and appears to require glycation, as tunicamycin blocks acquisition of binding activity (22). However, once the proreceptor acquires the ability to bind insulin, N-linked oligosaccharide removal with endoglycosidase H** does not diminish the proreceptor's ability to bind insulin (23). Thus, glycation may initiate conformational changes in the receptor that are ultimately responsible for generating binding activity.

---

* "Glycation" in place of "glycosylation" is recommended by the Nomenclature Committee of IUB and JCBN (see EJB 138, 5, 1984) for those situations where the product is not a glycosyl [Eds.].
** Mannosyl-glycoprotein endo-β-N-acetylglucosaminidase (EC 3.2.1.96) [Eds.].

Analysis of the nucleotide sequence suggests a stretch of four basic amino acids (position 720–723, numbering according to *16*) as a candidate for proteolytic cleavage separating the N-terminal α-subunit precursor from the C-terminal β-subunit precursor. Nineteen consensus sequences exist as potential sites for asparagine-linked glycation within the proposed α-subunit and extracellular domain of the β-subunit. Ullrich *et al.* (*16*) suggest that the absence of the predicted asparagines in positions 16 and 7 of the α and β subunits, respectively, during protein sequencing argues that these two sites are glycated.

The α-subunit contains 37 predicted cysteine residues, 26 of which reside within a stretch of 160 amino acids (Fig. 1). Similar cysteine-rich domains have been observed in the low-density lipoprotein (*24*) and epidermal growth factor (*18*) receptors. Such cysteine-

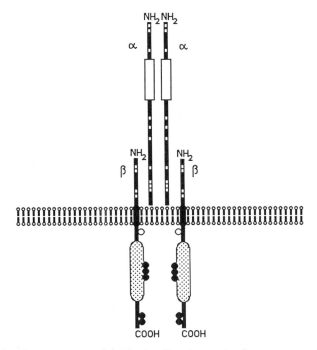

FIG. 1. Insulin receptor model. The insulin receptor is a heterotetrameric structure. Two α- and two β-subunits are linked by interchain disulfide bonds. The α-subunits reside entirely on the extracellular surface. White boxes, cysteine-rich domain; white dots, individual cysteine residues possibly involved in interchain disulfide bonds. Stippled area, tyrosine kinase domain; black circles, biochemically identified tyrosine phosphorylation sites; white circles, putative phosphorylation sites. Other, currently unidentified phosphorylation sites may exist.

rich regions within binding domains of transmembrane receptors may be associated with processes other than ligand binding (*17*). These may include intermolecular cross-linking between proteins, potentially resulting in receptor patching and capping. The high density of cysteines within the predicted α-subunit sequence probably provides the sulfhydryl groups that form the Class-I and Class-II disulfides linking α- and β-subunits into the receptor heterotetrameric structure (*25*).

A deduced stretch of 23 hydrophobic amino acids flanked by charged residues encodes the only region sufficient to encode a transmembrane domain. The three basic amino acids that are C-terminal to this sequence are characteristics of a "stop-transfer signal" used to anchor membrane proteins (*26*).

2. MEMBRANE ORIENTATION

Structural evidence provided by the insulin receptor cDNA in combination with biochemical evidence suggests a membrane orientation for the insulin receptor as shown in Fig. 1. The *a*-subunit lacks hydrophobic stretches of sufficient length to span the membrane or serve as a membrane anchor. The difference between the apparent molecular weight of the mature α-subunit and the α-subunit protein backbone, combined with the fact that 15 of 21 N-glycation sites reside on the α-subunit, suggest most of these sites may be glycated. Taken together, these facts suggest that the α-subunit resides entirely in the extracellular domain, held in place by disulfide bonds and interwoven tertiary structure to the β-subunit. The β-subunit contains the only plausible transmembrane domain. Thus, its amino terminus protrudes to the extracellular side of the cell membrane, while the C-terminal end, encoding the tyrosine kinase, resides within the cell cytoplasm. This orientation places four of six potential glycation sites in the β-subunit outside the cell.

3. PHOSPHORYLATION SITES

The β-subunit cytoplasmic domain has significant homology with the family of proteins known to encode tyrosine kinases (cf. Section I,B). The homology includes the consensus sequence Gly-Xaa-Gly-Xaa-Xaa-Gly and a lysine situated 22 amino acids toward the carboxy terminal from this sequence, which is crucial in tyrosine and serine/threonine kinases for ATP binding (*27*).

A prominent characteristic of tyrosine kinases is their ability to autophosphorylate. The insulin receptor tyrosine at position 960 (numbering according to *16*) is surrounded by a sequence homologous to the environment around the major phosphorylated tyrosine (number 1173) in the EGF receptor (*18*). The sequence that includes the major phosphorylation site in v-*src* (tyrosine 1150 in the insulin receptor) is also highly conserved within the insulin receptor. Stadtmauer and Rosen (*28*) synthesized synthetic peptides corresponding to the deduced amino-acid sequences 952–961 (containing a tyrosine at 960), 1142–1153 (containing Tyr-1146, Tyr-1150, and Tyr-1151), and 1313–1329 (Tyr-1316 and Tyr-1322). Peptide 1142–1153 was the best substrate when phosphorylated *in vitro* by affinity-purified insulin receptor. Sequencing of peptide 1142–1153 indicated Tyr-1150 to be the major site of phosphorylation. By *in vitro* autophosphorylation of the insulin receptor under nearly maximal kinase activity followed by protein sequencing, 70% of the [^{32}P]phosphotyrosine could be localized on tryptic peptides 1144–1152 and 1315–1329 (*29*). Tryptic peptide 1144–1152 was isolated in doubly and triply phosphorylated forms in a 1 : 2 molar ratio. Tyr-1146 was present in both forms. In the doubly phosphorylated form, tyrosine 1150 and 1151 were phosphorylated in a molar ratio 1 : 2. Peptide 1315–1329 was equally phosphorylated on Tyr-1316 and Tyr-1322.

The differences in phosphorylation observed between receptor autophosphorylation sites (*29*) and phosphorylation of homologous synthetic peptides (*28*) may result from differences in phosphorylation conditions, or may be due to stabilization of the phosphopeptide domains within the protein structure. Furthermore it is argued (*29*) that vicinal phosphotyrosines may contribute to such a stabilization and thus contribute to the autophosphorylation-induced kinase activation (*30*, *31*). Figure 1 shows the relative location of known and potential phosphorylation sites.

B. Homology to Other Tyrosine Kinases

1. THE INSULIN-LIKE GROWTH FACTOR-I (IGF-I) RECEPTOR

Elucidation of the cDNA sequence for the human placental IGF-I receptor (*19*) revealed that the biological, biochemical, and gross structural similarities of this receptor with the insulin receptor have a basis in the homology of their respective genes. Substantial homology exists between the genes of the two receptors. The deduced primary amino-acid structure, hydropathy, and structural domain distribution are all highly conserved. The highest level of identity between the receptor proteins resides within the tyrosine kinase domain (84%). Regions of the IGF-receptor α-subunit flanking cysteine-rich domains show 64–67% identity with the insulin receptor. The cysteine-rich domain itself shows less sequence identity (48%), despite conservation of 24 out of 26 cysteine residues between the two receptors. Fifteen of 26 potential asparagine-linked glycosylation sites in the IGF-I receptor are similarly positioned within the insulin receptor.

The C-terminal tails within the cytoplasmic domain of the insulin receptor and IGF-I receptor are the most divergent. Two other regions of dissimilarity reside within the tyrosine kinase domain of the receptors (Fig. 2). Four of 5 cysteines and 11 of 15 tyrosines in the IGF-I receptor are similarly placed in the insulin receptor, including the tyrosines identified in the insulin receptor as *in vitro* sites of phosphorylation (29).

The insulin receptor and IGF-I receptor transcripts are distinctly different. The insulin receptor cDNA hybridizes to 4 or 5 messages ranging in size from 5 to 11 kb.The IGF-I receptor cDNA hybridizes to two transcripts in human term placenta mRNA of 11 and 7 kb. The human insulin receptor gene is found on the distal short arm of chromosome 19 (17, 32). The IGF-I receptor gene resides on the distal long arm of chromosome 15 (19).

2. INSULIN RECEPTOR-RELATED GENE FROM *DROSOPHILA*

Petruzelli *et al.* (33) used a portion of the human insulin receptor cDNA to screen a *Drosophila* genomic library for insulin receptor-related clones. Two overlapping clones contained sequences homologous to the tyrosine-kinase domain of the insulin receptor. The longest open reading frame (900 nucleotides) yielded a deduced amino-acid sequence that is 53% identical to the insulin-receptor cDNA (Fig. 2). A stretch of 68 predicted amino acids within the tyrosine-kinase domain shares 90% identity with the insulin receptor cDNA. The cloned *Drosophila* DNA hybridizes to an 11-kb message from *Drosophila* RNA extracted during embryogenesis. Peak *Drosophila* insulin receptor-transcript accumulation occurs during 8–12 hours of embryogenesis and declines thereafter. Receptor message accumulation correlates well with the appearance of insulin-dependent protein kinase activity during embryogenesis, and the appearance of a protein of M_r 100,000 that specifically cross-links to insulin (34). Interestingly, the putative *Drosophila* insulin receptor kinase contains an insertion of 20 deduced amino acids at the same spot within the tyrosine-kinase domain where dissimilarity is found between the insulin receptor, the IGF-I receptor, and the genes of other cloned tyrosine kinases. This region has been proposed as a site of potential interaction with substrates (19, 35).

3. INSULIN RECEPTOR HOMOLOGY TO OTHER TYROSINE KINASES

Within the tyrosine-kinase region, the insulin receptor shows homology to all other members of the *src* family of tyrosine kinases. Nevertheless, it is evident that the catalytic domain of the insulin receptor is not identical to any of these genes. Given the recognition of the EGF receptor as the cellular homolog of the oncogene v-*erb*-B

```
DIR    1 -----vnPfYAS--------------mqYiPDdWEVlREnIiqLapLGQGSFGMVYEGilKsfppngVdrec
RIR    1 QPDGPmGPLYASSNPEYLSASDVFPsSVYVPDEWEVpREKITLLRELGQGSFGMVYEGNAKDIIKGEVETRV
HIR    1 QPDGPlGPLYASSNPEYLSASDVFPcSVYVPDEWEVsREKITLLRELGQGSFGMVYEGNArDIIKGEaETRV
IGFIR  1 nsrlgnGvLYASvNPEYfSA-----adVYVPDEWEVaREKITmsRELGQGSFGMVYEGVAkgvvKdEpETRV

      54 AiKTVNEnAtdRERtnFLsEASVMKeFdtyHVVrLLGvcSrGQPaLV-VMELMkkGDLKSyLRahRPeerdd
      73 AVKTVNESASLRERIEFLNEASVMKGFTCHHVVsLLGmVSKGQPTLV-VMELMAHGDLKShLRfLRP-----
      73 AVKTVNESASLRERIEFLNEASVMKGFTCHHVVRLLGVVSKGQPTLV-VMELMAHGDLKSYLRSLRP-----
      68 AiKTVNEaASmRERIEFLNEASVMKeFnCHHVVRLLGVVSqGQPTLViVMELMtrGDLKSYLRSLRP-----

     125 ghddvsnrigvtgnvqPPTygriyQMaiEIADGMAYLaAKKFVHRpfAARNCMVAdDlTVKIGDFGMTRDIY
     139 -------dAENNPGRPPPPTLQEMIQMtAEIADGMAYLNAKKFVHRDLAARNCMVAHDFTVKIGDFGMTRDIY
     139 -------EAENNPGRPPPTLQEMIQMAAEIADGMAYLNAKKFVHRDLAARNCMVAHDFTVKIGDFGMTRDIY
     135 -------EmENNPvlaPPSLskmIQMAgEIADGMAYLNAnKFVHRDLAARNCMVAeDFTVKIGDFGMTRDIY

     197 ETDYYRKGtKGLLPVRWMpPESLqawclllvpvtvfSFGVVLWEmailSLwrsP
     204 ETDYYRKGGKGLLPVRWMsPESL-KDGVFTaSSDMWSFGVVLWE--ITSLAEQPYQGLSNEQVLKFVMDGGY
     204 ETDYYRKGGKGLLPVRWMaPESL-KDGVFTTSSDMWSFGVVLWE--ITSLAEQPYQGLSNEQVLKFVMDGGY
     200 ETDYYRKGGKGLLPVRWMsPESL-KDGVFTTySDvWSFGVVLWE--IatLAEQPYQGLSNEQVLrFVMeGGl

     273 LDpPDNCPERlTDLMRMCWQFNPkMRPTFLEIVNLLKDDLHPSFPEVSFFySEENKAPESEELEMEFEDMEN
     273 LDqPDNCPERvTDLMRMCWQFNPnMRPTFLEIVNLLKDDLHPSFPEVSFFhSEENKAPESEELEMEFEDMEN
     269 LDkPDNCPdmlfeLMRMCWQyNPkMRPsFLEIissiKeemePgFrEVSFyySEENKlPEpEELdlEpEnMEs

     345 VPLD--RSS-------HCQREEAGcReGGSSLsiKRtYdEHIPYTHMNGGKKNGRvLTLPRSNPS
     345 VPLD--RSS-------HCQREEAGgRdGGSSLgfKRSYeEHIPYTHMNGGKKNGRiLTLPRSNPS
     341 VPLDpsaSSsslplpdrhsghkAengpGpgvLvlraSfdErqPYaHMNGGrkNeRaLpLPqSstc
```

FIG. 2. Homology of insulin receptor-related molecules. Primary amino-acid sequence of the tyrosine-kinase domain for putative *Drosophila* insulin receptor (DIR), spliced exons of the rat insulin receptor (RIR), human insulin receptor (HIR), and human IGF-I receptor. Mammalian sequences extend to the putative C-terminus.

(*24*) it is intriguing to speculate that the insulin receptor may have its own transforming counterpart. Placed in the appropriate viral construct, the insulin receptor tyrosine kinase does indeed exhibit oncogenic potential (*36*; also compare Section II,B). The highest degree of homology of the insulin receptor to any known oncogene is to the gene product of the UR2 avian sarcoma virus, v-*ros*. At the amino-acid level, there is 52% identity between regions 990–1251 of the insulin receptor (numbering of *16*) and residues 264–529 of v-*ros* (*37*). Regions flanking this amino-acid span do not appear to be related.

The insulin receptor diverges from all other tyrosine kinases (including its closest relative, the IGF-I receptor) within the kinase domain and at the C-terminus (Fig. 2). Rearrangements or translocations of the C-terminus can be a crucial part of activating transforming potential in *src* (*38, 39*) and EGF receptor/*erb*-B gene products (*40*), respectively. When an insulin receptor cDNA construct lacking the coding region of the 112 amino acids of the receptor C-terminal was transfected into Chinese hamster ovary cells (*41*) only the α-subunit from this construct was expressed, leading the authors to conclude that the β-subunit is susceptible to proteolysis and is rapidly degraded.

A striking observation is the presence of a substantial region of nonhomology in the middle of the catalytic domain of all tyrosine kinases. In v-*fms* (*42*) and the platelet-derived growth factor receptor (*20*), this region of dissimilarity extends 79 and 109 amino acids, respectively. In other members of the *src* tyrosine-kinase family, this region is much smaller, but, as with the C-terminus, the insulin receptor displays a marked difference in this region even with the IGF-I receptor. It is speculated that this region may be crucial for generating substrate specificity for each protein (*19*). There is support for this notion in that temperature-sensitive mutants of the v-*abl* kinase obtain that property from point mutations immediately flanking this region. A deletion mutation within this region confers temperature sensitivity to v-*src* (*43*).

C. Genomic Organization of the Insulin Receptor Cytoplasmic Domain

The intron/exon structure of the gene fragment encoding the cytoplasmic domain and 3′ untranslated region of the rat insulin receptor has been characterized (*44*). Two overlapping clones from a rat genomic library covering 18 kb of DNA include seven exons and six complete introns (Fig. 3). At the nucleotide level, the exons covering coding regions are 88% homologous to the human insulin receptor

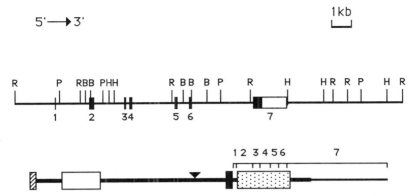

FIG. 3. Rat insulin receptor cytoplasmic domain gene structure. Upper line, gene fragment structure. Numbered boxes, exons; open box, untranslated region of exon 7. Restriction enzymes EcoRI, R; PstI, P; BamHI-B; HindIII, H. Lower line, schematic of human insulin prereceptor mRNA. Hatched box, signal sequence; open box, cysteine-rich region; closed box, transmembrane domain; stipled region, tyrosine-kinase domain; inverted triangle, putative proteolytic processing site; narrow line, untranslated region. Regions corresponding to the rat exons are numbered accordingly in the prereceptor schematic.

cDNA. The predicted 3′ untranslated region is only 60% homologous, but also contains substantial insertions and deletions. The predicted 3′ untranslated region of the rat is 152 nucleotides longer than its human homologue yet still contains the imperfect polyadenylation signal proposed for the human cDNA (16). The characterized introns are (5′ to 3′) 1.9, 1.4, 0.2, 1.9, 0.6, and 2.8 kb, respectively. Six of the seven putative intron/exon junctions split codons, thus restricting the number of alternative splicing combinations.

Most of nucleotide differences between rat and human genes are conservative. Consequently, the deduced amino-acid sequence of the cytoplasmic domain of the rat insulin receptor is 94% homologous to that of the human (Fig. 2). All tyrosines predicted in the human sequence are conserved in the rat except the tyrosine at position 132 of the human sequence in Fig. 2 (Tyr-1075, ref. 16) which corresponds to a histidine in the rat gene. There is one tyrosine in the rat (Tyr-323 in Fig. 2) that is a histidine in the human (His-1266 in ref. 16). These data on the rat insulin receptor gene sequence have recently been used to confirm five of the in vivo sites of phosphorylation on the β-subunit of the insulin receptor in rat hepatoma cells (45). The ATP-binding site sequence in human cDNA is strictly conserved in the rat gene. The tyrosine-kinase domain (as defined by homology to other tyrosine kinases) is coded for by exons 3–6 and portions of exons 2 and 7. The biochemically confirmed tyrosine phosphorylation sites (45) are encoded in exons 5 and 7. A tyrosine surrounded by an environment similar to that around the major phosphorylation site in the EGF receptor is coded for in exon 1. The entire 3' untranslated region is in exon 7 (Fig. 3).

II. Mutagenesis and Expression of the Insulin Receptor

The cloning of the insulin receptor cDNA has provided a tool with which to investigate the functional significance of various structural features within the protein. To elucidate the importance of any portion of the receptor to insulin action, the receptor must be functionally reconstituted. This was first demonstrated by the discovery of a 5-fold increase in the level of human insulin receptor expression over endogenous levels in Chinese hamster ovary cells, using cDNA transfection techniques (46). Recently, a human insulin receptor cDNA was transfected to NIH 3T3 fibroblasts, with greater than 10^7 receptors per cell being expressed (47).

A. Mutant Insulin Receptor Expression

Owing to its striking homology with other growth factor receptors and oncogene products, the tyrosine kinase of the insulin receptor is an obvious target for site-directed mutagenesis. The insulin receptor kinase is known to be activated by phosphorylation (30, 31), suggesting some functional significance for the sites of tyrosine phosphorylation of the β-subunit. Mutation of tyrosines 1162 alone, or 1162 and 1163 to phenylalanines results in expression of receptors that have markedly reduced ability to autophosphorylate and either little or no ability to phosphorylate exogenous substrate (41). Furthermore, the point mutations reduce the binding ability of a monoclonal antibody that inhibits insulin receptor kinase activity. Concomitant with these mutations in human receptors expressed in Chinese hamster ovary cells is a parallel decrease in 2-deoxyglucose uptake stimulated by insulin.

Similar blocking of signal transduction has been observed when the insulin receptor kinase activity is abrogated by a mutation blocking the ability of the receptor to bind ATP (48, 49). The consensus sequence for ATP binding within tyrosine and serine/threonine kinases (Gly-Xaa-Gly-Xaa-Xaa-Gly) requires a carefully positioned downstream lysine to be effective (27). Mutation of this lysine to alanine in the insulin receptor not only results in the loss of insulin-stimulated tyrosine phosphorylation, but in reduced sensitivity to insulin-stimulated deoxyglucose uptake, activation by ribosomal protein S6 kinase, endogenous substrate phosphorylation, glycogen synthesis, and thymidine incorporation into DNA (48). Although the possibility that the lysine-to-alanine mutation modifies properties of the receptor distinct from the kinase activity cannot be excluded, the simplest interpretation is that kinase activity is intimately involved in mediating insulin control over several metabolic processes.

Studies with receptors lacking the ability to bind ATP were recently extended (50) to explore the role of the receptor tyrosine kinase in insulin-mediated receptor down-regulation. There is a correlation of defective kinase activity with an inability of insulin receptor to internalize bound insulin, undergo short- or long-term down-regulation in response to insulin, demonstrate ligand-promoted receptor turnover, or be phosphorylated on either tyrosine or serine (50). A surprising observation is the absence of serine phosphorylation in the kinase deficient receptor. Exposure of cells to insulin stimulates phosphorylation of the insulin receptor on serine and threonine as well as tyrosine (51). The absence of phosphotyrosine can be ascribed to the inability of the receptor to autophosphorylate. However, the surprising lack of phosphoserine and phosphothreonine on the receptor in these *in vivo* assays suggests three possibilities: (1) the insulin receptor tyrosine kinase activates, presumably by phosphorylation, serine/threonine kinases, which in turn phosphorylate the receptor; (2) the tyrosine autophosphorylation of the insulin receptor is (at least in part) an allosteric mechanism that makes the receptor a suitable substrate by changing its conformation; or (3) insulin receptors require internalization to be phosphorylated by serine/threonine kinases. None of these possibilities is mutually exclusive of the other two.

In truncated forms of the insulin receptor, membrane localization is required for receptor-activated deoxyglucose uptake. Such truncated forms of the human insulin receptor cDNA expressed either membrane bound or cytosolic forms of the β-subunit tyrosine kinase (52). Deoxyglucose transport was constitutively activated only in cells containing the membrane-bound form of the receptor even though the high mannose content of the expressed protein and immunofluorescence studies with receptor-specific antibody indicated an intracellular location. No deoxyglucose transport activation was stimulated by the soluble protein in spite of the fact that the cytosolic form of the receptor had a tyrosine kinase activity *in vitro* almost 20 times that of the membrane-bound form. The authors conclude that receptor-dependent glucose uptake requires membrane localization, and that the extracellular domain inhibits the insulin receptor tyrosine kinase and receptor signaling capacity. Insulin relieves that inhibition. The results suggest that insulin receptor action is regulated by its extracellular domain in a similar manner to that of the EGF receptor (40).

B. Chimeric Constructs with the Insulin Receptor

Riedel *et al.* (53) demonstrated that the insulin receptor extracellular domain can efficiently couple hormone binding to EGF receptor kinase activation by expressing a chimeric construct of the two receptor domains. No data were given indicating whether the insulin receptor/EGF receptor chimera was coupled to biological activity. However, the ability to transduce hormone binding into a transmembrane response is not established by connecting any receptor extracellular domain to the transmembrane and cytoplasmic domain of any other receptor. Ellis *et al.* (54) were unable to identify a functional biological response by expression of the extracellular binding domain fused to the transmembrane and cytoplasmic domains of the bacterial asparate receptor. In spite of the fact that this chimera bound insulin, it blunted insulin-stimulated 2-deoxyglucose uptake generated via endogenous Chinese hamsters ovary receptors. The reason for this inhibition is unclear.

Fusion proteins generated by combining the ligand binding domain of the human insulin receptor with the transmembrane and cytoplasmic domain of v-*ros* can also generate insulin-stimulable kinase activity *in vivo* as well as *in vitro* (55). However, this construct could not generate a biological response. These results are consistent with those found with the insulin receptor/EGF receptor construct (53), suggesting that the α-subunit of the insulin receptor can control intrinsic kinase activity but that related kinases lack the specificity to generate insulin-associated biological signals. However, both insulin receptor/EGF receptor and insulin receptor/v-*ros* chimeric constructs utilized only the extracellular portion of the insulin receptor. Thus, it is unclear whether the absence of biological responsiveness is due to the lack of specificity of the tyrosine kinase, or some other portion of the cytoplasmic domain. More discrete substitutions within the insulin receptor tyrosine kinase may shed more light on this problem.

A construct inserting the DNA coding for the insulin receptor cytoplasmic domain into the UR2 genome in place of homologous sequences for the v-*ros* tyrosine kinase has been used to explore the oncogenic potential of the insulin receptor kinase. The modified virus expressed kinase activity in infected chicken embryo fibroblasts, which demonstrated the fusiform morphology of transformed cells and were able to form colonies in soft agar. The construct was unable to induce tumors in chickens but passage of the virus in culture resulted in a variant with enhanced transforming potential and a high efficiency of tumorigenicity. The precise difference in the variant virus that enhanced tumorigenicity was not determined. Although chicken embryo fibroblasts infected with UR2/insulin receptor chimeric genes have a different colony morphology than fibroblasts infected with wild-type UR2, it is apparent that the insulin receptor tyrosine kinase retains transformation potential demonstrable in the proper environment.

III. Future Directions

A. Receptor Signaling

Recent cloning of the human insulin receptor cDNA (16, 17) has provided a new and powerful tool for experimentation. Mutagenesis with the human cDNA has already yielded strong evidence that the tyrosine kinase is involved in insulin receptor signaling (48–50, 52). Yet it remains undetermined if the insulin receptor tyrosine kinase phosphorylates, and thus activates, other substrates or whether the receptor itself is the primary substrate. Clearly the possibilities are not mutually exclusive. There are also other more detailed questions ammenable to use of the receptor cDNA. Are all the known or putative phosphorylation sites important for signaling? Currently, mutagenesis of only two tyrosines has been reported. Furthermore, is the serine/threonine phosphorylation of the receptor observed *in vivo* physiologically important? What are the sites of serine and threonine phosphorylation, and must the insulin receptor be phosphorylated on tyrosine first to be subsequently phosphorylated on other residues? These aspects of receptor signaling are approachable using a combination of molecular biological and biochemical techniques.

B. Hormone Binding

Experiments have yet to be reported on using mutagenesis of the insulin receptor cDNA to identify sites on the α-subunit critical for insulin binding. Also, little is understood on how the binding event is translated through the plasma membrane to stimulate kinase activity. The high number and similar distribution of cysteines in the insulin receptor and other transmembrane proteins (18, 24) suggest a functional role for these amino acids. It may be reasonable to imagine that hormone-induced alteration or production of disulfide bonds between or within subunits may alter activity within the cytoplasmic domain. As chimeric recombinant transmembrane proteins are capable of hormone-induced activation of dissimilar tyrosine kinases (53, 55), the possibility exists that understanding signal transduction in one receptor system will lead to important advances in the understanding of other tyrosine kinase-containing receptors as well.

C. Regulation of Receptor Expression

Future reports will undoubtedly describe the 5' regulatory regions of the insulin receptor gene. Elucidation of cis regulatory elements and trans activating factors that control message synthesis will be crucial for a full understanding of insulin receptor gene expression.

IV. Conclusion

Mutagenesis of the insulin receptor cDNA has provided strong evidence that the tyrosine kinase encoded within the receptor β-subunit is required for normal receptor function (48–50). At least one domain containing autophosphorylation sites is also necessary (41). The entire cytoplasmic structure is important to signaling specificity as the related tyrosine kinase v-ros will not substitute for the insulin receptor kinase in a hormone-responsive fusion protein (55). Defined sequences within the cytoplasmic domain of various tyrosine kinases have been suggested as regions that may confer substrate specificity on each enzyme (19, 35). Undoubtedly mutagenesis and expression of the insulin receptor cDNA will continue to provide valuable information about the intermolecular and intramolecular mechanisms of receptor signaling.

References

1. M. P. Czech, *Annu. Rev. Physiol.* **47**, 557 (1985).
2. M. P. Czech, "Molecular Basis of Insulin Action." Plenum, New York, 1985.
3. C. R. Kahn, *Annu. Rev. Med.* **36**, 429 (1985).
4. L. M. Petruzelli, R. Herrera and O. M. Rosen, *PNAS* **81**, 3327 (1984).
5. M. Kasuga, Y. Fujita-Yamaguchi, D. L. Blith, M. F. White and C. R. Kahn, *JBC* **258**, 10973 (1983).
6. M. L. Standaert, S. D. Schimmel and R. J. Pollet, *JBC* **259**, 2337 (1984).
7. M. D. Resh *in* "Molecular Basis of Insulin Action" (M. P. Czech, ed.), p. 451. Plenum, New York, 1985.
8. T. J. Wheeler and P. C. Hinkle, *Annu. Rev. Physiol.* **47**, 503 (1985).
9. K. Sasaki, T. P. Cripe, S. R. Koch, T. C. Andreone, D. D. Peterson, E. G. Beale and D. K. Granner, *JBC* **259**, 15242 (1984).
10. T. Kono, F. W. Robinson, T. L. Blevins and O. Ezaki, *JBC* **257**, 10942 (1982).
11. Y. Oka, C. Mottola, C. L. Oppenheimer and M. P. Czech, *PNAS* **81**, 4028 (1984).
12. R. J. Davis and M. P. Czech, *EMBO J.* **5**, 653 (1986).

13. J. R. Gavin III, J. R. Roth, D. M. Neville, Jr., P. DeMeyts and D. B. Buell, *PNAS* **71**, 84 (1974).
14. L. S. Jefferson, *Diabetes* **29**, 487 (1980).
15. D. S. Straus, *Endocr. Rev.* **5**, 356 (1984).
16. A. Ullrich, J. R. Bell, E. Y. Chen, R. Herrera, L. M. Petruzelli, T. J. Dull, A. Gray, L. Coussens, Y.-C. Liao, M. Tsubokawa, A. Mason, P. H. Seeburg, C. Grunfeld, O. M. Rosen and J. Ramachandran, *Nature* **313**, 756 (1985).
17. Y. Ebina, L. Ellis, K. Jarnagin, M. Edeny, L. Graf, E. Clausner, J.-H. Ou, F. Masiarz, Y. W. Kan, I. D. Goldfine, R. A. Roth and W. J. Rutter, *Cell* **40**, 747 (1985).
18. A. Ullrich, L. Coussens, J. S. Hayflick, T. J. Dull, A. Gray, A. W. Tam, J. Lee, Y. Yarden, T. A. Libermann, J. Schlessinger, J. Downward, E. L. V. Mayes, N. Wittle, M. D. Waterfield and P. H. Seeberg, *Nature* **309**, 418 (1984).
19. A. Ullrich, A. Gray, A. W. Tam, T. Yang-Feng, M. Tsubokawa, C. Collins, W. Henzel, T. LeBon, S. Kathuria, E. Chen, S. Jacobs, U. Francke, J. Ramachandran and Y. Fujita-Yamaguchi, *EMBO J.* **5**, 2503, (1984).
20. Y. Yardin, J. A. Escobedo, W.-J. Kuang, T. L. Yang-Feng, T. O. Daniel, P. M. Tremble, E. Y. Chen, M. E. Ando, R. M. Harkins, U. Francke, V. A. Fried, A. Ullrich and L. T. Williams, *Nature* **323**, 226 (1986).
21. M. J. Bishop, *ARB* **52**, 301 (1983).
22. G. V. Ronnet, V. P. Knutson, R. A. Kohanski, T. L. Simpson and M. D. Lane, *JBC* **259**, 4566 (1984).
23. T. S. Olson and M. D. Lane, *JBC* **262**, 6816 (1987).
24. T. Yamamoto, C. G. Davis, M. S. Brown, W. J. Schneider, M. L. Casey, J. L. Goldstein and D. W. Russell, *Cell* **39**, 27 (1984).
25. M. P. Czech, *Cell* **31**, 8 (1982).
26. D. D. Sabatini, G. Kreibich, T. Morimoto and M. Adesnik, *JBC* **92**, 1 (1982).
27. T. Hunter, *Nature* **311**, 414 (1984).
28. L. Stadtmauer and O. M. Rosen, *JBC* **261**, 10000 (1986).
29. H. E. Tornqvist, M. W. Pierce, A. R. Frackelton, R. A. Nemenoff and J. Avruch, *JBC* **262**, 10212 (1987).
30. O. M. Rosen, R. Herrera, Y. Olowe, L. M. Petruzelli and M. H. Cobb, *PNAS* **80**, 3237 (1983).
31. K.-T. Yu and M. P. Czech, *JBC* **259**, 5277 (1984).
32. T. L. Yang-Feng, U. Franke and A. Ullrich, *Science* **228**, 728 (1985).
33. L. Petruzelli, R. Herrera, R. Arenas-Garcia, R. Fernandez, M. J. Birnbaum and O. M. Rosen, *PNAS* **83**, 4710 (1986).
34. L. Petruzelli, R. Herrera, R. Garcia-Arenas and O. M. Rosen, *JBC* **260**, 16072 (1985).
35. E. T. Kipreos, G. J. Lee and J. Y. J. Wang, *PNAS* **84**, 1345 (1987).
36. L.-H. Wang, B. Lin, S.-M. J. Jong, D. Dixon, L. Ellis, R. A. Roth and W. J. Rutter, *PNAS* **84**, 5725 (1987).
37. W. S. Nickameyer and L. H. Wang, *J. Virol.* **53**, 879 (1985).
38. R. Swanstrom, R. C. Parker, H. E. Varmus and J. B. Bishop, *PNAS* **80**, 2519 (1983).
39. T. Takeya and H. Hanafusa, *Cell* **32**, 881 (1983).
40. J. Schlessinger, *JCB* **103**, 2067 (1986).
41. L. Ellis, E. Clausner, D. O. Morgan, M. Edery, R. A. Roth and W. J. Rutter, *Cell* **45**, 721 (1986).
42. A. Hampe, M. Gobet, C. J. Sherr and F. Galibert, *PNAS* **81**, 85 (1984).
43. M. Nishizawa, B. J. Mayer, T. Takeya, T. Yamamoto, K. Toyoshima, H. Hanafusa and S. Kawai, *J. Virol.*, 743 (1985).
44. R. E. Lewis, M. P. Czech and M. A. Tepper, *BJ*, submitted.

45. H. E. Tornqvist, J. R. Gunsalas, R. A. Nemenoff, A. R. Frackelton, M. W. Pierce and J. Avruch, *JBC* **263**, 350 (1988).
46. Y. Ebina, M. Edery, L. Ellis, D. Standring, J. Beaudoin, R. A. Roth and W. J. Rutter, *PNAS* **82**, 8014 (1985).
47. J. Whittaker, A. K. Akamoto, R. Thys, G. I. Bill, D. F. Steiner and C. A. Hofmann, *PNAS* **84**, 5237 (1987).
48. C. K. Chou, T. J. Dull, D. S. Russell, R. Gherzi, D. Lebwohl, A. Ullrich and O. M. Rosen, *JBC* **262**, 1842 (1987).
49. Y. Ebina, E. Araki, M. Taira, F. Shimacka, M. Mori, C. S. Craik, K. Siddle, S. B. Pierce, R. A. Roth and W. J. Rutter, *PNAS* **84**, 704 (1987).
50. D. S. Russell, R. Gherzi, E. L. Johnson, C.-K. Chou and O. M. Rosen, *JBC* **262**, 11833 (1987).
51. M. Kasuga, F. A. Karlsson and C. R. Kahn, *Science* **215**, 185 (1982).
52. L. Ellis, D. O. Morgan, E. Clausner, R. A. Roth and W. J. Rutter, *Mol. Endocrinol.* **1**, 15 (1987).
53. H. Riedel, T. J. Dull, J. Schlessinger and A. Ullrich, *Nature* **324**, 68 (1986).
54. L. Ellis, D. O. Morgan, D. E. Koshland, Jr., E. Clausner, G. R. Moe, G. Bollag, R. A. Roth and W. J. Rutter, *PNAS* **83**, 8137 (1986).
55. L. Ellis, D. O. Morgan, S.-M. Jong, L.-H. Wang, R. A. Roth and W. J. Rutter, *PNAS* **84**, 5101 (1987).

Cap-Binding Proteins of Eukaryotic Messenger RNA: Functions in Initiation and Control of Translation

NAHUM SONENBERG

Department of Biochemistry and
  McGill Cancer Center
McGill University
Montreal, Quebec, Canada
  H3G 1Y6

The translation of messenger RNAs in eukaryotes is a very complex process that involves numerous components and is regulated at many steps. Understanding the intricacy of the initiation step of translation is of particular importance to the study of the many translational regulatory mechanisms known to operate in the cell (for recent reviews, see *1–3*). Several features of the 5′ noncoding region of eukaryotic mRNAs are of importance for translational control at the initiation level; these include the 5′ cap structure $[m^7G(5′)ppp(5′)N]$ (*4*) and the 5′ noncoding region (comprising primary and secondary

173

Progress in Nucleic Acid Research
and Molecular Biology, Vol. 35

structure determinants). As discussed below, there is a clear functional interrelationship between the cap structure and the degree of secondary structure within the mRNA 5' noncoding region of mRNAs. I first summarize the data about the structural features of the 5' noncoding region of eukaryotic mRNAs, and then describe the different studies conducted to elucidate the function of the cap structure in translation.

Many studies suggest that the cap structure mediates the ATP-dependent "melting" of the 5' secondary structure of mRNA through the activity of a cap-binding-protein complex, in conjunction with other initiation factors required for mRNA binding. A model explaining these activities is presented and discussed below, and I also discuss the possibility of internal binding of ribosomes to eukaryotic mRNAs in the light of recent evidence. It should be emphasized that our knowledge of the ribosome-binding process is far from adequate, particularly in light of the poor understanding of the function of the many initiation factors, eIF-4B in particular; consequently, the models I present contain major elements of a working hypothesis.

Recent *in vitro* studies demonstrate that the cap structure may also function in nuclear processes, including pre-mRNA splicing (5–7) and processing of the 3' end (8, 9). In addition, the cap structure serves to stabilize mRNAs in the cytoplasm (10) and pre-mRNAs in the nucleus (11) against 5' exonucleolytic degradation.

I. Structural Features of 5' Noncoding Region of Eukaryotic mRNAs

A. Eukaryotic mRNA Cap Structure

Eukaryotic mRNAs are structurally different from prokaryotic mRNAs. One of the striking differences is the presence of a unique structure that blocks the 5' end of eukaryotic mRNAs. This structure has the general composition $m^7G(5')ppp(5')N$ (where N is any nucleotide) and is generally termed "the cap structure" or "cap" for short (4). It is present on all eukaryotic cellular mRNAs (except in organelles) and most eukaryotic viral mRNAs (4, 12). A few eukaryotic viral mRNAs do not contain a cap; these include all members of the picornavirus group (entero-, cardio-, rhino-, and aphtoviruses: for review, see 12) and several plant viral RNAs [e.g., satellite tobacco necrosis virus (14, 15) and its helper virus (16), and cowpea mosaic virus (17, 18)]. In all these cases, except for satellite tobacco necrosis

virus (STNV), the genomic RNAs possess a small polypeptide (VPg)*
that is covalently bound to the 5'-terminal nucleotide (13). However,
this polypeptide does not substitute for the cap in translation (12).
STNV terminates with a 5' di- or triphosphate (p)ppA (14).

In addition to N-methylation to yield m^7G, the 3' hydroxyl groups
of the 5' penultimate and subpenultimate nucleotides are sometimes
methylated [reviewed in 12; see also several papers in Vol. 19 (1976)
of this series]. In general, the extent of methylation at the mRNA 5'
end is greater in higher eukaryotes: the simplest structure—
m^7GpppN ("cap-O")—is found in such lower eukaryotes as yeast
and is also the prevalent structure in *Dictyostelium discoideum*
(12). In higher eukaryotes, "cap-1" ($m^7GpppN_1m-N_2$) or "cap-2"
($m^7GpppN_1m-N_2m$) prevails (12). In contrast to the important function
of m^7G in the cap, it is not clear what function (if any) or significance
there is for gene expression in the additional methylation.

B. 5' Noncoding Region of Eukaryotic mRNAs

Most eukaryotic mRNAs possess 5' noncoding regions ~50–100
nucleotides in length devoid of AUG codons (19). However, 10 to 20%
of mRNAs have longer 5' noncoding regions, which might indicate a
potential function in control of protein synthesis. One of the longest 5'
noncoding regions known (1100 nucleotides) is that of one of the
transcripts from a *Drosophila melanogaster* Antennapedia locus (20).
It is also striking that many mRNAs coding for important regulatory
proteins of cellular growth and development (such as those encoding
oncogenes, growth factors, and homeotic gene products) have unusually long 5' noncoding regions.

Most of the long 5' noncoding regions contain from one to several
AUG codons followed shortly by in-frame termination codons upstream of the translation start site. However, except for a few examples, it is not clear that these upstream open reading frames are translated or that they have any biological significance. The only cases
where translation of 5' upstream reading frames has been documented
are viral mRNAs: the 16-S late RNA of SV40 (21) and the mRNA
encoding the Epstein–Barr virus nuclear protein, EBNA-2 (22), produce two polypeptides *in vivo*. The late–early (L_E) SV40 transcript
produces a short polypeptide from a cistron upstream of the T antigen

---

* VPg is defined by Vartapetian and Bogdanov in Vol. 34 of this series as "Viral
Protein Genome-Linked" (to the RNA genome of picornaviruses) in "Proteins Covalently Linked to Viral genomes" [Eds.].

genes both *in vivo* and *in vitro* (23). Another study demonstrated *in vitro* synthesis of a seven-amino-acid peptide encoded by the leader segment of Rous sarcoma virus RNA (24). In all of these cases, it is not clear whether the upstream open reading frames serve any function in the lytic cycle of the virus. In the case of the yeast GCN4 gene* there is good evidence indicating that the four upstream AUG codons (each of which initiates a short open reading frame of two or three codons) mediate translational control of GCN4 expression (25–27). However, it is not clear whether these short peptides are synthesized *in vivo*.

Another interesting feature of the 5′ noncoding region of eukaryotic mRNA, indicating potential posttranscriptional control, is the existence of genes containing an optional exon in that region of the mRNA. For example, 99% of the transcripts for the arginosuccinate synthetase gene from baboon liver contain an optional exon, whereas in human liver only 1% contain this exon (28). In another case, about half of the human and hamster transcripts for 3-hydroxy-3-methylglutaryl-coenzyme-A synthase (HMG-CoA synthase, EC 4.1.3.5) contain an optional exon in the 5′ noncoding region (29). Also, differential splicing in the α-amylase gene in humans provides different 5′ noncoding regions for the salivary and pancreatic mRNAs (30).

Both primary and secondary structures of the 5′ noncoding regions of eukaryotic mRNAs play a key role in determining translational efficiency and control of translation. Many of the 5′ noncoding regions of mRNAs can be folded by computer modeling into stable stem and loop structures; furthermore, evidence for the existence of secondary structure *in vitro* has been obtained by using nuclease mapping techniques (see, for example, 31). Several of these potential hairpin structures are of remarkable stability, e.g., the human *bcr*** mRNA whose 5′ noncoding region contains an inverted repeat with $\Delta G = -281$ kcal/mol (32, 33) and human ornithine decarboxylase mRNA, which contains a potential stem and loop structure of $\Delta G \sim -190$ kcal/mol (34). The 5′ noncoding regions of the HIV-1 mRNA (which contains the target sequence necessary for trans activation) also can assume a relatively stable secondary structure of $\Delta G = -37$ kcal/mol (35, 36); in this case, the putative secondary structure was confirmed experimentally by digestion with structure-specific RNases (36). Increased sec-

---

* GCN denotes "general control nondepressible." GCN4 is one of the gene products required for the general control-mediated response to amino-acid deprivation (24a).

** *bcr* denotes "breakage cluster region" gene, which becomes juxtaposed to the c-*abl* oncogene in most cases of chronic myelogenous leukemia (32, 33).

ondary structure in the mRNA 5' noncoding region reduces translational efficiency *in vitro* and *in vivo* (*37–38a*); the relationship between the degree of secondary structure and the requirement for the cap structure for translation is discussed below.

The 5' noncoding region plays an important function in translational control. The 5' noncoding regions of translationally controlled genes can confer the same translational control properties in cis to heterologous genes, as shown by the following examples: (1) the 5' noncoding region of heat-shock mRNAs can confer heat resistant translation (*39–41*); (2) the 5' noncoding region of poliovirus RNA can confer cap-independent translation (*42*); (3) the 5' noncoding region of human ferritin heavy-chain mRNAs can confer iron-mediated translational control (*43, 44*); (4) the 5' noncoding region of GCN4 mRNA confers general control of amino-acid synthesis (*45*). In all of these examples, the nature of trans-acting factors that interact with the mRNA 5' noncoding region is not known. Consequently, one of the important future areas of research will be to identify these factors.

II. Cap-Binding Proteins in Translation

A. Functions of the Eukaryotic mRNA Cap in Translation

The best studied and understood function of the cap is its role in promoting ribosome binding to mRNA. Numerous studies (e.g., *46–51*, reviewed in *4, 12, 52, 53*) show that the cap is important for translation. *In vitro* transcribed uncapped mRNAs (*47*) or mRNAs whose cap had been removed either chemically (*46*) or enzymatically (*49, 51*) function at a reduced efficiency in ribosome binding assays (*49*) or in translation *in vitro* (*46–48, 50, 51*). In addition, cap analogues specifically inhibit translation of capped mRNAs (*54–58*) by decreasing 40-S ribosomal subunit binding to mRNAs (*55*). The first experiments (*46, 47*) showed that *in vitro* translation of the capped mRNAs of reovirus, vesicular stomatitis virus, and globin mRNA is more efficient than their uncapped or decapped counterparts. However, it was subsequently shown that the extent of reduction in translational efficiency of uncapped mRNAs varies considerably among mRNAs and among different translation systems (for review, see *12*). For example, decapping of alfalfa mosaic virus 4 (AMV-4) RNA (or addition of cap analogues) has only a slight detrimental effect (a maximum reduction of 50%) on translation (*58a–60*) or ribosome binding (*61*). Also, translation in wheat germ extracts is more cap-dependent than that in a reticulocyte lysate (62–64). In addition, factors such as temperature, salt concentration, and initiation factor concentration affect the degree to which translation is dependent on the cap (64, and reviewed in 12, 65, 66). It was anticipated that binding of ribosomes to the mRNA is mediated by specific cap-binding proteins; consequently, considerable work has focused on the identification and purification of these factors.

B. Identification of Cap-Binding Proteins

Cap-binding proteins (CBPs) are proteins that can either cross-link specifically to the mRNA cap, or can bind to cap-affinity columns and be eluted with an excess of cap analogue (for previous reviews, see 53, 65–67). Since the cap is involved in translation initiation, it was reasoned that an initiation factor (IF) functions as a CBP. To help follow the description of the studies involving initiation factors, I have listed in Table I the known eukaryotic initiation factors (eIFs) and their probable function in translation. Early experiments using filter binding assays identified eIF-2 and eIF-4B as CBPs (68 and 69, respec-

TABLE I

EUKARYOTIC INITIATION FACTORS AND THEIR PROBABLE FUNCTION
IN TRANSLATION INITIATION[a]

Initiation factor	Subunit molecular mass (kDa)	Activity
eIF-1	15	Repositioning of Met-tRNA to facilitate mRNA binding
eIF-2	35, 50, 55	Ternary complex formation
eIF-2B, GEF	34, 40, 55, 65, 82	eIF-2 recycling
eIF-3	~10 subunits 28,000–160,000	Subunit antiassociation; binding to 40-S subunits
eIF-4A	50	mRNA binding to 40-S subunit; ATPase
eIF-4B	80	mRNA binding to 40-S subunit
eIF-4C	17	Subunit antiassociation; 60-S subunit joining
eIF-4E (24-kDa CBP; CBP I)	24	5' cap recognition (subunit of eIF-4F)
eIF-4F (CBP II, CBP complex)	24, 50, 220	mRNA binding to 40-S subunit; ATPase; mRNA melting activity
eIF-5	150	Release of eIF-2 and eIF-3; ribosome-dependent GTPase
eIF-6	25.5	Subunit antiassociation

[a] This table was compiled from many different sources, taking into account generally accepted functions (for reviews, see 1–3).

tively). However, these experiments suffered from several disadvantages (70) and the results were not confirmed by other means. A chemical cross-linking assay to identify polypeptides that can cross-link to the cap in a specific manner (71) identified such a polypeptide of 24 kDa in eIF preparations from rabbit reticulocytes and mouse ascites cells (72). Subsequently, a CBP of similar size was identified using the cross-linking assay in all eukaryotic species, including yeast (73), humans (74, 75), and plants (76, 77).

The molecular weights attributed to this polypeptide varied between 24,000 and 28,000, possibly reflecting differences in gel systems and oxidation states (78). However, the real sizes are now known from cDNA cloning and sequencing (see Section V). This polypeptide was termed the "24K cap-binding protein" (24K CBP in 72) and later eIF-4E, and its cross-linking to the mRNA 5' cap was independent of the presence of ATP-Mg^{2+} (72, 79). More recently, a photochemical cross-linking assay identified a similar 24-kDa polypeptide that cross-links specifically to the cap structure in an ATP-Mg^{2+} independent manner (80). In the presence of ATP-Mg^{2+}, additional polypeptides of approximately 28, 50, and 80 kDa from rabbit reticulocyte IF preparations became cross-linked to the oxidized cap in a cap-specific manner (60, 79). Cross-linking of the 28-kDa polypeptide was not always detected. A similar set of polypeptides was subsequently identified in IF preparations from HeLa cell extracts, but HeLa cells sometimes contain an additional polypeptide of 32 kDa that cross-links specifically to the cap structure (75). Nonhydrolyzable analogs of ATP did not substitute in the cross-linking reaction, leading to the proposal that energy generated by ATP hydrolysis is required for the binding of the 28-, 50-, and 80-kDa polypeptides to the cap structure (60, 79).

The identity of two of the ATP-dependent CBPs has been established. Anti-eIF-4A monoclonal antibody immunoprecipitates the cross-linked 50-kDa polypeptide in crude IF preparations (81). In addition (Milburn et al., unpublished), anti-eIF-4B polyclonal antibody immunoprecipitates the 80-kDa cross-linked polypeptide. Furthermore, eIF-4A in combination with eIF-4B can cross-link to the mRNA cap structure in an ATP-dependent manner (82). [It should be noted that eIF-4B preparations used in this experiment most probably contained a cap-binding-protein complex (described in Section II,C) as a contaminant (82).] Accordingly, I refer to the 50- and 80-kDa ATP-dependent cytoplasmic CBPs as eIF-4A and eIF-4B, respectively. The identity and significance of the 28- and 32-kDa ATP-dependent cap-specific polypeptides are not clear.

Cross-linking experiments similar to those described for the rabbit reticulocyte have also been performed with purified initiation factors from wheat germ using cap-oxidized reovirus mRNA (76, 77). The cross-linking pattern was similar to that obtained with rabbit reticulocyte initiation factors in that in the absence of ATP, only small polypeptides (24 to 28 kDa) can cross-link to the mRNA cap (76, 77). However, the presence of ATP-Mg^{2+} in the reaction mixture resulted in the cross-linking of eIF-4A (51 kDa) and a polypeptide of 65 kDa present in eIF-4B preparations, in a manner analogous to the cross-linking with rabbit reticulocyte initiation factors (76). Based on this analogy, the 65-kDa polypeptide present in eIF-4B preparations is the homologue of the mammalian 80-kDa eIF-4B. This is further substantiated by the recent finding of a new initiation factor that has properties of eIF-4B (see Section II,C). Wheat germ preparations that exhibit eIF-4B-like activity, purified in two different laboratories, contain an 80-kDa polypeptide (83, 84). However, a major problem with assigning eIF-4B activity is that there is no specific assay for this factor; the only activity measured is complementation of a reconstituted translation system (see Section II,C for further discussion of eIF-4B activity).

C. Isolation of Cap-Binding Proteins

Affinity chromatography as the only step, or in combination with conventional chromatography, has been used by several groups to purify CBPs. The first purification was performed by affinity chromatography on a m^{7}GDP-coupled Sepharose-4B column (85, 86). This procedure yielded an apparently homogeneous preparation of the 24-kDa CBP that could be cross-linked to the oxidized cap of reovirus mRNA (85), and that stimulated the translation of capped mRNAs, but not naturally uncapped RNAs, in a translation extract from HeLa cells (85, 87). The 24-kDa CBP was also isolated by conventional chromatography, assaying for an activity that reversed cap-analogue-induced inhibition of translation in a rabbit reticulocyte lysate (88). It was also purified by assaying for an activity that restores the translation of capped mRNAs in extracts prepared from poliovirus-infected cells (89; this restoring activity was probably due to the presence of a large complex of the 24-kDa CBP; see below). More recently an alternative affinity chromatography procedure to purify the 24-kDa CBP has also been described (90).

The ability of the 24-kDa CBP to associate with other proteins was originally noted by Bergmann et al. (91) who observed that it sedimented as a complex of about 200 kDa in sucrose gradients. Changes in the protocol used for the affinity-chromatography purification led to the isolation of a protein complex containing it and several major polypeptides of ~50, 55, and 200 kDa (92). This complex was termed CBP-II to distinguish it from uncomplexed 24-kDa CBP, now termed CBP-I (92). With a similar protocol, a complex was isolated comprising the 50- and 220-kDa polypeptides in addition to the 24-kDa CBP, which was referred to as the cap-binding protein (CBP) complex (81). A similar complex was isolated using a conventional protocol; it complemented a reconstituted rabbit reticulocyte translation system, and in light of this finding the CBP complex was given a bona fide initiation factor status and termed eIF-4F (93). In addition, all CBP complex preparations had the ability to restore translation of capped mRNAs in extracts from poliovirus-infected cells, whereas pure 24-kDa CBP had no such activity (81, 92, 93).

The 24-kDa polypeptide of eIF-4F corresponded to the 24-kDa cap-binding protein that interacts specifically with the cap structure (72, 85), while the 50-kDa polypeptide is very similar to eIF-4A (81, 93). Purified eIF-4A and the 50-kDa polypeptide component of the CBP complex comigrate in two-dimensional polyacrylamide gels (93), and a monoclonal antibody against eIF-4A reacts with the 50-kDa polypeptide of the CBP complex (81). Furthermore, comparative peptide map analyses of eIF-4A and the 50-kDa polypeptide of the CBP complex indicate that they are very similar, and it was suggested that the only difference is a modification of one of the tryptic peptides (81). Based on these findings, I refer to the 50-kDa polypeptide of the CBP complex as eIF-4A. However, in order to differentiate the complexed form of eIF-4A from the uncomplexed form, I refer to the former as eIF-4A$_c$ (c for complexed), and to the uncomplexed eIF-4A as eIF-4A$_f$ (f for free). The 220-kDa component (termed p220) has not been adequately characterized, although it appears to be required for full functioning of the CBP complex (see Section IV,A).

Cap-binding proteins have also been purified from other species, including yeast (73) and wheat germ (76, 84). In yeast, a 24-kDa polypeptide homologue of the mammalian 24-kDa CBP (eIF-4E) has been purified by affinity chromatography (73). This protein was used to raise monoclonal and polyclonal antibodies that were subsequently used to clone the gene for the 24-kDa CBP (73, and see Section V). Several other CBPs have since been identified and purified from yeast, including a 150-kDa polypeptide that cross-links specifically to the cap and is antigenically related to the 24-kDa CBP (C. Goyer, M. Altmann and N. Sonenberg, unpublished observations).

TABLE II

CHARACTERISTICS OF mRNA-BINDING INITIATION FACTORS

Initiation factor	Origin	Molecular mass (kDa)	Specific cross-linking to mRNA 5' cap		Activity[a]
			ATP dependent	ATP independent	
eIF-4A$_f$	Mammal	50	+	–	Stimulates translation; ATPase
	Plant	51	+	–	Stimulates translation; ATPase
	Yeast	?	?	?	?
eIF-4B	Mammal	80	+	–	Stimulates translation; stimulate eIF-4A and eIF-4F ATPase; AUG recognition; recycle eIF-4F
	Plant	59–65	+	–	Stimulates translation
	Yeast	?	?	?	?
eIF-4E (24-kDa CBP; CBP I)	Mammal	24		+	Binds cap structure
	Plant	26, 28		+	Binds cap structure
	Yeast	24		+	Binds cap structure
eIF-4F (cap-binding protein complex; CBP II)	Mammal	24, 50, 220	+(50 kDa)	+(24 kDa)	ATPase; mRNA unwinding; restoring activity; stimulates translation
	Plant	26, 220		+(26 kDa)	Stimulates translation; ATPase
		28, 80		+(28 kDa)	Stimulates translation; ATPase
		26, 28, 75		+(26 or 28 kDa)	Stimulates translation; ATPase
	Yeast	24, 150		+(24 and 150 kDa)	Stimulates translation
					?

[a] Activity indicated as "stimulation of translation" refers to stimulation of exogenous mRNA translation in a reconstituted translation system.

Several wheat germ CBPs have been purified by cap-affinity chromatography. Three different preparations were obtained by fractionation on a m⁷GTP–Sepharose column (84). These preparations contained polypeptides that cross-linked specifically to the cap (77). One preparation, termed eIF-4B, consisted of an 80-kDa polypeptide and a 28-kDa polypeptide (1 : 1 ratio); the latter could be cross-linked specifically to the cap (77). The second preparation, termed eIF-4F because of its structural similarity to the mammalian counterpart, consisted of a 220-kDa and a 26-kDa polypeptide; the latter could be cross-linked specifically to the cap (77). A third preparation, which contained a 110-kDa polypeptide and a 26-kDa cap-binding protein, is a degradation product of eIF-4F (77). An additional activity that stimulates binding of globin mRNA to ribosomes was separated from eIF-4B by chromatography on m⁷GTP–Sepharose. This activity copurified with a 59-kDa polypeptide and was termed eIF-4G (94). Furthermore, eIF-4G can cross-link to the mRNA cap in an ATP-Mg²⁺-dependent manner (J. Ravel, personal communication), a property characteristic of mammalian eIF-4B. These data, in conjunction with others (76), strongly indicate that the newly described eIF-4G may be the functional equivalent of mammalian eIF-4B; the factor originally termed (77) eIF-4B may be an isozyme of eIF-4F. The latter notion is also supported by the findings that wheat germ eIF-4B and eIF-4F are interchangeable in both a protein-synthesis system (84) and an RNA-dependent ATPase assay (95). A CBP complex termed "cap-specific factor" containing primarily polypeptides of 24, 26, and 75 kDA has been purified (76). Cross-linking experiments with oxidized reovirus mRNA showed that one of the small polypeptides interacts specifically with the mRNA cap (76). Although at present the relationship among the large mammalian, plant, and yeast CBPs is not clear, the evidence suggests similarity in the components involved in mRNA binding to ribosomes in all species examined. Table II summarizes the available data about CBPs and their function in translation initiation.

D. The 5′ Cap and Secondary Structure of Eukaryotic mRNAs

Is the requirement of the 5′ cap for translation related to the potential for secondary structure formation in the 5′ noncoding region of eukaryotic mRNAs? There are several indirect lines of evidence for a positive correlation. (1) Reovirus mRNA in which inosine is substituted for guanosine, with consequent reduction in stability of the mRNA secondary structure, shows a reduced requirement for the cap (and ATP) for ribosome binding (96, 97). However, it should be noted that the authenticity of the presumed initiation complexes containing inosine-substituted mRNA has been questioned (98). (2) A monoclonal antibody with anti-CBP activity inhibits initiation complex formation with native reovirus mRNA but not with inosine-substituted mRNA (60). (3) Translation *in vitro* of a naturally occurring capped mRNA, plant alfalfa mosaic virus 4 (AMV-4) RNA, is almost independent of the presence of the cap (59, 60). Nuclease digestion experiments show this mRNA to be predominantly single-stranded at its 5′-terminus (61). (4) AMV-4 RNA and inosine-substituted reovirus mRNAs are functional in initiation of translation in extracts prepared from poliovirus-infected cells (100), in which eIF-4F is inactivated (see Section IV,A). Because eIF-4F is inactivated in poliovirus-infected cells, these results are consistent with a cap-dependent, CBP-mediated mRNA unwinding process. (5) The *in vitro* mRNA translation of AMV-4 RNA or ribosome binding of inosine-substituted reovirus mRNA is resistant to inhibition by elevated K^+ concentrations, whereas other capped mRNA are not (99–101). Addition of eIF-4F reverses the inhibition of capped mRNA translation caused by high salt (101). Since high salt concentrations promote stable secondary structure (101a), this finding is consistent with the notion that eIF-4F is involved in melting mRNA secondary structure.

E. Mechanism of Action of Cap-Binding Proteins

The notion that CBPs are involved in the melting of secondary structure in the mRNA 5′ noncoding region, in an ATP-dependent mechanism to facilitate ribosome binding, was first adumbrated in 1981 (60, 79). This hypothesis was based on the finding that eIF-4A and eIF-4B cross-link to the cap structure only when energy derived from ATP is generated (60, 79, 81, 82, 93, 99), but the requirement for ATP is obviated when unstructured mRNAs were used (99). In addition, earlier reports pointed to a direct correlation between the requirement for the cap and the degree of mRNA secondary structure (96, 97). Subsequent experiments showed that cross-linking of highly purified eIF-4A and eIF-4B to the cap of reovirus mRNA occurs only in the presence of eIF-4F and ATP-Mg^{2+} (81, 93), suggesting that eIF-4A and eIF-4B interact with the cap subsequent to the initial interaction of eIF-4F via the 24-kDa CBP subunit. Consistent with this suggestion are the findings that the 24-kDa CBP, either as a purified polypeptide or as a subunit of eIF-4F, cross-links to the cap in an ATP-Mg^{2+}-independent fashion (102).

Several studies led to the suggestion that the initial binding of eIF-

4F to the mRNA, via the interaction of the 24-kDa CBP subunit with the 5' cap, occurs with equal efficiency to all mRNAs regardless of their 5' proximal secondary structure, and is therefore not a step at which mRNA discrimination occurs (see Section III). For example, cross-linking of the 24-kDa CBP occurs with equal efficiency to all mRNAs irrespective of the degree of secondary structure. Similarly, hybridization of cDNAs to the first 15 nucleotides downstream from the cap has no deleterious effect on the cross-linking of the 24-kDa CBP to the mRNA 5' cap (103). However, recent experiments (T. G. Lawson and R. E. Thach, personal communication; N. Parkin and N. Sonenberg, unpublished) indicate that the lack of accessibility of the cap structure (where the 5' terminal bases are paired) reduces the cross-linking to the 24-kDa CBP. This agrees with the finding that cap accessibility to tobacco acid pyrophosphatase correlates with translational efficiency of AMV mRNAs (103a).

In contrast to the general insensitivity of cross-linking the 24-kDa CBP to mRNA secondary structure, the ATP-Mg^{2+}-dependent cross-linking of eIF-4A and eIF-4B is reduced when secondary structure is increased at the 5' proximal region of the RNA, but not in more distal portions of the mRNA 5' noncoding region. The photochemical cross-linking of eIF-4B to mRNA is inhibited by the insertion of BamH1 linkers capable of "hairpin" formation 7 nucleotides from the 5' cap, whereas a similar structure 37 nucleotides downstream from the cap has no effect (80). Similarly, an oligodeoxynucleotide complementary to sequences 16 nucleotides downstream from the cap has only a small negative effect on the cross-linking of the eIF-4A subunit of eIF-4F and eIF-4B, whereas an oligodeoxynucleotide complementary to sequences immediately downstream from the cap strongly inhibits the cross-linking of these polypeptides (103). These findings have implications for the model of unwinding of 5' mRNA secondary structure, as discussed in Section II,G.

Incubation of reovirus mRNA with eIF-4F in the presence of ATP, but not in its absence, results in increased sensitivity to single-strand-specific nucleases (104). This activity was inhibited specifically by cap analogues. Furthermore, eIF-4F melted a short (20 base-pairs) RNA–DNA heteroduplex in an ATP and cap-dependent manner. The melting activity was augmented by the addition of eIF-4B (104). The component of eIF-4F directly responsible for its melting activity is most probably eIF-$4A_c$.

Several lines of evidence support this conclusion. (1) Rabbit reticulocyte eIF-4A possesses an ATPase activity that is single-stranded RNA-dependent (105). Similarly eIF-4F possesses ATPase activity, but unlike that of eIF-4A, it is inhibited by cap analogues. Furthermore, eIF-4B stimulates the *in vitro* ATPase activity of either eIF-4A or eIF-4F in the presence of RNA and consequently also the proposed eIF-4F melting activity (*105*). Plant eIF-4A$_f$ enhances RNA-dependent ATP hydrolysis in the presence of either eIF-4B or eIF-4F (*95*). (2) eIF-4A$_c$ possesses an ATP-binding site as shown by photoaffinity labeling of eIF-4F with ATP or dATP (*106*). In addition, UV-irradiation-induced cross-linking of ATP to eIF-4A$_c$ is ~60-fold more efficient than cross-linking of ATP to eIF-4A$_f$, suggesting that eIF-4A$_c$ is the active form responsible for generating energy to be consumed in the mRNA melting process (*106*). It is possible that the interaction of the eIF-4A$_c$ subunit with the other subunits in eIF-4F enhances its catalytic activity. Also, the ATP analogue, 5'-fluorosulfonylbenzoyl adenosine, strongly inhibits the activity of free wheat germ eIF-4A$_f$ (*107*). Consistent with these studies is the presence of a putative ATP-binding site in the amino-acid sequence of eIF-4A (*108*), Gly-Xaa-Gly-Lys-Thr, which is highly conserved in ATP-binding proteins (*109*). (3) eIF-4F from which eIF-4A$_c$ was ablated is inactive in destabilization of mRNA higher structure (*104*).

An additional property of eIF-4A$_f$ that is probably important in RNA melting is its ability to bind single-stranded RNA in an ATP-dependent, sequence-nonspecific manner (*110*). This binding is significantly stimulated by eIF-4B, and is cap-independent (*110*). It was therefore postulated that eIF-4A$_f$ binds to single-stranded RNA and prevents it from forming secondary structures (*110*). According to this view, the function of eIF-4A$_f$ is to maintain the mRNA in a denatured state.

F. Mechanism of Action of eIF-4B

What is the function of eIF-4B in translation initiation? Of the factors involved in mRNA binding the mechanism of function of eIF-4B is the least understood. The facts established with mammalian eIF-4B are (1) eIF-4B is absolutely required for mRNA binding to ribosomes in an ATP-dependent reaction (*111, 112*). (2) eIF-4B can cross-link to the cap, but only in the presence of eIF-4F and ATP (*81*). It is required for the ATP-dependent cross-linking of eIF-4A to the cap (*81*). (3) eIF-4B stimulates the mRNA binding and ATPase activities of eIF-4A$_f$ and eIF-4F (*105, 110*), and the cross-linking of ATP to eIF-4A$_c$ (*106*). However, no specific function has yet been uniquely and unequivocally attributed to eIF-4B.

These findings argue for a catalytic role of eIF-4B in the melting activity of eIF-4F. However, there are several other observations that argue for alternative or additional functions of eIF-4B. An activity of eIF-4B that is responsible for the "recycling" of the 24-kDa CBP component of eIF-4F (and possibly other components of eIF-4F) in mRNA binding has been described (113). Another activity attributed to eIF-4B is the recognition of the AUG translation initiator codon. Originally, an 80-kDa polypeptide from wheat germ, considered to be eIF-4B (as discussed in Section III,B, it is not clear that it is homologous to mammalian eIF-4B), binds and specifically protects the initiator AUG of STNV RNA (83). The interaction of rabbit reticulocyte eIF-4B with poly($1,N^6$-ethanoadenylic acid), as measured by fluorescence spectroscopy, is specifically inhibited by the AUG triplet (114). These latter experiments raise the interesting possibility that eIF-4B, while important in the melting process, plays a key role in ribosome recognition of the appropriate initiator AUG.

The importance of eIF-4B notwithstanding, the results have to be interpreted cautiously as eIF-4B preparations obtained so far are admittedly only 60–80% pure (114, 115). Consequently, activities attributed to eIF-4B might be in fact due to associated proteins. Preparations of eIF-4B used in the late 1970s and early 1980s contained as one impurity eIF-4F (93). Consequently, eIF-4B was originally thought to be the factor inactivated in poliovirus-infected cells (see Section IV,A) and a translation discriminatory factor (115), properties now unequivocally attributed to eIF-4F.

G. A Model for mRNA "Melting" by Initiation Factors

The notion that secondary structure must be disrupted for ribosomes to bind has been around for many years (see, for example, 116). The identification, purification, and the characterization of CBPs led to the proposal that they are involved in the melting of mRNA 5' secondary structure (60, 61, 65, 79, 99, 103, 104). Here, I extend the model to accommodate the new data available concerning eIF-4A$_f$ and eIF-4B and propose the term "melting model." I emphasize that several features of the model are speculative and the model should therefore better be viewed as a working hypothesis.

The key steps in the model are eIF-4F binds to the cap structure via the 24-kDa CBP; subsequently, the eIF-4A subunit of eIF-4F (eIF-4A$_c$) in conjunction with eIF-4B melts the mRNA 5' secondary structure in a processive mechanism that requires ATP hydrolysis. Free eIF-4A (eIF-4A$_f$) maintains the mRNA in a single-stranded configuration by binding to the denatured region of the mRNA in an ATP hydrolysis-mediated event, thus shifting the equilibrium between the structured and unstructured configurations of the RNA toward the

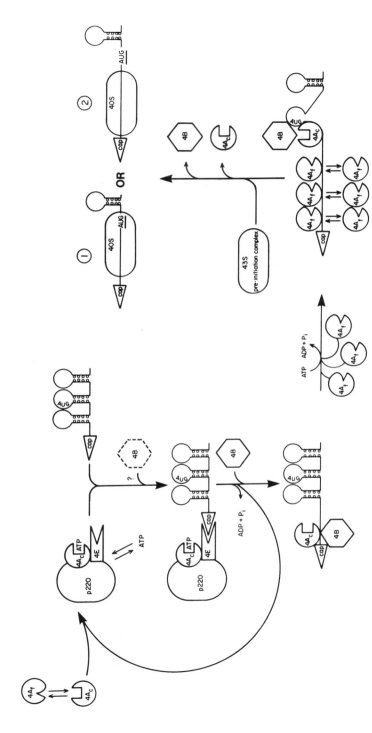

FIG. 1. A model to explain the function of initiation factors involved in ribosome mRNA binding.

unstructured form. This is followed by ribosome binding. No strict provision is made in this model for the binding site of ribosomes. This model can accommodate ribosome binding near the 5' end of the mRNA as well as directly to the initiator AUG. The model is depicted in Fig. 1.

As discussed above, secondary structure at the 5' noncoding region generally inhibits translation, but has differential effects on the interaction of eIF-4A and eIF-4B with the cap depending on the position of the secondary structure relative to the cap (80, 103). One way to explain these findings in light of the melting model is that the initial interaction of eIF-4A$_c$ and eIF-4B with the cap is strongly inhibited by secondary structure adjacent to the 5' end of the mRNA. However, further melting of downstream secondary structure, facilitated by eIF-4A$_f$, can overcome higher energy barriers.

The mRNA melting model does not necessarily contradict the prevailing ribosome scanning mechanism to explain the selection of AUG initiation codons (19, 97). It has been argued that the 40-S ribosomal subunit binds at or near the cap and scans the mRNA until it encounters the appropriate AUG initiation codon. This is followed by the association of the 60-S subunit and formation of a functional 80-S initiation complex (19, 97). However, significantly, the melting model opens the intriguing possibility that scanning of the mRNA 5' noncoding region is carried out by the melting eIF-4F (including eIF-4B) itself rather than by ribosomes. Furthermore, in light of the affinity of eIF-4B for the AUG triplet (114), the possibility arises that selection of the initiator AUG is accomplished by eIF-4B and this signals ribosome binding to the initiation codon.

The RNA melting model could also accommodate bona fide internal mRNA ribosome binding as reported recently (117–119), as an alternative pathway to mRNA 5' binding of ribosomes. This pathway could be explained by the direct binding of eIF-4A$_f$ and eIF-4B to internal regions of the mRNA devoid of secondary structure (based on the ability of eIF-4A$_f$ to bind independently to single-stranded RNA regions; 110), followed by ribosome binding and internal initiation of translation. This pathway is expected to function in a cap-independent manner and indeed it has been shown that eIF-4A and eIF-4B are required whereas eIF-4F is not required (as discussed in Section IV,A) for translation of naturally uncapped mRNAs such as poliovirus and EMC (120, 121). I suspect that more cases of internal initiation will emerge with the future identification of proteins arising from internal initiation. The model for internal initiation is schematically summarized in Fig. 2.

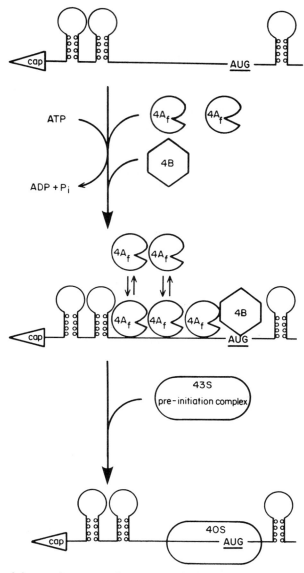

FIG. 2. A model to explain internal initiation of translation on eukaryotic mRNAs.

III. Translational Discriminatory Activity

Binding of eukaryotic mRNAs to ribosomes is generally considered to be the overall limiting step in translation (122, 123). Consequently, the limiting component (in amount) among the initiation factors participating in this step, eIF-4F (due to the low abundance of 24-kDa CBP) is a priori a prime candidate for modulating the rate of ribosome binding to mRNAs. Indeed, several reports attribute a translational discriminatory activity to eIF-4F. Addition of eIF-4F relieves the translational competition between reovirus and globin mRNAs in a fractionated protein-synthesizing system from Krebs ascites cells (124). In another study, eIF-4F relieved the translational competition between endogenous α- and β-globin mRNAs in a rabbit reticulocyte lysate. Other IF factors possessed no such activity (125), contrary to previous reports in other translation systems. In the earlier studies eIF-4B, eIF-4A (126), and eIF-2 (127) relieved the translational competition between α- and β-globin mRNAs either in a fractionated protein-synthesizing system derived from rabbit reticulocytes (126) or in a rabbit reticulocyte extract treated with micrococcal nuclease (127). In addition, eIF-4B and, to a lesser extent, eIF-4A$_f$ relieve the translational competition between globin and EMC virus mRNAs in a reconstituted protein-synthesizing system from Krebs ascites cells (115), and eIF-4A relieves the translational competition between reovirus and globin mRNAs in the same system (124).

How can these discrepancies be explained? First, the early studies showing the translational competition-relieving property of eIF-4B (115, 126) are most probably explained by the fact that the eIF-4B preparations used contained significant amounts of eIF-4F (72, 93). Thus, eIF-4B is apparently not a discriminatory factor. Second, there is no straightforward explanation for the discriminatory effect of eIF-2 on the ratio of α- to β-globin chain synthesis. However, this effect has not been reproduced in several other systems (125, 126, 128) and it has been suggested that nuclease treatment of rabbit reticulocyte lysates renders a usually nondiscriminatory factor limiting for translation (128). Third, the discriminatory activity of eIF-4A might be indirect and reflect the fact that it is a subunit of eIF-4F.

How does eIF-4F function as a discriminatory factor? Brendler *et al.* (128) developed a kinetic model to explain competition between mRNAs. Although this model showed that the hierarchy of competition is not dependent on the presence or absence of the cap, it could be applied to explain the relief of translational competition between reovirus and globin mRNAs by eIF-4A$_f$ and eIF-4F. Recognition of the cap is not required for the discriminatory activity, since relief of translational competition is achieved when either capped or uncapped reovirus mRNAs are used, according to similar hierarchies (128). Consequently, it was proposed that each mRNA contains sequence determinants, apart from the cap, that are recognized by eIF-4A and eIF-4F and determine its initiation efficiency under competitive conditions (128).

In contrast to this model, it was proposed (125) that the discriminatory factor (eIF-4F) binds initially to the cap of all mRNAs with similar affinity. (However, see exceptions discussed in Section II,E.) During a subsequent step involving melting of the mRNA (in conjunction with eIF-4A$_f$ and eIF-4B), the affinity of the discriminatory factor for the mRNA will vary in inverse proportion to the amount of mRNA secondary structure. This could be envisaged by a mechanism of attenuation, whereby the probability of eIF-4F falling or idling on the mRNA increases in direct proportion to the increase in mRNA secondary structure. This is also consistent with the postulated mode of action of eIF-4A$_f$ by which it binds to single-stranded RNA regions and prevents base-pairing with complementary sequences (110).

IV. Control of Translation by Cap-Binding Proteins

The cap structure modulates translational activity through the cap-binding proteins (CBPs). Regulation of translation by modulation of eIF-4F activity was best documented in the studies of the shut-off of host protein synthesis after poliovirus infection (for recent reviews, see 129, 130). Several other instances of translational control in which eIF-4F was implicated have been described. In addition, eIF-4A and eIF-4B are also involved in translational control. However, the molecular mechanisms involved in the latter controls are not well understood.

A. Regulation of Translation in Poliovirus-Infected Cells

Poliovirus infection of HeLa cells causes a selective inhibition of host protein synthesis followed by exclusive synthesis of viral proteins (129–132). A model to explain the mechanism of the shut-off was originally based on the finding that poliovirus RNA is not capped: genomic RNA, a positive strand RNA, contains a small polypeptide (VPg)* that is covalently bound to the 5' terminal U residue (133, 134). Poliovirus polysomal RNA does not contain the VPg protein (135,

---

* See footnote about VPg on page 175.

136), which is removed by a cytoplasmic enzyme to yield a 5' terminal pU residue (137). Consequently, it was postulated that translation of poliovirus proceeds by a cap-independent mechanism, and that inactivation of a CBP would cause the shut-off of cellular protein synthesis, with no deleterious effects on poliovirus protein synthesis (138–140).

Considerable evidence supports this model, the most significant derived from *in vitro* studies, as follows.

1. Cell extracts from poliovirus-infected cells mimic the *in vivo* translation pattern in that they are capable of translating poliovirus RNA (140) or other naturally uncapped RNAs (EMC, 75; STNV, 100), but not most naturally capped mRNAs (75)—there are some exceptions (e.g., AMV-4 RNA, 100).

2. Cross-linking of the 24-kDa CBP, eIF-4A and eIF-4B, to the cap is impaired in IF preparations prepared from poliovirus-infected cells (75). Furthermore, the latter fractions contain an activity that causes a reduction in the cross-linking of CBPs from mock-infected cells to the cap (75).

3. Preparations of IF from mock-infected cells, but not from poliovirus-infected cells, can restore the translating ability of capped mRNAs in extracts prepared from poliovirus-infected cells (140). The protein that possesses the restoring activity has been identified as eIF-4F (81, 92, 93). Earlier experiments identifying other IFs (139, 141) as containing restoring activity can now be explained by the findings that these IFs contained eIF-4F (72, 93).

4. The large subunit of eIF-4F (p220) is proteolyzed in poliovirus-infected cells (102, 142). The kinetics of proteolysis roughly parallels the kinetics of the translational shut-off (142). A modified CBP complex containing the proteolytic cleavage products of p220 and the 24-kDa CBP has been isolated (102). Proteolysis of the p220 occurs before the onset of viral protein synthesis (142), and also occurs in the presence of guanidine or 3-methylquercetin (143), compounds that inhibit poliovirus RNA replication. It was therefore concluded (143) that small amounts of the poliovirus mediator of p220 proteolysis are sufficient for the proteolysis.

5. eIF-4F activity is impaired in extracts prepared from poliovirus-infected cells (144).

6. A causal relationship between p220 proteolysis and the shut-off of host protein synthesis after poliovirus infection was shown by isolation of a mutant (145) containing an amino-acid insertion in poliovirus protein 2A, a proteinase implicated in the cleavage of two Tyr-Gly amino-acid pairs in the poliovirus polyprotein (146). The mutant virus

generated small plaques and lost the ability to mediate the selective inhibition (shut-off) of host protein synthesis in CV-1 and HeLa cells (*145*). Furthermore, infection of cells with the mutant virus gave no cleavage of p220 (*145*). This implicates protein 2A as the mediator of p220 cleavage. In support of this contention, *in vitro* synthesis of 2A led to cleavage of p220 in a rabbit reticulocyte translation system (*147*). However, other experiments suggest that 2A does not cleave p220 directly. Antibodies directed against 2A have no effect on the *in vitro* proteolysis of p220 (*148*). More significantly, p220 proteolyzing activity did not copurify with 2A, implying that 2A activates a cellular component that subsequently cleaves p220. This component might be involved in the physiological turnover of p220 and as such might modulate eIF-4F activity. The direct involvement of the second poliovirus protease, 3C (*149*), in the cleavage of p220 was considered to be unlikely (*150, 151*); antibodies against 3C did not inhibit the cleavage of p220 *in vitro*. Again, more significantly, protease 3C did not copurify with the p220 proteolyzing activity (*150*).

Recent evidence indicates that cleavage of p220 by itself is not sufficient to induce the complete shut-off of cellular protein synthesis (*143*). Infection of HeLa cells with poliovirus in the presence of guanidine leads to incomplete inhibition (70%) of host protein synthesis, whereas p220 is completely cleaved (*143*). These results imply the existence of a second viral-induced function that is involved in the inhibition of host protein synthesis.

B. Regulation of Translation by Other Viruses

Viruses other than poliovirus inhibit host-cell protein synthesis in a manner that implicates cap-binding proteins, although the molecular mechanisms involved in this inhibition are not understood (reviewed in *129, 130*). Of the other picornaviruses, rhinoviruses (human rhinovirus 14; *151a*) and enteroviruses (E. Ehrenfeld, personal communications) appear to exert the host-cell protein synthesis shut-off by proteolysis of p220, whereas EMC virus (*152*) and mengovirus (J. Hershey and J. Lucas-Lenard, personal communication) do not proteolyze p220. It is not clear how the latter mRNAs cause the shut-off of cellular protein synthesis and several hypotheses have been proposed including competition between mRNAs (reviewed in *129, 130*).

1. REOVIRUS

During reovirus infection there occurs a transition from synthesis of capped mRNAs early in infection to uncapped, pG-terminated mRNAs late in infection (153, 154). Furthermore, late reovirus mRNAs can be translated efficiently in extracts prepared from reovirus-infected cells (at late times after infection), whereas capped reovirus mRNAs transcribed *in vitro* are not translated in these extracts (155). However, unpredictably, translation of uncapped late reovirus mRNAs is sensitive to inhibition by the cap analogue, m⁷GTP (155), suggesting that reovirus infection does not induce a transition from cap-dependent to cap-independent translation. To explain this, it was postulated that a factor is present in infected cells that preferentially stimulates the translation of late viral uncapped mRNA (156). Consistent with this hypothesis, recent experiments (157) indicate that a viral protein "sigma 3" (156a) can selectively stimulate translation of late viral mRNAs. Furthermore, L-cell lines expressing this protein from the cloned S4 gene were established, and extracts prepared from these cells translated late reovirus mRNA more efficiently than extracts from control cells (158).

Some of the conclusions reached in these studies have been questioned (159, 159a). Studies of the shut-off of host protein synthesis in extracts prepared from reovirus-infected SC-1 cells grown in monolayers and also in L-cells growing in suspension led to the conclusion that the major mechanism regulating protein synthesis after reovirus infection is competition between viral and cellular mRNAs for a limiting message-discriminatory factor (159, 159a). However, direct competition experiments between L-cell mRNAs and late reovirus mRNAs in extracts prepared from reovirus-infected L-cells did not support this conclusion (156). The conflicting results are probably mainly due to the use of different cell lines.

2. SEMLIKI FOREST VIRUS (SFV)

Infection of neuroblastoma cells with SFV causes inhibition of cellular mRNA translation late in infection concomitantly with a transition from early to late viral mRNA translation (160). The inhibitor is the major viral capsid protein that interdicts the activity of eIF-4B and the 24-kDa CBP (161). Late SFV mRNA is apparently less dependent on these factors for translation, compared to early SFV mRNA and cellular mRNAs, consistent with it being less sensitive to cap analogue inhibition, even though it is capped (162).

C. Control of Translation during Development

Most of the maternal mRNA present in oocytes from different species is translationally inactive before fertilization (163, 164). Translational activation after fertilization occurs at the level of translation initiation, as demonstrated first in sea urchin oocytes (165). There are different explanations for the mechanism of translational repression in oocytes (163, 164). I will refer only to those explanations that implicate the cap structure or cap-binding proteins in this control. One hypothesis is that the cap in oocytes is either not present or lacking the methyl group resulting in poor translational efficiency. Several reports are consistent with this hypothesis. m^7GMP appears in RNA of mouse one-cell embryo only 3 hours after fertilization (166). There appear to be no cap structures in insect oocyte RNA (167). Fertilization of sea urchin embryos leads to an increase in mRNA cap methylation of early histone genes H1, H4, and H6 (168). Thus, it is possible that fertilization induces the activity of masked cap-methylating enzymes that apparently exist in the unfertilized sea urchin oocyte but cannot methylate specific sets of mRNAs (168).

An RNA melting activity increases dramatically when *Xenopus* oocytes are induced to mature (169, 170). This activity exists at high levels in eggs and early embryos, but is almost absent in oocytes and late blastula embryos (169). It was suggested that this melting activity might be responsible for the translational control of maternal mRNAs in amphibian oocytes (169). Since most polyadenylated RNAs in oocytes are not translated *in vivo* (171), but are translated after fertilization, it is possible that the RNA melting activity is induced or activated following fertilization and causes the dissociation of RNA hybrid regions. An interesting speculation is that this melting activity is in fact eIF-4F (CBP complex). This is consistent with the finding that translation of mRNA injected into oocytes is very sensitive to secondary structure in the 5' noncoding region, compared to other *in vitro* translation systems (N. Parkin, A. Darveau and N. Sonenberg, unpublished observations). Extracts from unfertilized sea urchin eggs contain an inhibitor of eIF-4F that prevents mRNA translation in translation systems derived from 2-hour sea urchin embryos and from rabbit reticulocytes (172). Thus, it is possible that eIF-4F is present in oocytes but is repressed, and this repression is relieved upon fertilization.

The involvement of the cap per se was also invoked in the translation of rat insulinoma insulin-2 mRNA (173). The levels of the two allelic rat insulin mRNAs in rat insulinoma were similar, but protein levels differed by a factor of 10. When the mRNAs were capped *in vitro*, the ratio of the proteins changed to 1 : 1, suggesting that one of the mRNAs was not capped and therefore translated inefficiently (173).

D. Phosphorylation of the 24-kDa Cap-Binding Protein and Modulation of Translation

Another structural modification of eIF-4F that could modulate its translational activity is phosphorylation of the 24-kDa CBP subunit. Several studies showed that 24-kDa CBP can be phosphorylated at several serine residues in different tissues (reticulocytes, 174; HeLa cells, 175, 176). Phosphorylation of the 24-kDa CBP was also detected in yeast (M. Jaramillo and M. Altmann, unpublished observations) and a serine protein kinase isolated from yeast is capable of phosphorylating yeast and human erythrocyte 24-kDa CBP *in vitro* (177).

A direct correlation exists between the phosphorylation state of the 24-kDa CBP and the translation of cellular mRNAs during heat shock. In response to heat shock, translation of most cellular mRNAs in many eukaryotes is reduced, whereas translation of heat-shock mRNAs is enhanced (178–182). The major translational inhibition occurs at the level of polypeptide chain initiation (182). Concomitant with cellular mRNA translational reduction, the level of 24-kDa CBP phosphorylation is reduced (176). In contrast, immunoblot analyses indicated an increase in the phosphorylation of eIF-2 and eIF-4B. Examination of the activity of IF in heat-shocked HeLa cells indicated partial impairment of the factors that underwent changes in their phosphorylation state [eIF(3 + 4F), eIF-4B, and eIF-2] (183). Nevertheless, there is no evidence to indicate that the phosphorylation state of IF has any causal significance in the translation control in this system. Further implication of eIF-4F function in the heat-shock response is indicated by the facts that protein synthesis in extracts, prepared from Ehrlich ascites cells after heat shock, is inhibited and synthesis is restored by the addition of eIF-4F, but not by other IFs (184). Moreover, addition of eIF-4F preferentially stimulated translation of non-heat-shock protein mRNAs. Consistent with these findings is also the report that translation of heat-shock protein mRNAs are more resistant to inhibition by poliovirus infection that inactivates eIF-4F (184a). Thus, it is an interesting possibility that dephosphorylation of 24-kDa CBP reduces the activity of eIF-4F under heat-shock conditions.

A similar situation occurs in HeLa cells in mitosis. Protein synthesis in mitotic cells is reduced to approximately 25% of that in cells in interphase (185, 186). The extent of 24-kDa CBP phosphorylation is reduced in mitotic cells and the ability of the 24-kDa CBP to crosslink to the mRNA cap structure is also reduced (187). Furthermore, translation of endogenous mRNA in extracts prepared from cells in mitosis is reduced compared to control cells; addition of eIF-4F can partially overcome this translational block (187). Thus, in two different systems, a positive correlation has been established between the degree of eIF-4E phosphorylation and translational activity. However, no direct proof is provided to link the decrease in 24-kDa CBP phosphorylation and the reduced rate of protein synthesis in mitotic cells. In an examination of the phosphorylation state of the 24-kDa CBP in poliovirus-infected HeLa cells, no change from uninfected cells was found (175).

V. 24-kDa Cap-Binding Protein (eIF-4E) Genes

Understanding the mechanism of function of the 24-kDa cap-binding-protein (eIF-4E) will benefit considerably from the present availability of cDNA and genomic clones encoding this protein from several species. cDNA clones have been obtained from human (188) and mouse (J. Pelletier, M. Jaramillo, I. Edery and N. Sonenberg, unpublished). Both cDNA and genomic clones have been obtained from yeast (189). Comparison of the nucleotide sequences and the deduced protein sequences (Fig. 3) reveals several interesting features. (1) There is strong conservation on both the nucleotide and protein level between mouse and man (more than 95% identity of amino-acid sequences). In addition, there is a significant homology in the amino-acid sequences between the mammalian and yeast 24-kDa CBP (~30%; when considering conservative changes in amino acids, the homology is 50%), indicating a strongly conserved and important function of the 24-kDa CBP. (2) The amino-acid sequence of the 24-kDa CBP from all species analyzed contains a high proportion of tryptophans (eight) that is remarkably evolutionarily conserved in number and position between such diverse species as mammal and yeast. This might be of special significance in light of the report that tryptophans (particularly those flanked by negatively charged amino acids) might be involved in cap recognition (190). It is also of interest that one of the tryptophans is located in an evolutionarily conserved sequence (position 36 of human or mouse 24-kDa CBP) that is highly homologous to a sequence (position 360) found in the influenza cap-binding protein (PB2, 191). This sequence is Lys-Xaa-Xaa-Xaa-Gln-Xaa-Baa-Trp-Ala-Leu (Xaa is any amino acid and Baa is a basic amino acid) (188).

The availability of the 24-kDa CBP yeast gene will facilitate studies of its mechanism of function by genetic manipulations. The yeast gene is essential for growth, as shown by gene disruption (189). Of

```
              1        10          20           30             40
human    MATVEPETTPTPNPPTTEEEKTESNQEV----ANPE------HYI-KHPLQ
mouse    MATVEPETTPTTNPPPAEEEKTESNQEV----ANPE------HYI-KHPLQ
yeast    MSVEEVSK----------KFEENVSVDDTTATPKTVLSDSAHFDVKHPLN

                  50          60          70          80       90
human    NRWALWFFKN--DKSKTWQANLRLISKFDTVEDFWALYNHIQLSSNLMPGCD
mouse    NRWALWFFKN--DKSKTWQANLRLISKFDTVEDFWALYNHIQLSSNLMPGCD
yeast    TKWTLWYTKPAVDKSESWSDLLRPVTSFQTVEEFWAIIQNIPEPHELPLKSD
         ☆  ☆      ☆       ☆            ☆

                100         110         120         130
human    YSLFKDGIEPMWEDEKNNRGGRWLITLNKQQRRS---DLDRFWLETLLCLIG
mouse    YSLFKDGIEPMWEDEKNKRGGRWLITLNKQQRRS---DLDRFWLETLLCLIG
yeast    YHVFRNDVRPEWEDEANAKGGKWSFQL-----RGKGADIDELWLRTLLAVIG
                   ☆            ☆              ☆

                140         150         160         170         180
human    ESFDDYSDDVCGAVVNVRAKGDKIAIWTT----ECENREAVTHIGRVYKERL
mouse    ESFDDYSDDVCGAVVNVRAKGDKIAIWTT----ECENRDAVTHIGRVYKERL
yeast    ETIDEDDSQINGVVLSIRKGGNKFALWIKSEDKEPLLR-----IGGKFKQVL
                              ☆

                190         200         210     217
human    GFPPKIVIGYQSHADTATKSGSTTKNRFVV*
mouse    GLPPKIVIGYQSHADTATKSGSTTKNRFVV*
yeast    KLTDDGHLEFFPH-------SSANGRHPQPSITL*
```

NUMBER OF MATCHED AMINO ACIDS (HUMAN VS MOUSE) = 211
NUMBER OF MATCHED AMINO ACIDS (MOUSE VS YEAST) =   76

FIG. 3. Comparison of amino-acid sequences of the 24-kDa cap-binding proteins from different species. Gaps have been introduced to maximize homology between the mammalian and yeast protein. Stars indicate the conserved tryptophans in the sequence. Amino acids are expressed in the one-letter system [*JBM* **260**, 17 (1985)].

great importance for the studies of cap recognition will be the elucidation of the crystal structure of the 24-kDa CBP.

VI. Conclusions and Perspectives

Considerable progress has been gained in the last years studying the initiation factors involved in the binding of ribosomes to eukaryotic mRNAs. The molecular mechanisms of this process are beginning to emerge, but by and large, the details are still moot. From the studies I have described, it is clear that several initiation factors (eIF-4A, eIF-4B, and eIF-4F) interact with the mRNA *prior* to ribosome binding. I emphasize "prior" because it is often assumed (particularly by the uninitiated) that ribosomes attach directly to eukaryotic mRNAs, in analogy to prokaryotic mRNAs, without the prior interaction of initiation factors with the mRNA. All of the initiation factors involved in the binding of ribosomes to mRNA interact specifically with the cap. However, the interaction of eIF-4F with the cap can occur in the absence of ATP-Mg^{2+}, whereas interaction of eIF-4A and eIF-4B with the cap is dependent on ATP hydrolysis. Based on the available data, a model is postulated stating that eIF-4F is the first initiation factor to interact with the cap. This is followed by melting of the 5' proximal secondary structure. These events lead then to ribosome binding.

It is important to stress that it is unclear what determinants on the mRNA or factors the ribosome recognizes for binding. Analyses of 40-S initiation complexes have not revealed the presence of eIF-4A or eIF-4B (e.g., 192). However, similar analyses have not been carried out for eIF-4F, whereas the 24-kDa CBP has been detected on polysomes (193). An interesting role for eIF-4B in directing ribosomes to the initiator AUG could also be envisaged. Thus, it is possible that scanning of the 5' noncoding region of eukaryotic mRNAs is performed by initiation factors followed by internal binding of ribosomes.

In light of the initial binding of eIF-4F to the mRNA, it is of interest that this factor has been implicated in the regulation of protein synthesis in several systems (poliovirus infection, heat shock, mitosis), and is a prime candidate in determining the translation efficiency of an mRNA.

Major important questions concerning mRNA ribosome binding are still unanswered. These include (1) the precise function of eIF-4B and its mode of interaction with other initiation factors and with mRNA, (2) the elements within the mRNA 5' noncoding region that signal ribosome binding—current evidence negates the likelihood of the direct recognition of the 5' cap structure by the ribosome, and (3) the involvement of other initiation factors that are unjustifiably ignored in this review, particularly the role of eIF-2 and eIF-3. The lack of discussion of the possible roles of these other factors in mRNA ribosome binding is chiefly because of two reasons. (1) There is no consensus about the participation of eIF-3 and eIF-2 in mRNA ribosome binding. A direct role for eIF-3 in mRNA ribosome binding has not been documented, but since eIF-3 binds to the 40-S subunit prior to the 43-S preinitiation complex formation (111, 112), it is already present during mRNA ribosome binding. However, it may also play an active role in mRNA ribosome binding. As for eIF-2, it binds specifically to mRNA in an *in vitro* filter binding assay (194, 195), although these results were challenged by others (125, 126, 128). In addition, eIF-2 binds to the initiation codon of several eukaryotic mRNAs (STNV, 196; mengovirus, 197), which led to the suggestion that eIF-2 participates in the selection of AUG initiation codons (196, 197). (2) An attempt to accommodate eIF-3 and eIF-2 into the melting model for mRNA ribosome binding would have been very cumbersome because there are so few data to relate the functions of these IFs with those involved in mRNA binding that even intelligent guesses would be futile.

In conclusion, despite the advances in understanding the mechanism of function of the initiation factors involved in mRNA binding to ribosomes, it is unclear how and what the ribosome recognizes on the mRNA for its initial binding. Future cloning of the genes coding for the different initiation factors and the ability to mutate them for functional analysis will undoubtedly significantly increase our understanding of one of the more complex processes in the living cell. Understanding the mechanisms involved in translation initiation will aid in unraveling additional examples of control of gene expression at the level of translation. This will certainly make the research on translation initiation in eukaryotes both exciting and rewarding.

ACKNOWLEDGMENTS

The work cited from the author's laboratory was supported by the Medical Research Council of Canada and the National Cancer Institute of Canada. I thank Jerry Pelletier, Isaac Edery, Michael Altmann, and Neil Parkin for their useful criticism and the colleagues who communicated their results before publication.

REFERENCES

1. K. Moldave, *ARB* **54**, 1109 (1985).
2. V. M. Pain, *BJ* **235**, 625 (1986).
3. R. Kaempfer, *in* "Comprehensive Virology" (H. Fraenkel-Conrat and R. R. Wagner, eds.), Vol. 19, p. 99. Plenum, New York, 1984.
4. A. J. Shatkin, *Cell* **9**, 645 (1976).
5. M. M. Konarska, R. A. Padgett and P. A. Sharp, *Cell* **38**, 731 (1984).
6. I. Edery and N. Sonenberg, *PNAS* **82**, 7590 (1985).
7. E. Patzelt, E. Thalman, K. Hartmuth, D. Blaas and E. Kuechler, *NARes* **15**, 1387 (1987).
8. O. Georgiev, J. Mous and M. Birnstiel, *NARes* **12**, 8539 (1985).
9. R. P. Hart, M. A. McDevitt and J. R. Nevins, *Cell* **43**, 677 (1985).
10. Y. Furuichi, A. LaFiandra and A. J. Shatkin, *Nature* **266**, 235 (1977).
11. M. Green, D. Melton and T. Maniatis, *Cell* **32**, 681 (1983).
12. A. K. Banerjee, *Microbiol. Rev.* **44**, 175 (1980).
13. E. Wimmer, *Cell* **28**, 199 (1982).
14. E. Wimmer, A. Y. Chang, J. M. Clark, Jr. and M. E. Reichman, *JMB* **38**, 59 (1968).
15. D. W. Leung, K. S. Browning, J. E. Heckman, U. L. RajBhandary and J. M. Clark, *Bchem* **18**, 1361 (1979).
16. J. A. Lesnaw and M. E. Reichman, *PNAS* **66**, 140 (1970).
17. J. Klootwijk, I. Klein, P. Zabel and A. Van Kammen, *Cell* **11**, 73 (1977).
18. S. D. Daubert, G. Bruening and R. C. Najarian, *EJB* **92**, 45 (1978).
19. M. Kozak, *Microbiol. Rev.* **47**, 1 (1983).
20. V. L. Stroeher, E. M. Jorgensen and R. L. Garber, *MCBiol* **6**, 4667 (1986).
21. G. Jay, S. Nomura, C. W. Anderson and G. Khoury, *Nature* **291**, 346 (1981).

202 NAHUM SONENBERG

22. K. Hennessy, F. Wang, E. Woodland Bushman and E. Kieff, *PNAS* **83**, 5693 (1986).
23. K. Khalili, J. Brady and G. Khoury, *Cell* **48**, 639 (1987).
24. P. B. Hackett, R. B. Petersen, C. H. Hensel, F. Albericio, S. I. Gunderson, A. C. Palmenberg and G. Barany, *JMB* **190**, 45 (1986).
24a. M. Wolfner, D. Yep, F. Messenguy and G. R. Fink, *JMB* **96**, 273 (1975).
25. G. R. Fink, *Cell* **45**, 155 (1986).
26. P. P. Mueller and A. B. Hinnebusch, *Cell* **45**, 201 (1986).
27. P. Tzamarias, D. Alexandraki and G. Thireos, *PNAS* **83**, 4849 (1986).
28. S. O. Freitag, A. L. Beaudet, H. G. O. Bock and W. E. O'Brien, *MCBiol* **4**, 1978 (1984).
29. G. Gill, J. R. Smith, J. L. Goldstein and M. S. Brown, *PNAS* **84**, 1863 (1987).
30. R. A. Young, O. Hagenbüchle and U. Schibler, *Cell* **23**, 451 (1981).
31. G. N. Pavlakis, R. E. Lockard, N. Vamvakopoulos, L. Rieser, U. L. RajBhandary and J. N. Vournakis, *Cell* **19**, 91 (1980).
32. A-M. Mes-Masson, J. McLaughlin, G. Q. Daley, M. Paskind and O. N. Witte, *PNAS* **83**, 9763 (1986).
33. I. K. Hariharan and J. M. Adams, *EMBO J.* **6**, 115 (1987).
34. M. Barbinc, L. McConlogue, T. van Daalen Wetters and P. Coffino, *PNAS* **85**, 2200 (1988).
35. T. Okamoto and F. Wong-Staal, *Cell* **47**, 29 (1986).
36. M. A. Muesing, D. H. Smith and D. J. Capon, *Cell* **48**, 691 (1987).
37. J. Pelletier and N. Sonenberg, *Cell* **40**, 515 (1985).
38. S. B. Baim, D. F. Pietras, D. C. Eustice and F. Sherman, *MCBiol* **5**, 1839 (1985).
38a. M. Kozak, *PNAS* **83**, 2850 (1986).
39. R. Klemenz, D. Hultmark and W. J. Gehring, *EMBO J.* **4**, 2053 (1985).
40. T. J. McGarry and S. Lindquist, *Cell* **42**, 903 (1985).
41. S. Lindquist, *ARB* **55**, 1151 (1986).
42. J. Pelletier, G. Kaplan, V. Racaniello and N. Sonenberg, *MCBiol* **8**, 1103 (1988).
43. M. W. Hentze, T. A. Rouault, S. W. Caughman, A. Dancis, J. B. Harford and R. D. Klausner, *PNAS* **84**, 6730 (1987).
44. N. Aziz and H. N. Munro, *PNAS* **84**, 8478 (1987).
45. P. P. Mueller, S. Harashima and A. L. Hinnebusch, *PNAS* **84**, 2863 (1987).
46. S. Muthukrishnan, G.W. Both, Y. Furuichi and A. J. Shatkin, *Nature* **255**, 33 (1975).
47. G. W. Both, A. K. Banerjee and A. J. Shatkin, *PNAS* **72**, 1189 (1975).
48. J. K. Rose and H. F. Lodish, *Nature* **262**, 32 (1976).
49. G. W. Both, Y. Furuichi, S. Muthukrishnan and A. J. Shatkin, *Cell* **6**, 185 (1975).
50. M. Zan Kowalczewska, M. Bretner, H. Sierakowska, E. Szczesna, W. Filipowicz and A. J. Shatkin, *NARes* **4**, 3065 (1977).
51. A. Wodnar-Filipowicz, E. Szczesna, M. Zan Kowalczewska, S. Muthukrishnan, U. Szybiak, A. B. Legocki and W. Filipowicz, *EJB* **92**, 69 (1978).
52. W. Filipowicz, *FEBS Lett.* **96**, 1 (1978).
53. A. J. Shatkin, *Cell* **40**, 223 (1985).
54. E. D. Hickey, L. A. Weber and C. Baglioni, *PNAS* **73**, 19 (1976).
55. R. Roman, J. D. Brooker, S. N. Seal and A. Marcus, *Nature* **260**, 359 (1976).
56. E. D. Hickey, L. A. Weber, C. Baglioni, C. H. Kim and R. H. Sarma, *JMB* **109**, 173 (1977).
57. D. Canaani, M. Revel and Y. Groner, *FEBS Lett.* **64**, 326 (1976).
58. W. Filipowicz, Y. Furuichi, J. M. Sierra, S. Muthukrishnan, A. J. Shatkin and S. Ochoa, *PNAS* **73**, 1559 (1976).

58a. D. S. Shih, R. Dasgupta and P. Kaesberg, *J. Virol.* **19**, 637 (1976).
59. L. Van Vloten-Doting, J. Bol, L. Neeleman, T. Rutgers, D. Van Dalen, A. Castel, L. Bosch, G. Marbaix, G. Huez, E. Hubert and Y. Cleuter, *in* "NATO Advanced Studies on Nucleic Acids and Protein Synthesis in Plants" (L. Bogorad and M. Weil, eds.), p. 387. Plenum, New York, 1977.
60. N. Sonenberg, D. Guertin, D. Cleveland and H. Trachsel, *Cell* **27**, 563 (1981).
61. L. Gehrke, P. E. Auron, G. J. Quigley, A. Rich and N. Sonenberg, *Bchem* **22**, 5157 (1983).
62. S. Muthukrishnan, M. Morgan, A. K. Banerjee and A. J. Shatkin, *Bchem* **15**, 5761 (1976).
63. H. F. Lodish and J. K. Rose, *JBC* **252**, 1181 (1977).
64. L. A. Weber, E. D. Hickey, D. L. Nuss and C. Baglioni, *PNAS* **74**, 3254 (1977).
65. N. Sonenberg, I. Edery, A. Darveau, M. Humbelin, H. Trachsel, J. W. B. Hershey and K. A. W. Lee, *in* "Protein Synthesis: Translational and Posttranslational Events" (A. K. Abraham, ed.), p. 23. Humana Press, Clifton, New Jersey, 1983.
66. R. E. Rhoads, *Prog. Mol. Subcell. Biol.* **9**, 104 (1985).
67. I. Edery, J. Pelletier and N. Sonenberg, *in* "Translational Regulation of Gene Expression" (J. Ilan, ed.), p. 335. Plenum, New York, 1987.
68. R. Kaempfer, H. Rosen and R. Israeli, *PNAS* **75**, 650 (1978).
69. D. A. Shafritz, J. A. Weinstein, B. Safer, W. C. Merrick, L. A. Weber, E. D. Hickey and C. Baglioni, *Nature* **261**, 291 (1976).
70. N. Sonenberg and A. J. Shatkin, *JBC* **253**, 6630 (1978).
71. N. Sonenberg and A. J. Shatkin, *PNAS* **74**, 488 (1977).
72. N. Sonenberg, M. A. Morgan, W. C. Merrick and A. J. Shatkin, *PNAS* **75**, 4843 (1978).
73. M. Altmann, I. Edery, N. Sonenberg and H. Trachsel, *Bchem* **24**, 6085 (1985).
74. J. Hansen and E. Ehrenfeld, *J. Virol.* **38**, 438 (1981).
75. K. A. W. Lee, and N. Sonenberg, *PNAS* **79**, 3447 (1982).
76. S. N. Seal, A. Schmidt, A. Marcus, I. Edery and N. Sonenberg, *ABB* **246**, 710 (1986).
77. K. S. Browning, S. R. Lax and J. M. Ravel, *JBC* **262** 11228 (1987).
78. W. Rychlik, P. R. Gardner, T. C. Vanaman and R. E. Rhoads, *JBC* **261**, 71 (1986).
79. N. Sonenberg, *NARes* **9**, 1643 (1981).
80. J. Pelletier and N. Sonenberg, *MCBiol* **5**, 3222 (1985).
81. I. Edery, M. Humbelin, A. Darveau, K. A. W. Lee, S. Milburn, J. W. B. Hershey, H. Trachsel and N. Sonenberg, *JBC* **258**, 11398 (1983).
82. J. A. Grifo, S. Tahara, J. Leis, M. A. Morgan, A. J. Shatkin and W. C. Merrick, *JBC* **257**, 5246 (1982).
83. J. S. Butler and J. M. Clark, Jr., *Bchem* **23**, 809 (1984).
84. S. Lax, W. Fritz, K. Browning and J. Ravel, *PNAS* **82**, 330 (1985).
85. N. Sonenberg, K. M. Rupprecht, S. M. Hecht and A. J. Shatkin, *PNAS* **76**, 4345 (1979).
86. K. M. Rupprecht, N. Sonenberg, A. J. Shatkin and S. M. Hecht, *Bchem* **20**, 6570 (1981).
87. N. Sonenberg, H. Trachsel, S. M. Hecht and A. J. Shatkin, *Nature* **285**, 331 (1980).
88. G. M. Hellmann, L.-Y. Chu and R. E. Rhoads, *JBC* **257**, 4056 (1982).
89. H. Trachsel, N. Sonenberg, A. J. Shatkin, J. K. Rose, K. Leong, J. E. Bergmann, J. Gordon and D. Baltimore, *PNAS* **77**, 770 (1980).

90. N. R. Webb, R. V. J. Chari, G. DePillis, J. W. Kozarich and R. E. Rhoads, *Bchem* **23**, 177 (1984).
91. J. E. Bergmann, H. Trachsel, N. Sonenberg, A. J. Shatkin and H. F. Lodish, *JBC* **254**, 1440 (1979).
92. S. M. Tahara, M. A. Morgan and A. J. Shatkin, *JBC* **256**, 7691 (1981).
93. J. A. Grifo, S. M. Tahara, M. A. Morgan, A. J. Shatkin and W. C. Merrick, *JBC* **258**, 5804 (1983).
94. K. S. Browning, D. M. Maia, S. R. Lax and J. M. Ravel, *JBC* **262**, 538 (1987).
95. S. R. Lax, K. S. Browning, D. M. Maia and J. M. Ravel, *JBC* **261**, 15632 (1986).
96. M. A. Morgan and A. J. Shatkin, *Bchem* **19**, 5960 (1980).
97. M. Kozak, *Cell* **19**, 79 (1980).
98. S. M. Tahara, M. A. Morgan and A. J. Shatkin, *JBC* **258**, 11350 (1983).
99. K. A. W. Lee, D. Guertin and N. Sonenberg, *JBC* **258**, 707 (1983).
100. N. Sonenberg, D. Guertin and K. A. W. Lee, *MCBiol* **2**, 1633 (1982).
101. I. Edery, K. A. W. Lee and N. Sonenberg, *Bchem* **23**, 2456 (1984).
101a. J. W. Holder and J. B. Lingrel, *Bchem* **14**, 4209 (1975).
102. K. A. W. Lee, I. Edery and N. Sonenberg, *J. Virol.* **54**, 515 (1985).
103. T. G. Lawson, B. K. Roy, J. T. Dodds, J. A. Grifo, R. D. Abramson, W. C. Merrick, D. F. Betsch, H. L. Weith and R. E. Thach, *JBC* **216**, 13979 (1986).
103a. T. Godefroy-Colburn, M. Ravelonandra and L. Pinck, *EJB* **147**, 549 (1955).
104. B. K. Ray, T. G. Lawson, J. C. Kramer, M. H. Cladaras, J. A. Grifo, R. D. Abramson, W. C. Merrick and R. E. Thach, *JBC* **260**, 7651 (1985).
105. J. A. Grifo, R. D. Abramson, C. A. Salter and W. C. Merrick, *JBC* **259**, 8648 (1984).
106. G. Sarkar, I. Edery and N. Sonenberg, *JBC* **260**, 13831 (1985).
107. S. N. Seal, A. Schmidt and A. Marcus, *PNAS* **80**, 6562 (1983).
108. P. J. Nielsen, G. K. McMaster and H. Trachsel, *NARes* **13**, 6867 (1985).
109. K. Walker, M. Saraste, M. Runswick and N. Gay, *EMBO J.* **8**, 945 (1982).
110. R. D. Abramson, T. E. Dever, T. G. Lawson, B. K. Ray, R. E. Thach and W. C. Merrick, *JBC* **262**, 3826 (1987).
111. H. Trachsel, B. Erni, M. H. Schreier and T. Staehelin, *JMB* **116**, 755 (1977).
112. R. Benne and J. W. B. Hershey, *JBC* **253**, 3078 (1978).
113. B. K. Ray, T. G. Lawson, R. D. Abramson, W. C. Merrick and R. E. Thach, *JBC* **261**, 11466 (1986).
114. D. J. Goss, C. L. Woodley and A. J. Wahba, *Bchem.* **26**, 1551 (1987).
115. F. Golini, S. S. Thach, C. H. Birge, B. Safer, W. C. Merrick and R. E. Thach, *PNAS* **73**, 3040 (1976).
116. J. Ilan and J. Ilan, *PNAS* **74**, 2325 (1977).
117. R. C. Herman, *J. Virol.* **58**, 797 (1986).
118. D. Hassin, R. Korn and M. S. Horwitz, *Virology* **155**, 214 (1986).
119. E. Nagy, R. Duncan, P. Krell and P. Dobos, *Virology* **158**, 211 (1987).
120. T. Staehelin, H. Trachsel, B. Erni, A. Boschetti and M. H. Schreier, *Proc. FEBS Meet.* **41**, 309 (1975).
121. S. Daniels-McQueen, B. M. Detjen, J. A. Grifo, W. C. Merrick and R. E. Thach, *JBC* **258**, 7195 (1983).
122. R. Jagus, W. F. Anderson and B. Safer, *This Series* **25**, 127 (1981).
123. W. E. Walden, T. Godefroy-Colburn and R. E. Thach, *JBC* **256**, 739 (1981).
124. B. K. Ray, T. G. Brendler, S. Adya, S. Daniels-McQueen, J. Kelvin Miller, J. W. B. Hershey, J. A. Grifo, W. C. Merrick and R. E. Thach, *PNAS* **80**, 663 (1983).

125. G. Sarkar, I. Edery, R. Gallo and N. Sonenberg, *BBA* **783**, 122 (1984).
126. D. Kabat and M. R. Chappell, *JBC* **252**, 2684 (1977).
127. G. Di Segni, H. Rosen and R. Kaempfer, *Bchem* **18**, 2847 (1979).
128. T. Brendler, T. Godefroy-Colburn, R. D. Carlill and R. E. Thach, *JBC* **256**, 11755 (1981).
129. E. Ehrenfeld, *in* "Comprehensive Virology" (H. Fraenkel-Conrat and R. R. Wagner, eds.), Vol. 19, p. 177. Plenum, New York, 1984).
130. N. Sonenberg, *Adv. Virus Res.* **33**, 175 (1987).
131. D. Baltimore, *in* "The Biochemistry of Viruses" (H. B. Levy, ed.), p. 101. Dekker, New York, 1969).
132. J. M. Lucas-Lenard, *in* "The Molecular Biology of Picornaviruses" (R. Perez-Bercoff, ed.), p. 78. Plenum, New York, 1979.
133. Y. F. Lee, A. Nomoto, B. M. Detjen and E. Wimmer, *PNAS* **74**, 59 (1977).
134. J. B. Flanagan, R. Petterson, V. Ambros, M. J. Hewlett and D. Baltimore, *PNAS* **74**, 961 (1977).
135. M. J. Hewlett, J. K. Rose and D. Baltimore, *PNAS* **73**, 327 (1976).
136. A. Nomoto, Y. F. Lee and E. Wimmer, *PNAS* **73**, 375 (1976).
137. V. Ambros, R. F. Petterson and D. Baltimore, *Cell* **15**, 1439 (1978).
138. R. Fernandez-Munoz and J. E. Darnell, *J. Virol.* **18**, 719 (1976).
139. J. K. Rose, H. Trachsel, K. Leong and D. Baltimore, *PNAS* **75**, 2732 (1978).
140. T. Helentjaris and E. Ehrenfeld, *J. Virol.* **26**, 510 (1978).
141. T. Helentjaris, E. Ehrenfeld, M. L. Brown-Leudi and J. W. B. Hershey, *JBC* **254**, 10973 (1979).
142. D. Etchison, S. C. Milburn, I. Edery, N. Sonenberg and J. W. B. Hershey, *JBC* **257**, 14806 (1982).
143. A.-M. Bonneau and N. Sonenberg, *J. Virol.* **61**, 986 (1987).
144. D. Etchison, J. Hansen, E. Ehrenfeld, I. Edery, N. Sonenberg, S. Milbrun and J. W. B. Hershey, *J. Virol.* **51**, 832 (1984).
145. H. D. Bernstein, N. Sonenberg and D. Baltimore, *MCBiol* **5**, 2913 (1985).
145a. R. R. Rueckert and E. Wimmer, *J. Virol.* **50**, 957 (1984).
146. H. Toyoda, M. J. H. Nicklin, M. G. Murray, C. W. Anderson, J. J. Dunn, F. W. Studier and E. Wimmer, *Cell* **45**, 761 (1986).
147. H. G. Krausslich, M. J. H. Nicklin, H. Toyoda, D. Etchison and E. Wimmer, *J. Virol.* **61**, 2711 (1987).
148. R. E. Lloyd, H. Toyoda, D. Etchison, E. Wimmer and E. Ehrenfeld, *Virology* **150**, 299 (1986).
149. R. Hanecak, B. L. Semler, C. W. Anderson and E. Wimmer, *PNAS* **79**, 3973 (1982).
150. R. E. Lloyd, D. Etchison and E. Ehrenfeld, *PNAS* **82**, 2723 (1985).
151. K. A. W. Lee, I. Edery, R. Hanecak, E. Wimmer and N. Sonenberg, *J. Virol.* **55**, 489 (1985).
151a. D. Etchison and S. Fout, *J. Virol.* **54**, 634 (1985).
152. J. Mosenkis, S. Daniels-McQueen, S. Janovec, R. Duncan, J. W. B. Hershey, J. A. Grifo, W. C. Merrick and R. E. Thach, *J. Virol.* **54**, 643 (1985).
153. H. Zarbl, D. Skup and S. Millward, *J. Virol.* **34**, 497 (1980).
154. D. Skup and S. Millward, *J. Virol.* **34**, 490 (1980).
155. D. Skup and S. Millward, *PNAS* **77**, 152 (1980).
156. R. Lemieux, H. Zarbl and S. Millward, *J. Virol.* **51**, 215 (1984).
156a. W. J. Joklik, *in* "The Reoviridae" (W. K. Joklik, ed.), p. 9. Plenum, New York, 1983.

157. R. Lemieux, G. Lemay and S. Millward, *J. Virol.* **61**, 2472 (1987).
158. G. Lemay and S. Millward, *Virus Res.* **6**, 133 (1986).
159. B. Morgan-Detjen, W. E. Walden and R. E. Thach, *JBC* **257**, 9855 (1982).
159a. A. Munoz, M. Alonso and L. Carrasco, *J. Gen. Virol.* **66**, 2161 (1985).
160. H. Van Steeg, A. Thomas, S. Verebek, M. Kasperaitis, H. O. Voorma and R. Benne, *J. Virol.* **38**, 728 (1981).
161. H. Van Steeg, M. Kasperaitis, H. O. Voorma and R. Benne, *EJB* **138**, 473 (1984).
162. H. Van Steeg, M. Van Grinsven, F. Van Mansfield, H. O. Voorma and R. Benne, *FEBS Lett.* **129**, 62 (1981).
163. E. H. Davidson, "Gene Activity in Early Development," 3rd ed. Academic Press, New York, 1986.
164. R. A. Raff and R. M. Showman, in "The Biology of Fertilization" (C. B. Metz and A. Monroy, eds.). Academic Press, New York, 1983.
165. T. Humphreys, *Dev. Biol.* **26**, 201 (1971).
166. R. J. Young, *BBRC* **76**, 32 (1977).
167. W. H. Kastern, M. Swindelhurst, C. Aaron, J. Hooper and S. J. Berry, *Dev. Biol.* **89**, 437 (1982).
168. D. C. Caldwell and C. P. Emerson, Jr., *Cell* **42**, 691 (1985).
169. M. R. Rebagliati and D. A. Melton, *Cell* **48**, 599 (1987).
170. B. L. Bass and H. Weintraub, *Cell* **48**, 607 (1987).
171. J. D. Richter, D. Smith, D. M. Anderson and E. H. Davidson, *JMB* **173**, 227 (1984).
172. L. J. Hansen, W.-I. Huang, and R. Jagus, *JBC* **262**, 6114 (1987).
173. B. Cordell, D. Diamond, S. Smith, J. Punter, H. H. Schone and H. M. Goodman, *Cell* **31**, 531 (1982).
174. W. Rychlik, P. R. Gardner, T. C. Vanaman and R. E. Rhoads, *JBC* **261**, 71 (1986).
175. B. Buckley and E. Ehrenfeld, *Virology* **152**, 497 (1986).
176. R. Duncan, S. C. Milburn and J. W. B. Hershey, *JBC* **262**, 380 (1987).
177. Y. Yanagita, M. Abdel-Ghany, D. Raden, N. Nelson and E. Racker, *PNAS* **84**, 925 (1987).
178. M. J. Schlesinger, M. Ashburner and A. Tissieres (eds.), "Heat Shock from Bacteria to Man." Cold Spring Harbor Laboratory, Cold Spring Harbor, New York, 1982.
179. R. V. Storti, M. P. Scott, A. Rich and M. L. Pardue, *Cell* **22**, 825 (1980).
180. M. E. Mirault, M. Goldschmidt-Clermont, L. Moran, A. P. Arrigo and A. Tissieres, *CSHSQB* **42**, 819 (1978).
181. M. P. Scott and M. L. Pardue, *PNAS* **78**, 3353 (1981).
182. W. McCormick and S. Penman, *JMB* **39**, 315 (1969).
183. R. Duncan and J. W. B. Hershey, *JBC* **259**, 11882 (1984).
184. R. Panniers, E. B. Stewart, W. C. Merrick and E. C. Henshaw, *JBC* **260**, 9648 (1985).
184a. A. Munoz, M. A. Alonso and L. Carrasco, *Virology* **137**, 150 (1984).
185. H. Fan and S. Penman, *JMB* **50**, 655 (1970).
186. M. A. Tarnowka and C. Baglioni, *J. Cell. Physiol.* **99**, 359 (1979).
187. A.-M. Bonneau and N. Sonenberg, *JBC* **262**, 11134 (1987).
188. W. Rychlik, L. L. Domier, P. R. Gardner, G. M. Hellman and R. E. Rhoads, *PNAS* **84**, 945 (1987).
189. M. Altmann, C. Handschin and H. Trachsel, *MCBiol* **7**, 998 (1987).
190. T. Ishida, M. Katsuta, M. Inoue, Y. Yamagata and K. Tomita, *BBRC* **115**, 849 (1983).
191. S. Fields and G. Winter, *Cell* **28**, 303 (1982).

192. D. T. Paterson, W. C. Merrick and B. Safer, *JBC* **254**, 2509 (1979).
193. M. Goerlach and K. Hilse, *EMBO J.* **5**, 2629 (1986).
194. R. Kaempfer, R. Hollender, W. R. Abrams and R. Israeli, *PNAS* **75**, 209 (1978).
195. R. Kaempfer, R. Hollender, H. Soreq and U. Nudel, *EJB* **94**, 591 (1979).
196. R. Kaempfer, J. Van Emmelo and W. Fiers, *PNAS* **78**, 1542 (1981).
197. R. Perez-Bercoff and R. Kaempfer, *J. Virol.* **41**, 30 (1982).

Physical Monitoring of Meiotic and Mitotic Recombination in Yeast

James E. Haber,
Rhona H. Borts,
Bernadette Connolly,
Michael Lichten,
Norah Rudin, and
Charles I. White

*Rosenstiel Basic Medical Sciences
Research Center and
Department of Biology
Brandeis University
Waltham, Massachusetts 02254*

Progress in Nucleic Acid Research
and Molecular Biology, Vol. 35

The use of polymorphic chromosomal markers to identify products of recombination was first applied in 1931 to demonstrate that genetic crossing-over actually involves an exchange of chromosomal segments (1, 2).* In the past several years, this same principle has been applied to a detailed molecular analysis of recombination in several organisms to determine at a molecular level when and how recombination occurs. The advent of recombinant DNA techniques has made it possible to create very well-defined genetic intervals in which to examine recombination in great detail. Moreover, the ability to follow recombination in "real time," by isolating DNA from cells undergoing recombination, has made it possible to begin to determine the way in which recombination events are initiated, what types of molecular intermediates are generated, and how these intermediates are resolved.

It is not our intention to review here all aspects of recombination, nor to discuss all of the enzymatic activities that appear to play a role in catalyzing efficient recombination. Rather, we focus our attention on the substrates of these enzymes: homologous sequences undergo-

---

* *Nomenclature:* The biochemical analysis of DNA undergoing recombination is inextricably enmeshed 'in a web of genetic nomenclature. For the uninitiated, the distinctions between *LEU2*, *leu2*, and *Leu+* persuade the reader that only an elect few can decipher the geneticist's code. A few guideposts are presented here to help the reader understand the important points.

Genetic nomenclature: In standard yeast genetic nomenclature, each gene is identified by a three-letter name. The names attempt to indicate the function of the gene product or the phenotype of a mutation in that gene. For example, the *FLP* gene of the naturally occurring yeast plasmid, 2μ-DNA, encodes an enzyme that causes the isomerization (flipping) of the 2μ plasmid by promoting recombination between two identical sites in inverted orientation. The *LEU2* gene encodes a protein (3-isopropylmalate dehydrogenase) that catalyzes a step in the biosynthesis of leucine. The wild-type (dominant) variant of that gene is given in capital letters (e.g., *LEU2* or *FLP*); recessive mutations in the gene are designated by lower case (e.g., *leu2* or *flp*). The *phenotype* of the organism (whether it can grow without leucine or not) is given by Leu+ or Leu−.

The mating type of yeast is determined by codominant alleles of the *MAT* locus. Cells of opposite mating type (*MATa* and *MATα*) conjugate to form a *MATa/MATα* diploid that is nonmating and capable of undergoing meiosis. Most haploid strains of yeast are heterothallic, that is they express only one mating type. Homothallic (*HO*) strains are capable of switching from one mating type to the other, resulting in the formation of nonmating diploid cells.

Construction of novel strains: The use of the yeast *Saccharomyces cerevisiae* as an organism to study recombination has benefited from the same powerful genetic techniques that have been applied to the study of gene regulation and cell biology. Yeast can be transformed with autonomously replicating plasmids that carry a DNA segment of interest plus a selectable marker (such as *URA3* to complement a *ura3* mutation on the chromosome and allow the cell to grow without uracil). These plasmids can be stably maintained with a low copy number by inserting into such plasmids a small,

ing gene conversion and crossing-over. In the yeast *Saccharomyces cerevisiae,* recombination events can be induced at such high frequency and with sufficient synchrony that one can hope to isolate intermediate steps in recombination and to test specific predictions of various models of recombination. This review is of necessity a progress report, as the approaches being undertaken are new and the questions under investigation are complex.

Recombination occurs in both meiotic and mitotic cells. In many ways, these recombination events appear quite different. For example, gene conversion events in meiosis are generally accompanied by crossing-over about half of the time (3), while mitotic gene conversions involve exchanges much less often (4). There are also significant differences in gene conversion tract length in meiosis and mitosis. Moreover, from studies on various recombination-defective mutations, it is also clear that there are mutants that specifically block meiosis without having any significant effect on mitotic events, and vice versa (4–6).

This review considers both general recombination events (intragenic and intergenic recombination on both normal and artificial

---

cloned segment from a yeast centromere (*CEN*). In addition, linear restriction fragments of yeast DNA can be transformed into yeast, whereupon they will recombine with, and replace, the homologous DNA sequences; by such "gene replacement" techniques, various *in vitro*-generated mutations can readily be introduced into yeast chromosomes.

Genetic measurements of recombination: If a diploid yeast strain carries two different alleles of the same gene, for example *leu2-K* and *leu2-R*, the cell is Leu⁻. If the two alleles are mutations at two different locations within the gene, wild-type Leu⁺ recombinants can be generated by intragenic recombination. These Leu⁺ recombinants can be detected by plating a large number of cells on an agar plate lacking leucine and scoring the number of colonies able to grow in the absence of that nutrient. Most intragenic recombination events are nonreciprocal, that is, the formation of a wild-type *LEU2* gene on one chromosome is usually not accompanied by the formation of the double mutant (*leu2-K,R*) on the opposite homologous chromosome. Such nonreciprocal exchanges of information are termed *gene conversions.* Gene conversions might occur either by the transfer of a single strand of DNA to form heteroduplex DNA, followed by repair of the mismatched basepair(s), or by filling in of a double-stranded gap in one DNA by copying the region from the intact homologous DNA. Gene conversions are sometimes accompanied by a reciprocal crossover in a flanking region of the chromosome.

Crossing-over in the interval between two genetic markers on the same arm of a chromosome (intergenic recombination) can be detected by determining the linkage of the flanking markers in meiotic segregants. Tetrad analysis is carried out, in which all four products of meiosis are recovered as spores, separated by micromanipulation, allowed to grow into colonies, and then tested by replica plating for various phenotypes such as amino-acid auxotrophy, temperature sensitivity, or antibiotic resistance.

chromosomes) and several well-studied site-specific recombination events (*FLP*-mediated crossing-over in 2μ-DNA, ω conversion in mitochondria, and *MAT* switching).

I. Meiotic Recombination in *Saccharomyces*

Diploid yeast cells can be induced to initiate meiosis and sporulation by transferring cells from nitrogen-containing growth medium to a 1% potassium acetate solution. Sporulation is also inhibited by glucose, so that sporulation efficiency is improved by cultivating vegetative cells in a nonfermentable carbon source, or by allowing glucose-grown cells to adapt to growth on ethanol as the cells reach stationary phase. Compared to a normal 2–3 hour vegetative cell cycle, the completion of meiosis and subsequent spore formation are quite slow, with most strains taking 12–18 hours to produce spores. Moreover, sporulation does not occur with great synchrony. In strains derived from originally wild-type homothallic diploids, such as strains SK1 or Y55, meiosis and sporulation occur more rapidly than in most hybrid laboratory strains; nevertheless, the time to complete meiotic DNA synthesis or other discrete steps in meiosis still covers a period of 2–3 hours (*7–10*). Consequently, our ability to detect short-lived intermediates of recombination is limited.

A. Timing of Meiotic Recombination

As a prelude to more detailed studies of molecular intermediates arising during meiotic recombination, one first needs to define the period in which interesting molecular events will occur. In yeast, one can define a "commitment to meiotic recombination" by removing cells from sporulation medium and plating back to vegetative conditions. Cells committed to recombine will then exhibit meiotic levels of intragenic and intergenic recombination (*11, 12*). The time at which cells become committed to recombination does not necessarily reflect the time at which recombination actually occurs. To establish when crossing-over actually occurs, a strategy was developed (*9*) that allowed the monitoring of recombination in real time, by Southern blot analysis of DNA extracted at intervals during meiosis. For any chromosomal interval flanked by pairs of polymorphic restriction sites, a crossover in the interval yields novel-sized restriction fragments. The particular interval studied is composed primarily of the plasmid pBR322 and the yeast *URA3* and *LEU2* sequences, flanked by a duplication of the mating-type (*MAT*) genes (Fig. 1). *MATa* and *MATα* are codominantly expressed alleles of the mating-type gene; a haploid

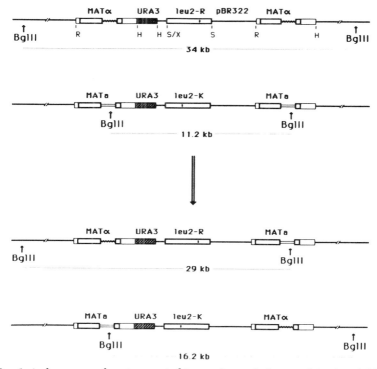

FIG. 1. A chromosomal region created to monitor meiotic recombination. A 11.2-kb nontandem duplication of the mating-type (*MAT*) locus was created by integrative transformation of a pBR322 plasmid containing the 3.5-kb *Eco*RI–*Hin*dIII *MAT* fragment, the 1.1-kb *Hin*dIII *URA3* fragment, and a 2.2-kb *Xho*I–*Sal*I restriction fragment carrying one of two different *leu2* alleles. The diploid contains an a-mating and an α-mating duplication. Crossing-over in this interval results in a tetrad containing two nonmating spores that express both *MAT*a and *MAT*α. Because *MAT*a contains a *Bgl*II site not present in *MAT*α, crossing-over can be detected physically by the appearance of two novel *Bgl*II restriction fragments that are different from the two parental restriction fragments. The presence of the *leu2-K* and *leu2-R* heteroalleles can also be used to monitor the time of appearance of Leu+ recombinants. (Adapted from *10*.)

segregant containing both *MAT*a and *MAT*α exhibits a nonmating phenotype while haploids carrying two copies of MATa or *MAT*α are a- and α-mating, respectively. Thus, a reciprocal exchange in the interval between the flanking *MAT* genes yields a tetrad with one a-, one α-, and two nonmating segregants. The frequency of reciprocal exchange in this interval is quite high; approximately 22% of all tetrads contain an exchange in this 11.2 kb (kilobase) interval. Recombination in this interval (1.4 cM/kb)* is approximately four times more frequent than the average chromosomal level of exchange (0.4 cM/kb) (13), although this is well within the range of normal frequencies of exchange seen in other chromosomal intervals. With such a high frequency one can readily detect recombination at the DNA level.

Because *MATa* contains a *BgI*II site not found in *MATα*, a *BgI*II restriction endonuclease digest of DNA from a [*MATa–MATa*]/ [*MATα–MATα*] diploid yields restriction fragments of 11 and 34 kb, respectively (Fig. 1). Crossing-over in this interval yields two new fragments of 29 and 16 kb, that correspond to the [*MATα–MATa*] and [*MATa–MATα*] segregants, respectively. Because crossing-over occurs in 22% of all tetrads, each of these two recombined DNA restriction fragments accounts for approximately 5.5% of total DNA homologous to a pBR322 probe.

It is possible to detect as little as 0.5% of total hybridized DNA in a well-resolved band; thus, one can readily follow the time course of appearance of recombined DNA in Southern blots of samples taken during meiosis. An example is shown in Fig. 2A, where it is evident that the 16 kb recombined [*MATa–MATα*] band is not present at the beginning of meiosis but increases to approximately 5% of pBR322-homologous DNA by approximately 10 hours. The 29-kb band identifying the reciprocal [MATα–MATa] product can also be seen on shorter exposures of autoradiograms, but is generally not well-enough resolved to be monitored.

We can relate the time of appearance of recombined DNA to other landmark events in meiosis (Fig. 2B). Here, the appearance of the

---

* cM = centiMorgan, a genetic map distance equivalent to 1% meiotic recombination [Eds.].

FIG. 2. (A) A Southern blot of *BgI*II-digested DNA samples taken at intervals after the initiation of meiosis. The blot is probed with ^{32}P-labeled pBR322. The appearance of the 14-kb and a 29-kb restriction fragments, indicative of the completion of crossing-over begins to appear after 6 hours. Two other novel restriction fragments of 13 and 8 kb are also visible. These two minor bands reflect "ectopic" recombination between the 2.2-kb leu2 region within the *MAT* duplication and the *leu2* locus, 100 kb on the opposite of the centromere of the same chromosome. In DNA from populations of germinated spores (lanes A and B), the *MATa–MATα* and *MATα–MATa* restriction fragments are visible, but the bands reflecting ectopic recombination are absent, as expected if such ectopic recombinants are inviable. (B) Time of appearance of the 16.2-kb *BgI*II restriction fragment (■) relative to the time of premeiotic DNA synthesis (●), the time of appearance of Leu2$^+$ recombinants (○), and the time of the first meiotic division (+).

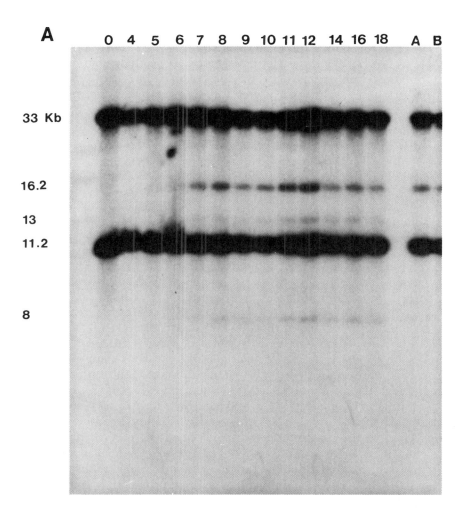

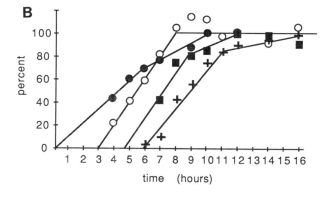

[*MATa–MATα*] *Bgl*II restriction fragment is plotted relative to other landmark events in meiosis. In this construction, the two parental configurations carry two different alleles of the *leu2* gene, so that one can also assess the time at which cells became committed to undergo meiotic levels of intragenic recombination, even when returned to growth medium. A 1–2 hour delay was observed from the time cells became committed to intragenic recombination (Leu$^+$) to the time of appearance of physically recombined DNA in the interval embracing the *leu2* alleles (9). This suggests that there may be a significant delay between the time at which recombination events are initiated (or committed to be initiated) and the time at which actual crossing-over is completed. The notion that a recombination event may take 60 minutes or more to complete is reinforced by recent studies of mitotic recombination (described in Section III).

It must be pointed out that we have not actually measured the physical appearance of the novel restriction fragment produced by gene conversion between *Kpn*I$^-$ and *Eco*RI$^-$ alleles of *leu2*, because the frequency with which these events occur in the *MAT–MAT* interval is too low to be detected by physical means (*14*). It is possible, however, to visualize the appearance of gene conversion events by Southern blots of the same pair of *leu2* alleles at their normal chromosomal location, on the left arm of chromosome III (Fig. 3). Intragenic recombination between *leu2-K* and *leu2-R* yields a Leu$^+$ recombinant. Digestion of genomic DNA with both *Eco*RI and *Kpn*I reveals a 400-bp *Eco*RI$^+$ *Kpn*I$^+$ fragment present only in a Leu$^+$ recombinant). Leu$^+$ recombinants arise at a frequency of approximately 1.3% of all spores, so that only 1.3% of all DNA strands will contain the 400-bp fragment characteristic of this recombinant. This is approximately one-fifth the level of exchanges in the *MAT–MAT* interval; consequently one tends to observe an all-or-none appearance of this recombined DNA (Fig. 3). Nevertheless, the time of appearance of the 400-bp *LEU2* fragment occurs at approximately the same time that reciprocal exchange occurs in the *MAT–MAT* interval (R. H. Borts, M. Lichten and J. E. Haber, unpublished). A more detailed analysis of the relation between gene conversion events and reciprocal exchange could be carried out using restriction site polymorphisms surrounding the *LEU2* locus.

Recently J. Game and R. K. Mortimer (personal communication) extended this approach by examining the timing of crossing-over anywhere along the length of a single chromosome, separating chromosomes by OFAGE* (*15*) to detect changes in chromosome size and

---

* OFAGE = orthogonal field alternating gel electrophoresis.

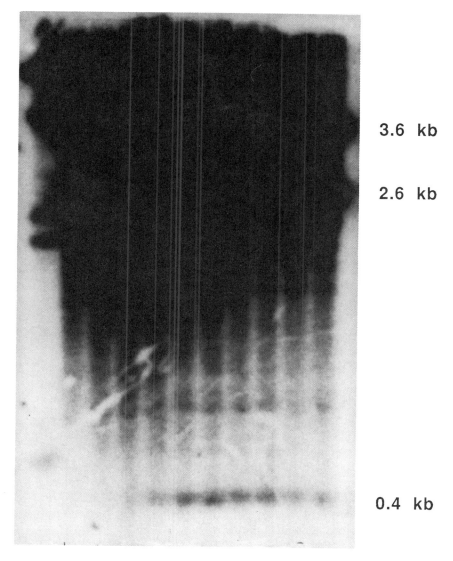

3.6 kb

2.6 kb

0.4 kb

0 6 7 8 9 10 11 12 13 14

hours

FIG. 3. Appearance of a 400-bp EcoRI–KpnI LEU2 fragment arising by gene conversion between leu2-R (EcoRI⁻) and leu2-K (KpnI⁻) heteroalleles. DNA isolated at hourly intervals during meiosis was digested with both EcoRI and Asp-718, a KpnI "isoschizomer." The Southern blot was probed with ³²P-labeled EcoRI–KpnI 400-bp fragment of LEU2. Approximately 1% of LEU2-homologous DNA is visible as the recombinant band, consistent with a 1.3% frequency of LEU2 recombinants among random spores.

structure. Meiotic recombination between a haploid-viable ring chromosome III and a normal linear chromosome frequently generates linear dicentric tandem duplications of chromosome III (16, 17). Using OFAGE, one can examine whole chromosomes extracted from cells undergoing meiosis. Ring chromosomes fail to enter OFAGE gels, and linear dicentric chromosomes resulting from a crossing-over between the ring and rod can readily be detected as a novel band of approximately twice the size of a normal chromosome III. DNA corresponding to three times the normal chromosome III length that may have arisen by three-strand multiple crossings-over have also been seen. Using this approach, one is not limited to examining specific regions bounded by pairs of restriction endonuclease polymorphisms. Moreover, by using diploids carrying two circular chromosomes, one can also look for linear derivatives of these ring chromosomes that would be expected to appear if recombination is frequently initiated by double-strand breaks.

B. Physical Detection of Recombination between Short, Homologous Regions at Distant Chromosomal Locations (Ectopic Recombination)

The ability to detect recombination directly, without analysis of viable progeny, has led to the discovery that yeast cells exhibit very high levels of "ectopic" recombination between homologous regions at different chromosomal locations. While following the appearance of reciprocally recombined products in the [MAT–URA3–leu2–MAT] interval, two other, less abundant novel restriction fragments of approximately 13 and 8 kb appearing at the same time were noted (9) (Fig. 2B). These fragments were products of reciprocal exchange between the 2.2-kb leu2 fragment inserted in the MAT–MAT region and the normally resident LEU2 locus, about 100 kb away on the opposite side of the chromosome III centromere.

The frequency with which these "ectopic" recombinants appear is approximately 10% of the level of reciprocal exchange within the MAT–MAT interval. Given that the size of the recombining leu2 regions is 2.2 kb compared to 11.2 kb for the entire [MAT–MAT] interval, these ectopic recombinants appear to occur at nearly the same frequency per kb of homology as the normal (allelic) recombination events. This is a striking result, suggesting that, at least in a lower eukaryote like yeast (with little heterochromatic or repeated DNA), pairing and recombination between homologous sequences are nearly as probable between short homologous segments at different chromosomal locations as they are between the same segments embedded in continuous homology on two homologous chromosomes.

Reciprocal exchanges between *leu2* and [*MAT–leu2–MAT*] result in deficiency circular or dicentric chromosomes that are not viable; consequently we would not have found evidence for such high-frequency ectopic recombination by standard genetic analysis of meiotic progeny. Indeed, when sporulated cultures containing the restriction fragments indicative of crossing-over between dispersed copies of *leu2* are allowed to germinate and grow, one discovers that the viable progeny do not contain the restriction fragments indicative of ectopic crossing-over (Fig. 2B).

1. Position Effects on Allelic Recombination

These results have prompted a more detailed examination of ectopic recombination using a combination of genetic and physical analysis of meiotic recombination (*14*). We inserted the same pair of *leu2* alleles in five different chromosomal locations and examined both *allelic* (both alleles at the same chromosomal location) and ectopic gene conversions and their associated crossings-over. These experiments showed that there are substantial position effects on allelic recombination, so that Leu$^+$ recombinants when the *leu2-K* and *leu2-R* alleles are at the normal *leu2* locus are over 40 times more frequent than when these alleles are located at *HML* (Fig. 4). These results argue that sequences outside the 7.8-kb construct that contains the *leu2* alleles profoundly influence the frequency with which the *leu2* sequences are able to undergo recombination. Thus, some chromosomal regions are intrinsically "hot" while others are not.

2. Ectopic Recombination Frequencies

When ectopic recombination was examined between the same two *leu2* alleles inserted in different locations, in some cases ectopic events were found to occur more frequently than when both alleles were at allelic locations (*14*) (Fig. 4). As a general rule, the locus that shows the highest level of allelic recombination is the *recipient* in an ectopic interaction (i.e., becomes Leu$^+$). In two instances, we could also ask how often ectopic interactions were accompanied by crossing-over. Because there are no essential genes between *his4* and *leu2*, all of the Leu$^+$ recombinants between *his4* :: *leu2-R* and *leu2-K* are viable; indeed about 50% of these events are accompanied by crossing-over. When one of the interacting alleles is on chromosome III and the other is inserted at *URA3*, on chromosome V, about 22% of these ectopic events between nonhomologous chromosomes are

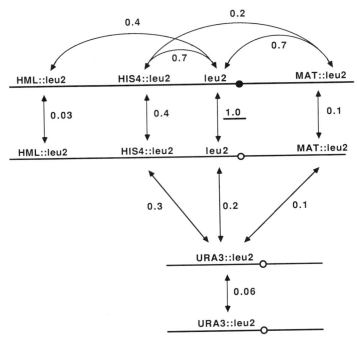

Fig. 4. Relative frequencies of meiotic allelic and ectopic recombination of the same pair of *leu2* heteroalleles inserted at five different chromosomal locations. *Allelic recombination* is indicated by vertical arrows between the same sites on homologous chromosomes. Plasmids containing the *leu2-K* and *leu2-R* alleles were integrated at four different chromosomal locations; in each diploid where recombination was tested at a novel location, the normal *leu2* locus contained the *leu2-K,R* double mutant. As a control, the same pair of alleles was also introduced at *leu2* without pBR322 sequences. The frequency of Leu+ spores from recombination at the normal *leu2* locus was 1.3 × 10⁻²; this frequency has been normalized to a value of 1.0. *Ectopic recombination* is shown by arrows between two different chromosomal locations. A series of diploids were constructed, with *leu-K* at one location and an integrated *leu2-R* allele at another location. In all cases involving the normal *leu2* locus, *leu2* contained the *leu2-K* allele. The frequency of Leu+ random spores was determined for each case illustrated; all are normalized to the allelic frequency at the normal *leu2* locus. All of the Leu+ conversions between *leu2-K* and *his4* :: *leu2-R* are viable; 50% of the events were accompanied by crossing-over. Other ectopic recombinations (e.g., *leu2-K* with *MAT* :: *leu2-R* or *HML* :: *leu2-R*) have not been corrected for inviability of some recombinants. (HML = homothallism donor, left arm of chromosome III.) (Summary of data in *14*.)

accompanied by crossing-over. These results are true for other ectopic interactions; similar conclusions have been drawn from studies of ectopic recombination between the yeast *URA3* gene and a cloned *ura3* segment inserted at two other chromosomal locations (*18, 19*).

3. CONSTRAINTS ON CROSSING-OVER

We have used the term **ectopic** recombination to distinguish these events from "unequal" exchange events between tandemly duplicated DNA sequences. One interesting observation concerning unequal recombination events is that gene conversions between two *his4* alleles in tandem duplication on the same chromatid are much less frequently associated with an exchange of flanking markers than when the interacting alleles are on homologous chromosomes (*20*). These results showed a significant constraint on *crossing-over* (but not on the total frequency of His$^+$ gene conversions) when the interactions are intrachromosomal or even when they involve unequal pairing between sister chromatids. These results extended and supported previous observations (*21, 22*) that intrachromosomal gene conversions are rarely accompanied by exchange.

We have asked if this is also true with ectopic interactions between *leu2* regions, and find that this constraint on crossing-over associated with gene conversion is markedly dependent on the distance between the two interacting alleles (M. Lichten and J. E. Haber, unpublished). When the markers are inserted 20 kb apart (when *leu2-K* is inserted at *HIS4* and *leu2-R* is at its normal chromosomal location), we confirmed the earlier result (*20*) for duplicated *his4* markers approximately 20 kb apart. However, when the interacting alleles are 100 kb apart, there is no apparent constraint on crossing-over. Because recombination events between *leu2* and *MAT* :: *leu2* are lethal, we approached this experiment by looking again for novel restriction fragments created by crossing-over. Taking advantage of restriction site polymorphisms distal to the *leu2* locus, we distinguished recombination events between [*MAT–leu2–MAT*] and the homologous *leu2* region on the same or opposite chromosome (Fig. 5A). The Southern blot (Fig. 5B) demonstrates that ectopic crossing-over occurs as frequently between *leu2* regions on the same chromosome and those on opposite chromosomes. One possible explanation for this difference between markers 20 kb apart (where the intrachromosomal constraint is seen) and 100 kb apart (where there is no apparent constraint) is that *other* normal exchange events, between homologous chromosomes, in the interval between the two *leu2* segments, effectively place the two regions on different chromosomes. Thus a crossing-over in the region between *MAT* and *LEU2* (which occurs about 40% of the time) would place the *MAT* :: *leu2-K* allele on the chromosome opposite *leu2-R*. If this interpretation is correct, we would expect most crossings-over between alleles located on the same chromosome to be accompanied by another crossing-over event in the interval between them. If this conclu-

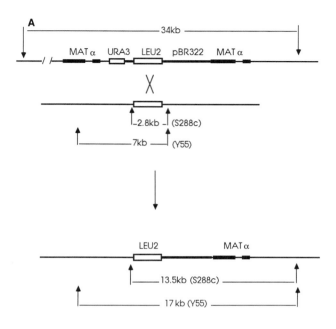

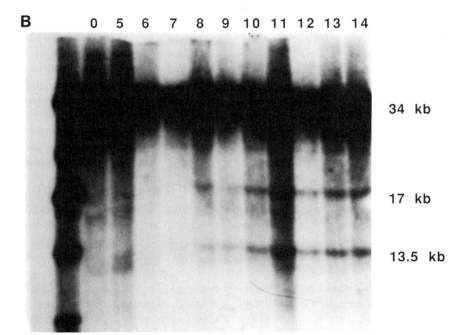

sion is correct, it also suggests that ectopic crossing-over occurs at the same time as, or later than, normal meiotic crossing-over; otherwise, how could the interacting *leu2* regions "know" that they were on different chromosomes and cross over? Although our ability to follow the kinetics of ectopic recombination is limited by the lower frequency of these events, we note that the timing experiments (9) did not distinguish between the time of appearance of ectopic exchange events and the time of crossings-over in the [*MAT–MAT*] interval.

C. Characterization of Meiotic Mutants by Physical Analysis of DNA

In *Saccharomyces* there are many meiotic-defective mutations that fail to produce viable progeny (reviewed in 5). It is difficult to assess at what stage of meiosis these mutations are blocked, both because there are no meiotic progeny and because many of these mutants lead to inviability even of cells returned to vegetative growth. Recently, several complementary approaches have emerged to characterize the stage at which these mutations affect meiosis and recombination.

One approach (23–25) takes advantage of a mutation (*spo13*) that bypasses the first meiotic division to produce two diploid spores that have essentially undergone a mitotic division. Using *spo13* strains, it has been possible to demonstrate that both *rad50* and *spo11* are mutations that completely prevent gene conversion and crossing-over between homologous chromosomes. Recombination-deficient mutants of this sort experience massive levels of meiotic nondisjunction and yield nearly all inviable haploid progeny; however, in *spo13* diploids one recovers diploid spores with a parental configuration of markers. In contrast, *spo13* diploids carrying *rad52* or *rad57* fail to yield viable spores, suggesting that these mutations are blocked at some stage in meiosis where intermediates of recombination cannot be properly repaired or resolved. The fact that *spo13 rad50 rad52* diploids yield viable progeny argues that *rad50* mutants block cells prior to the point

---

FIG. 5. Physical detection of intrachromosomal and interchromosomal ectopic recombination. (A) Interchromosomal and intrachromosomal crossing-over between *MAT : : leu2* and a normal *leu2* locus can be distinguished by *BglII* restriction site differences between the *leu2* region on the same chromosome and the opposite chromosome. In the diploid used, the *MAT : : leu2* region was constructed in the Y55 background and then crossed to a strain carrying a *leu2* locus derived from strain S288c. (B) A Southern blot of *BglII*-digested DNA taken at intervals from a synchronously sporulating culture, probed with ^{32}P-labeled pBR322. Two ectopic recombinant bands of 17 kb and 13.5 kb appeared after 8 hours. The two bands are of approximately equal intensity.

where *RAD52* function is necessary. Thus, some meiotic mutants can be ordered with respect to each other.

A complementary approach is to look directly at the DNA of cells carrying meiotic mutants. Neutral and alkaline sucrose gradient sedimentations, to assess the average size of DNA during meiosis, indicate that *rad52* diploids accumulate a significantly large number of single-strand breaks or gaps during meiosis, but do not accumulate double-strand lesions (26). Similarly, *rad57* cells accumulate single-strand breaks, while *rad50* cells appear normal (M. Resnick, personal communication). All of these results are consistent with the phenotypes of *spo13 rad50* and *spo13 rad52* (or *rad57*) mutants.

A third strategy is to examine the effects of meiotic-defective mutants by physical monitoring of crossing-over. We have examined the effects of these mutants on recombination in the [*MAT–MAT*] interval, to ask if some meiotic-defective mutants can actually initiate or complete exchange events (even if the progeny are inviable). Given that the average yeast cell undergoes perhaps 100 crossings-over per meiosis (27, 28), only a small fraction of these events would have to fail in order to abolish spore viability. Physical monitoring of exchanges allows us to determine if these mutants are in fact unable to complete recombination. Five meiotic-defective mutants in diploids containing the [*MAT–MAT*] region were examined (10). Consistent with the results of *spo13* analysis and physical analysis of DNA, diploids homozygous for either *rad50* or *spo11* failed to yield any evidence of a recombined [*MATa–MATα*] restriction fragment (Fig. 6A). In contrast, we were surprised to discover that diploids homozygous for *rad52* exhibited 30% of the wild-type level of crossing-over (Fig. 6B). Furthermore, both *rad57* and *rad6* diploids displayed nearly wild-type levels. Thus, despite the fact that none of these three *rad* mutants permit the recovery of viable haploid progeny,* it is clear that they are not completely defective in the production of physically recombined DNA. These experiments do not establish the nature of the lethal defects of the *rad* mutants. It is possible that a fraction of recombination events is aberrant, leading, for example, to unrepaired

---

* These studies also illustrate the necessity of carrying out experiments in a defined genetic background. While Borts *et al.* (10) failed to recover viable meiotic progeny from *rad52* diploids, Resnick *et al.* (8) did recover viable recombinant progeny when cells were removed from sporulation medium and grown on synthetic medium. However, on rich media (yeast extract and peptone), there were no viable intragenic recombinants. Presumably the difference in these experiments reflects some difference in strain background; possibly the Y55 strain background does not permit repair of DNA in *rad52* cells that strain SK1 can carry out, at least on nutrient-poor medium.

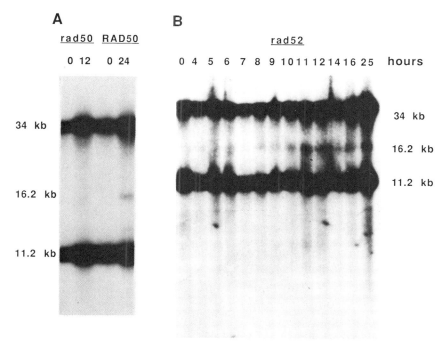

FIG. 6. Physical monitoring of crossing-over in the 9-kb *MAT–URA3*–pBR322–*MAT* interval in meiotic-defective mutants. (A) Recombination in a *rad50* diploid (−), compared to a *RAD50* (+) strain. DNA samples were collected at 0 and 12 or 24 hours. No 14-kb recombinant band was detected in the mutant strain. (B) Recombination in a *rad52* diploid. DNA was isolated at hourly intervals during meiosis. The 14-kb band indicative of crossing-over appears after 8 hours and accumulates to a level approximately 30% of the wild-type level. (Adapted from *10*.)

double-strand breaks that are lethal. Such a conclusion is consistent with our finding that mitotic intragenic recombination in *rad52* diploids frequently results in a crossing-over, with the coincident loss of one of the two participating chromatids (29).

Further work must be undertaken to establish the molecular defects of various meiotic-defective mutants. It is possible, for example, that although one detects physically recombined molecules on native agarose gels, a large fraction of these exchange events contains single-strand breaks or gaps that would only be detected by running denaturing gels. It is also possible that these mutations accumulate other, more complex intermediates of recombination that cannot be detected on these gels because of the other, more strongly hybridizing bands.

Alternative approaches to detect such intermediates will be discussed below (Section I,D,3).

D. Detection of Intermediates of Meiotic Recombination

The ultimate object of physical studies of meiotic recombination is to establish the molecular events that occur from the initiation to the resolution of gene conversion and exchange events. Studies of fungal recombination have revealed several phenomena that any molecular mechanism of recombination must fulfill, including heteroduplex DNA formation (as evidenced by post-meiotic segregation), the polarity of gene conversion events, and the positions of associated crossings-over. Detailed studies of these phenomena are just beginning in several laboratories, but one can already see some promising results from their various approaches.

1. INITIATION OF RECOMBINATION: MEIOTIC "HOT SPOTS"

A wealth of genetic data demonstrates that meiotic recombination events do not occur with equal frequency along a chromosome. Beyond the reduction of crossing-over seen near the centromere (30), some chromosomal regions exhibit much higher levels of exchange than others, even when the same pairs of alleles are inserted in different locations used to measure intragenic recombination (14). Gene conversion studies within a single gene also provide strong evidence that recombination events often occur more frequently at one end of a gene than the other. Such polarity of gene conversion has been seen for arg4 (31), his1 (32), his2 (R. Malone, personal communication), his4 (R. H. Borts and J. E. Haber, unpublished), and others. In every case where the direction of transcription has been established, the 5' end of the gene is the high conversion end. Various molecular models have interpreted polarity of gene conversion as putative evidence that the initiation of the transfer of genetic information [either by the creation of a single-strand nick (33) or a double-strand break (34)] occurs outside the gene, at the high conversion end. The sites at which recombination is initiated may be analogous to the Chi sequence (5'-GCTGGTGG-3') which serves as a "hot spot" for recombination in E. coli and phage λ (35–38).

Recently several labs have identified regions of DNA adjacent to several genes exhibiting high levels of gene conversion. For example, deletion of a 200-bp region 5' to the ARG4 gene appears to reduce meiotic gene conversion of arg4 alleles by a factor of approximately 4 (A. Nicolas, D. Trico, N. Shultes and J. Szostak, personal communication). This region overlaps the promoter region of ARG4 and raises the question if there is a correlation between the high gene conversion end of a gene and the chromatin structure or other features of promoter regions.

In another yeast, *Schizosaccharomyces pombe*, A. S. Ponticelli, E. Sena and G. F. Smith (personal communication) have carried out the molecular characterization of the M26 allele of the *ade6* gene that had been shown (39) to be a "hot spot" for recombination. To date, it has not been possible to carry out a time-course analysis of meiotic recombination in *S. pombe*, because diploid cells are unstable and cannot normally be synchronized as can *S. cerevisiae*. However, construction of a stable diploid that can be thermally induced to enter meiosis has now been constructed (A. S. Ponticelli, personal communication), so that a search for single-strand nicks or double-strand breaks within or adjacent to these DNA sequences may now be possible. One must remember, however, that M26 or other such sites important for stimulating recombination might be involved in the resolution, rather than initiation, of meiotic recombination (an issue raised by Stahl, 40). Alternatively, these hot spots may stimulate recombination in ways that do not lead to a (single-strand) nick or a (double-strand) cut at one site. One possibility is that these sites are analogous to recognition sites for type-I restriction endonucleases, that then cleave DNA at some (more or less random) distance from the recognition site. Were this the case, one might not see cleavage of a specific DNA fragment (but one might see conversion of a circular plasmid carrying the hot spot into a linear molecule). Alternatively, recombination may be stimulated by exchange of DNA strands in a 4-stranded DNA structure (*41, 42*) by topoisomerases that do not leave a long-lived nicked or cut substrate.

It should also be possible to follow specific recombination and DNA repair events in meiosis initiated by a specific double-strand break. The site-specific *HO* endonuclease that initiates mitotic switching of the yeast mating-type genes (Section III) can also be used to induce recombination in meiotic cells (*43*). Thus, meiotic recombination can be initiated by double-strand breaks induced by a galactose-inducible *HO* gene. A small restriction fragment of the *MAT* locus can be inserted in any other region to become a "hot spot" for meiotic gene conversion (*43*). These genetic experiments demonstrated that approximately half of the gene conversion events are accompanied by exchange. It would be most interesting to assess the kinetics of these events by physical monitoring, especially since *MAT* switching in mitotic cells is a surprisingly slow process, requiring an hour from the time HO endonuclease cleaves *MAT* to the time switching is complete (*90*). It is possible that one or more steps that are rate-limiting in mitotic switching of *MAT* would be much more rapid in meiotic cells, where some rate-limiting recombination or DNA repair enzyme might already be present at much higher levels.

2. FORMATION OF HETERODUPLEX DNA

Exchanges of single strands of DNA may result in the formation of heteroduplex DNA containing mismatched base pairs. When such mismatches are not repaired, they are detected as postmeiotic segregation (PMS) events. Mismatch repair leads either to gene conversion or to restoration (which can sometimes be inferred from the presence of an unconverted marker lying between two or more gene converted markers) (*44*). It does not follow, however, that loci with a high level of gene conversion involve the frequent formation of heteroduplex DNA; the double-strand break repair model (*34*) postulates that many gene conversion events result from "gap repair" in which heteroduplex DNA is confined to small regions adjacent to large converted regions. Thus, it is of great interest to determine whether loci with high levels of gene conversion also contain long stretches of heteroduplex DNA (a result that would support some models, e.g., *33*).

One approach to detection of heteroduplex DNA has been to look for restriction fragments in which one strand contains a large (single-stranded) heterology. This technique was first applied (*45*) to demonstrate the formation of heteroduplex DNA in phage λ. More recently, a similar approach to examine heteroduplex DNA involving the *ade8-18* locus of *S. cerevisiae* has been applied (A. Plessis, J. H. White and S. Fogel, personal communication). The *ade8-18* allele exhibits very high levels of postmeiotic segregation. DNA sequence analysis revealed that this mutation is actually a 38 base-pair deletion that creates a novel *Bss*HI restriction site while deleting a *Xho*I site. Thus, while homoduplex *ADE8* DNA would be cut by *Xho*I and *ade8-18* DNA would be cut by *Bss*HI, a heteroduplex (*ADE8 : ade8-18*) should not be cut by either enzyme. DNA taken from spores of a strain heterozygous for *ade8-18/ADE8* yields a band consistent with the formation of heteroduplex DNA, while DNA from strains homozygous for *ade8-18* or *ADE8* do not accumulate this band (Plessis *et al.*, personal communication).

A time-course analysis of DNA taken during meiosis of *ade8-18/ADE8* should demonstrate the time at which heteroduplex DNA is formed; however, because heteroduplex DNA at this locus must mostly be unrepaired, one cannot ask when mismatch repair of such a heteroduplex takes place. Not all gene conversion events involving large heterologies yield a high level of PMS (3, 46, and S. Fogel, personal communication). In fact, *ade8-18* seems to be an exception. Thus, it may be possible to use the same approach with other deletions or insertions to look for unique restriction fragments containing heteroduplex DNA and follow the appearance and subsequent disappearance of heteroduplex DNA.

An alternative approach is to monitor heteroduplexes involving only very small mismatches or heterologies. The basis of this approach has been developed (47). Small DNA fragments containing a single mismatched base pair migrate more slowly on high temperature, denaturing gradient polyacrylamide gels (47). The mismatched base pair lowers the melting temperature of the DNA fragment (which is reflected by denaturation at a lower concentration of urea). Thus, one can identify a region of DNA containing a mismatch; by extension, one should be able to determine when such mismatched DNA is present during meiosis.

To follow the kinetics of formation of heteroduplex DNA and its repair, one wishes to examine DNA for a locus that shows high levels of gene conversion but a low level of PMS. Many loci in *Saccharomyces* fulfill this requirement; for example, restriction site mutations in both the *leu2* and *his4* genes exhibit gene conversion frequencies (both 3 : 1 and 1 : 3) as high as 15% (*13*; R. H. Borts, unpublished), with PMS frequencies of much less than 1%. A first step will be to determine how often a region is included in a heteroduplex when subsequent mismatch repair events are blocked. This should be accomplished with mutations such as *pms1* (*48*), which leads to the appearance of a high level of PMS and a reduction in gene conversions. The maximum level of heteroduplex DNA one can expect in the region can be assessed by constructing diploids homozygous for the *pms1* mutation and extracting DNA late in meiosis. If most gene conversion arises from heteroduplex DNA rather than from double-strand gap repair, one would expect to detect as much as 6% of the DNA fragment covering one of these mutations in heteroduplex. A failure to see a significant level of heteroduplex in a *pms1* strain showing genetically a high level of PMS might indicate that the *pms1* mutation blocked DNA repair at some intermediate step that led to a more labile heteroduplex-containing structure.

If heteroduplex DNA is readily detected in a *pms1* diploid, a failure to see heteroduplex accumulate to any appreciable extent during a time-course with a wild-type strain would probably indicate that the half-life of the heteroduplex is too short, relative to the synchrony of the meiosis. By these approaches it should be possible to establish the kinetics of the metabolism of heteroduplex DNA.

3. FORMATION AND RESOLUTION OF BRANCHED STRUCTURES ARISING FROM RECOMBINATION

Strand invasion and isomerization of interacting DNA molecules lead to the formation of multistranded, or branched, structures. The most often discussed of these structures was proposed by Holliday (49). Direct electron micrographic evidence for these symmetrical structures was first obtained in yeast (50) in the examination of intrachromosomal recombination between two homologous inverted repeated regions within 2μ plasmid DNA molecules extracted during meiosis. Normally, during isolation of branched, restriction-digested molecules, Holliday structures would be expected to be highly unstable and be lost by branch migration, whereby the position of the crossed strands moves toward the ends of the DNA fragments until the structure falls apart into two unconnected double-stranded molecules. In 2μ-DNA, however, the inverted, homologous regions are flanked by two nonhomologous loops, such that $EcoRI$-digested 2μ-DNA containing a Holliday structure gave rise to a Chi (χ) structure that contained four nonhomologous arms. Approximately 0.1% of supercoiled 2μ-DNA isolated from the pachytene stage of meiosis migrated as Chi structures that were subsequently visualized by electron microscopy.

It appears that this approach can be extended to answer a variety of questions. The time-course of Holliday structure formation and resolution could be assessed, as could the effect of various meiotic mutants. One problem in using 2μ-DNA is that it encodes an enzyme, designated FLP, that catalyzes a site-specific isomerization of 2μ-DNA by recombination between the inverted repeated segments (51, 52). It is unlikely that the crossovers seen by Bell and Byers (50) reflected FLP activity (for example, no Chi structures were seen in mitotic cells), but recent advances in studying FLP-mediated recombination could be incorporated into future experimental design (see Section IV,A). Cells carrying a mutation in the FLP gene or mutations in the FLP recognition site are unable to carry out this recombination and are stabilized in one isomeric form. Thus all of the recombination one sees in meiosis would be by homologous meiotic recombination. Moreover, using Southern blots of total genomic DNA rather than first isolating supercoiled 2μ-DNA might increase the recovery of these branched structures, as most DNA might not be supercoiled at these moments during recombination.

These approaches could also be extended to study recombination of other DNA sequences, even in the genome. For example, ectopic recombination should yield Chi structures flanked by nonhomologous segments that would prevent branch migration. Beyond asking how long-lived these structures appear to be and when they appear relative to other events in recombination, one might be able to use this approach to ask more detailed questions about the relation of Holliday structures to crossing-over. As we noted earlier (Section I,B), ectopic sister-strand (intrachromosomal) gene conversions occur about as often as interchromosomal events, but crossovers accompanying gene conversion occur much more often when the sequences are on different homologues. It would be of profound interest to ask if gene conversions that were generally resolved without crossing-over nevertheless stemmed from Holliday structure intermediates. The relative abundance of diagnostic Chi structures from intrachromosomal and interchromosomal ectopic recombinations might answer that question.

An alternative approach to examine branched intermediates of recombination would be to use DNA cross-linking agents such as psoralen to "freeze" such intermediates of recombination. This approach has been used to identify both single and double Holliday structures in DNA extracted at the pachytene stage (50). Cross-linking offers the advantage that one can look at structures formed between completely homologous regions without loss of the structures by branch migration; it has the disadvantage that one examines randomly selected structures rather than repeated events within one known DNA segment.

Bell and Byers (50) also explored the use of two-dimensional gel electrophoresis to identify branched DNA structures arising by either DNA replication or recombination. Figure 7, provided by E. Sena from her study of replication and recombination in yeast mitochondrial DNA, illustrates the resolution achieved by this method. Branched structures, both χ and Y-forms migrate "off the diagonal." To date this type of analysis has been carried out with yeast mitochondrial DNA stabilized by psoralen cross-linking, and on replication intermediates of yeast DNA containing an origin of replication (ARS) (91, 92), but the same approach could be taken with yeast DNA from cells undergoing meiosis. This approach may be especially valuable to look for asymmetric structures such as strand invasion products envisioned by the Meselson-Radding model (33).

Once conditions have been established to detect the formation and

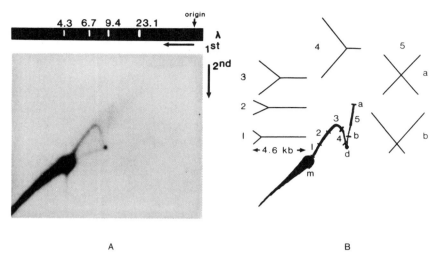

A   B

FIG. 7. Two-dimensional gel analysis of branched DNA structures arising by recombination between mitochondrial DNA molecules (A). Mitochondrial DNA was cleaved with the restriction enzyme HhaI, separated by two-dimensional gel electrophoresis, and probed with ³²P-labeled homologous DNA. The branched structures diagrammed in (B) were confirmed by electron microscopy. The spots labeled "m" and "d" are linear molecules of either monomer (4.6-kb) or dimer (9.2-kb) size. Data provided by Dr. Elissa Sena (unpublished).

loss of branched intermediate structures, these methods can also be applied to the analysis of mutations that may lack the ability to resolve Holliday structure intermediates. Mutations blocked late in recombination, such as *rad52* and *rad57* (*10*), or other mutants such as those that alter the proportion of conversion events with and without exchange (*6*, and R. E. Esposito, personal communication), may be interesting to test for the accumulation of χ structures. Several labs have recently identified a cruciform-cleaving activity in yeast that may be involved in cleaving Holliday junctions. "Reverse genetics" [purifying the protein, making an antibody, finding a cloned gene segment that contains an epitope recognized by the antibody (*53*)] should lead to the isolation of a gene encoding a Holliday-junction-cutting enzyme. *In vitro* mutagenesis and "gene replacement" (*54, 55*) would then allow testing of mutants in this function.

E. Studies of Gene Conversion and Meiotic Recombination in a Small Interval

Following meiotic recombination in real time depends on the existence (or creation) of novel restriction sites in a chromosomal region that frequently undergoes meiotic crossing-over. With the advent of gene-replacement techniques (55, 56) it is now possible to create novel markers in regions containing no expressed genes. The introduction of these markers also allows one to study the consequences of recombination in a very well-defined region.

Recently two groups have created a series of restriction site ablations or linker insertions spaced along a chromosomal region in order to establish (1) where crossing-over has occurred, and (2) how often such exchange events are accompanied by gene conversion. Borts and Haber (57) examined exchanges in the 9-kb [MAT–URA3-pBR322–MAT] interval where they previously studied the timing of recombination. L. S. Symington and T. D. Petes (personal communication) focused their attention on events in the 25-kb interval between LEU2 and the centromere of chromosome III (CEN3). Both found that a high proportion (50–60%) of events detected as crossing-over also involves gene conversion of one or more marker(s) in the interval. This is clearly a minimum estimate, as some of the restriction site markers were more than 1.5 kb apart, so that some conversion events were undoubtedly missed. Previous classical genetic experiments (32, 58) had approached this question from the other end: among tetrads containing a gene conversion approximately half were associated with crossing-over. Thus, the correlation between crossing-over and gene conversion holds in both directions; this suggests there is not a large class of crossover events that occur by some other mechanism that occurs without gene conversion of extensive regions.

1. A SURPRISE: MULTIPLE HETEROLOGIES ALTER THE TYPES OF RECOMBINATION EVENTS THAT OCCUR

The introduction of 9 heterologies across the 9-kb [MAT–MAT] interval (Fig. 8) had a profound effect on crossing-over (54). In the absence of these heterologies, 22% of the tetrads contained a crossover; when the heterologies were present this number dropped to about 11%. The loss of exchange events cannot be attributed to the destruction of a particular "hot spot" by one of the restriction site changes, as diploids homozygous for either of the two sets of modifications shown in Fig. 8 also recombine in 22% of all tetrads.

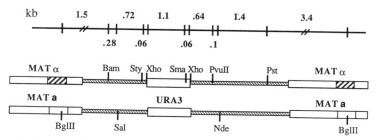

FIG. 8. Positions of nine restriction site mutations into the *MAT–MAT* interval to monitor gene conversion associated with crossing-over. The *PstI⁻* mutation is a single base-pair substitution; the remaining mutations were 4-bp insertions created by filling in various restriction sites. (Adapted from 57.)

The reductions in exchange events were in fact not due to a reduction in recombination within the interval; rather, there were significant increases in events that occurred only infrequently without the heterologies. One set of events was gene conversions (with and without exchange) of one of the flanking *MAT* regions, yielding a tetrad with only one nonmating segregant. These events were associated with unusually long tracts of gene conversion (57). The second set of aberrant events was apparent intrachromosomal recombination events between the two flanking homologous *MAT* regions, yielding a tetrad with one segregant that lacked *URA3* and pBR322. These two exceptional events increased from about 2% in the strains homozygous for the inserted markers to 11% in strains heterozygous for the 9 markers.

The increase in these unusual events and the loss of simple crossovers have been interpreted (57) as evidence that mismatch repair of heteroduplex DNA (including one or more of the restriction site ablations) frequently results in a second, repair-induced recombination event. This repair-induced recombination event is postulated to result from a double-strand break, resulting from the excision of one or more mismatches, as suggested by Hastings (44) (Fig. 9). From other work

FIG. 9. Consequences of repair-induced recombination resulting from mismatch repair of heteroduplex DNA during meiosis. In the model illustrated, the primary reciprocal recombination event involved the formation of a long region of heteroduplex DNA (A). Subsequently, the convergence of two independent repair events leads to the formation of a double-strand break or gap (B), as suggested by Hastings (44). This gap may be enlarged. The broken chromatid can be repaired with either a sister (C) or nonsister (D) chromatid as a template. If a sister chromatid was used as a template for repair of the double-strand break (C), sites initially included in heteroduplex DNA might be restored to their parental configuration. If a nonsister chromatid was involved in double-strand gap repair (D), one may recover a tetrad in which one of the flanking

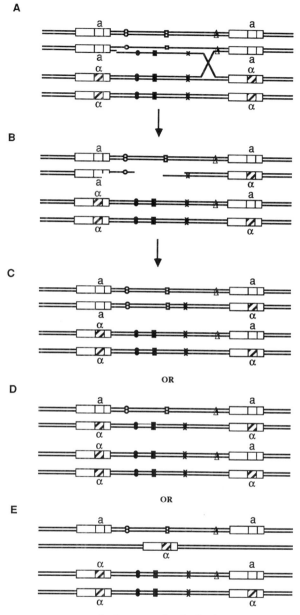

MAT regions was gene converted. Alternatively, the broken chromatid can be repaired by an intrachromosomal recombination event involving flanking regions of homology (in this case, the *MAT* regions), to yield one segregant that has lost the plasmid sequences (E). These novel classes of tetrads are found frequently in diploids carrying multiple heterozygosities in the *MAT–URA3*–pBR333–*MAT* interval. In the absence of flanking regions of homology, repair-induced recombination may be inferred from tetrads in which three DNA strands appear to be involved in a gene conversion event (57; see also Fig. 9.)(Adapted from 57. Copyright 1987 by the AAAS.)

in our laboratory on mating-type switching (see Section III,D,1), the introduction of a double-strand break between two regions of homology very frequently results in repair of this event by recombination between the two flanking regions, with the loss of all of the intervening sequences. In the meiotic case, this would result in $MAT \times MAT$ recombination with loss of pBR322 and $URA3$.

Another consequence of the second, repair-induced recombination event is that it might involve a third chromatid that had not participated in the original strand-exchange. Indeed, about 15% of the events we have analyzed give evidence of three strands participating in what initially looked like a simple exchange event.

Thus, we are confronted with what, at least in our laboratory, we term the Borts Uncertainty Principle: to monitor recombination within an interval one must introduce heterologies, but the heterologies perturb the event one wishes to study.

2. CONVERSION TRACT LENGTH

Despite the problem that inserting markers perturbs the measurement, one can look at the association of gene conversion in those tetrads that appear to have a simple crossing-over between two strands. Among these events, we find that about 60% have a detectable conversion of one or more marker(s) adjacent to the point of crossing-over. This is obviously an underestimate, as some conversion tracts, even some greater than 1.5 kb, may lie between two restriction site markers. The average conversion tract length among 29 tetrads proved to be 1.5 ± 1.2 kb, which is consistent with more classical genetic observations that gene conversions generally do not extend beyond one gene.

A more recent extension of this approach has allowed us to address another long-standing question, namely, are conversion tract lengths different in those tetrads where there is an associated crossing-over from those in which conversion was not exchange-associated (59, 60)? R. H. Borts and J. E. Haber (unpublished) have constructed similar regions, with fewer heterologies but also heterozygous for $URA3/$ $ura3:Nco^-$ (Fig. 10). With fewer heterologies, the frequency of crossover tetrads is restored to 22%. Gene conversions of $URA3$ (both 3:1 and 1:3 for Ura$^+$) arise in 9.5% of all tetrads. Approximately 60% of all conversions were associated with crossing-over. By measuring coconversions of the flanking SalI, XhoI, SmaI, and NdeI sites, we find no significant difference in conversion tract length among $URA3$ convertants with and without an associated exchange.

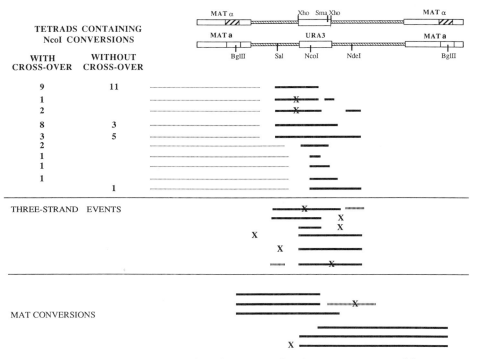

FIG. 10. Gene conversion tract lengths associated with gene conversion of the NcoI mutation within the URA3 gene. In this experiment, the 6 restriction site heterozygosities did not significantly alter the frequency of crossing-over (21%) in the interval. Approximately 10% of all tetrads exhibited a gene conversion ($3^+ : 1^-$ or $3^- : 1^+$) of the URA3/ura3 :: NcoI locus. Southern blot analysis of restriction fragments from each member of a tetrad containing a conversion of URA3 was used to determine which adjacent restriction sites had undergone coincident gene conversion, both in instances accompanied by crossing-over and those without an associated exchange. Conversion tracts are marked by solid bars; cases in which additional events occurred on another chromatid are marked by a stippled bar. In most gene conversion events where there is an associated crossover, the position of the crossover within the conversion tract cannot be determined; events in which the position of a crossover could be assigned are marked by an X. There is no difference in conversion tract length between events associated with crossing-over and those without crossing-over. A significant number of events appear to have involved the pariticipation of three chromatids.

Finding an equivalence of conversion tract length in tetrads with and without an associated crossover stands in contrast to one study of mitotic gene conversion (61), in which a plasmid containing two heteroalleles of his3 in inverted orientation and containing several restriction site mutations in the HIS3 flanking regions was constructed.

His$^+$ recombinants were scored for crossing-over and for the gene conversion of adjacent restriction site markers. His$^+$ events in which a crossing-over occurred contained significantly longer conversion tracts than conversion events without an associated exchange (*61*).

3. GENE CONVERSIONS NEAR CENTROMERES

L. S. Symington and T. D. Petes (personal communication and *93*) examined gene conversions of a set of restriction site heterologies in tetrads that had crossed over in the *LEU2–CEN3* interval. Conversion tracts averaged several kb in length. Approximately 30% of the cross-overs in this 23-kb interval occur within 7 kb of the centromere; thus crossing-over in the region close to the centromere seems to be unaffected by the presence of the centromere. This is especially striking in view of the work of Lambie and Roeder (*30*) who used gene replacement techniques to simultaneously delete *CEN3* from its normal location and insert a functional centromere sequence more than 20 kb distal to *LEU2*. When the centromere was moved, recombination in the *cen3Δ–LEU2* interval increased 4-fold, indicating that a functional centromere represses crossing-over in the surrounding interval. One explanation for both sets of results would be that the region close to *CEN3* contains a hot spot for meiotic recombination that is repressed about 4-fold by the presence of the centromere. It would be interesting to know in which subinterval between *LEU2* and *CEN3* these increased exchanges occur when the centromere is inactivated.

Symington and Petes extended their analysis to include a study of recombination events involving the centromere itself. By including a nutritional marker on one side of the chromosome-III centromere and one or more restriction site markers on the opposite side of *CEN3*, L. S. Symington and T. D. Petes (personal communication and *94*) also made the striking observation that approximately 25% of gene conversions on one side of the centromere are accompanied by coconversions of a marker on the other side of the centromere. This clearly demands that we revise the conventional view that a centromere represents a point on the chromosome where no recombination occurs, as gene conversion events can extend across the centromere.

II. Physical Monitoring of Mitotic Gene Conversion in Yeast Mitochondria

Mating between two yeast strains is accompanied by a high level of recombination between mitochondrial DNA (*62*). The number of mitochondrial DNA (mtDNA) molecules that participate in recombination in the zygote and the random partitioning of mtDNA to buds precludes systematic recovery of the reciprocal products of a single recombination event; nevertheless it is clear that several different types of recombination events occur. Both gene conversions and apparent crossings-over have been described for a number of different loci. In addition, there are at least two examples of unidirectional gene conversion events. All of these types of recombination have been followed by physical analyses of DNA after mating. These studies reveal a wealth of detail about the way in which these events occur.

Dujon (63) described the conversion of an intron-less 21-S rRNA gene (ω^-) by a 21-S rRNA gene that contains an intron (ω^+). The ω^+ intron encodes a protein product (*FIT1*) that catalyzes this conversion event (64). By isolating DNA from cells after mating, several investigators (65–67) demonstrated that this conversion from ω^- to ω^+ is initiated by a double-strand break within ω^- DNA, catalyzed by the *FIT1* protein (68). The restriction fragment characteristic of the ω^+ conversion product first appears approximately 4 hours after mating. At approximately the same time, the appearance of a double-strand break within ω^- DNA was detected (66). Conversion of ω^- to ω^+ appears to be a gene conversion event catalyzed by a site-specific double-strand break. Thus, physical monitoring of DNA following conjugation clearly reveals the molecular mechanism by which ω^+ conversion occurs. This system has not been followed in more detail to establish the actual kinetics of the conversion process, from the time of appearance of the double-strand break to the time of completion of the event, nor have intermediates of recombination been sought.

A second unidirectional conversion event involves the transfer of a 48-bp (G+C)-rich segment from a *VAR1* gene containing the insert (a^+) to a *VAR1* gene that lacks this element (a^-). Recent physical analysis of this event has revealed that it, too, is accompanied by a site-specific double-strand break in a^- DNA (69). This unidirectional gene conversion event is not dependent on the presence of ω^+ DNA (and the *FIT1* protein). The creation of a double-strand break is reminiscent of early events in the transposition of the bacterial Tn10 element (70).

The kinetics of these events have recently been compared with recombination at another mtDNA locus, COB, where one can recover both reciprocal products of recombination between two regions flanked by restriction site polymorphisms (71). The time-course of appearance of all three types of recombination events occurs with similar kinetics, despite the fact that each event appears to be carried out by separate recombinational pathways.

III. Physical Monitoring of Yeast Mating-Type Switching

The mating-type (*MAT*) genes of *Saccharomyces cerevisiae* undergo an efficient substitution/recombination event in which approximately 650 bp specifying *MAT*a are replaced by 750 bp of nonhomologous sequences specifying *MAT*α, or vice versa (reviewed in 72–74). In essence, this switch of *MAT* alleles is a highly efficient mitotic gene conversion, in which part of the *MAT* locus is replaced by sequences copied from one of two donor (silent copy) loci, *HML* and *HMR* (Fig. 11). Switching can occur as often as every cell division.

Conversion of the *MAT* locus is initiated by the creation of a double-strand cleavage of *MAT* DNA by a site-specific endonuclease encoded by the *HO* gene (75, 76). The series of molecular events that would then result in switching from one mating type to the other has not been defined in detail. Several models proposed (72, 75) to describe *MAT* switching resemble the double-strand break-repair model of Szostak *et al.* (34), but differ in a number of important respects. All of these models presume that one or more cut end of *MAT* DNA "invades" an intact, homologous DNA locus and initiates strand transfer that eventually results in the replacement of Ya or Yα sequences at *MAT* with those copied from the donor. One such model is shown in Fig. 12.

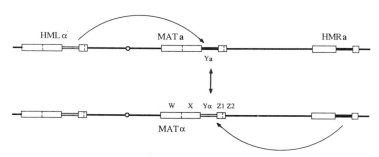

FIG. 11. Homothallic switching of yeast mating-type (*MAT*) genes. A double-strand break, created by the endonuclease endcoded by the *HO* gene, is repaired using one of the two "silent copy" genes, *HMLα* or *HMRa*. *MAT*, *HMR*, and *HML* all share homologous regions X and Z1. *MAT* and *HML* share additional regions of homology, W and Z2. Switching of *MAT*a to *MAT*α or of *MAT*α to *MAT*a involves the replacement of 650–750 bp of nonhomologous Ya or Yα sequences.

Genetic studies provide a number of observations that must be incorporated into molecular models of *MAT* switching. For example, the fact that *MAT* can be switched using a donor that is deleted for approximately 100 bp on either side of the *HO* endonuclease cleavage site implies that there must be some process to expose homologous regions shared by *MAT* and the donor, to allow switching (77), leading

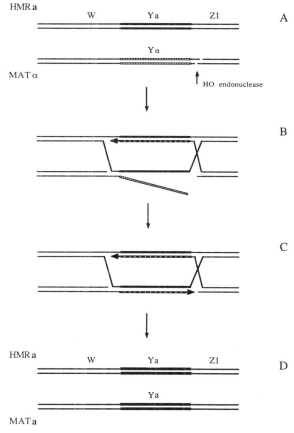

FIG. 12. A molecular model of *MAT* switching. In this model (72), the 3' end of the *MAT* Z1 region, created by *HO* endonuclease cleavage, invades homologous sequences at *HMR*a. New DNA synthesis is initiated by the invading strand, resulting in the displacement of a donor strand that, in turn, can invade and pair with homologous sequences in the *MAT* X region. During this process, the nonhomologous Y region at *MAT* must be removed. The 3' end of the exposed *MAT* X region can then also initiate new DNA synthesis, to complete the repair (and conversion) of the *MAT* locus. This model is similar to more general double-strand break repair models (34).

to the postulate that there may be an exonuclease that not only "chews back" from the cut ends in this unusual case, but is also responsible for removing the Y region when opposite mating-type information is donated. Furthermore, several experiments have demonstrated that *MAT* switching may involve the formation of heteroduplex DNA between *MAT* and *HML* or *HMR* (Section III,A).

A. What Sequences Are Transferred?

The structure of *MAT* and its donors and the position of the *HO* endonuclease cutting site suggest that the replacement of Ya or Yα must also involve the replacement of at least some of the X and Z1 regions. For example, infrequent switches of *inc* mutations that alter the *HO* endonuclease cutting site and prevent efficient switching always result in the replacement of the altered sequence with a normal cutting site (78, 79).

In considering what other regions of *MAT* are replaced, two general possibilities may be entertained (1) *MAT* conversions extend a variable distance into the adjacent, homologous sequences, or (2) a fixed segment of DNA is transferred from the donor locus. To establish how sequences are transferred, J. N. Strathern (personal communication) has marked *MAT* with *XhoI* or *SmaI* linkers at different sites within *MAT* and then asked if these sites are always or sometimes converted when *MATα* switches to *MATa*. His results show that a variable segment must be transferred; the probability that an insertion in the X region is replaced is proportional to its distance from the X-Y border (where all of Yα was replaced by Ya).

A more detailed analysis of these results has led Strathern (personal communication) to conclude that the replacement of sequences in the X region often involves the formation of heteroduplex DNA. When pairs of cells derived from a single switching event are examined, one may retain the linker insert while the other loses it. For a marker close to the Y-Z border, as many as 40% of the switching events apparently leave a heteroduplex structure. One implication of these results is that small heterologies are not often subjected to mismatch correction.

Similar conclusions have been reached about replacement of the Y region itself. For example, in "homologous" switching between *mata1-1* (a mutation in Ya) and the HMR donor carrying *hmra-2* (a different mutation in Ya), about 7% of the switches result in the formation of a *MATa⁺* locus rather than *mata-2* (81). Recovering these wild-type recombinants suggests that heteroduplex DNA must have been formed between the donor and recipient alleles. More recently, evidence for heteroduplex DNA when large (up to 2.3 kb) insertions in Yα are replaced by *HMLα* as the donor has been obtained (B. Connolly and J. E. Haber, unpublished). For an insertion approximately 440 bp from the cutting site, more than 50% of the switching events result in unrepaired heteroduplex DNA, so that one daughter cell contains a normal *MATα* locus and the other retains the *matα::LEU2* locus. These experiments suggest that single strands of DNA are transferred from donor to *MAT* and then used as templates for replication.

B. Kinetics of *MAT* Switching

The molecular models inferred from genetic experiments can be verified and extended by a physical analysis of DNA from synchronized cells undergoing switching. This approach was made possible by construction of plasmids placing the *HO* endonuclease gene under the control of a galactose-inducible (*GAL10*) promoter (*82*) and deleting sequences that normally restrict expression both to the G_1 phase of the cell cycle and to mother cells (*76*). This construct has been used to induce *HO* in cells synchronized by prior arrest at the G_1 stage of the cell cycle with α-factor (B. Connolly, C. I. White and J. E. Haber, *90*). Addition of galactose to cells released from G_1 arrest results in the induction of *HO* endonuclease, which can be assayed *in vitro* by the cleavage of an end-labeled linearized plasmid containing *MATα*. Transfer of these cells to glucose-containing medium shuts off *HO* transcription; the rapid turnover of the *HO* protein leaves no detectable activity after another 30 minutes. The progress of switching in these induced cells can be monitored by Southern blot analysis, shown in Fig. 13. After 45 minutes, approximately 50% of the *MATa* DNA has been cleaved by *HO* endonuclease, to yield predicted *Hind*III fragments of 2.8 and 1.2 kb. In the absence of *HO* endonuclease activity, these fragments remain for more than an hour, without any evidence of progressive exonucleolytic shortening of the cut DNA (although the 1.2-kb band appears to become less abundant before the 2.9-kb band is depleted). Sixty minutes after *HO* cleavage, the product of switching—*MATα*—is detected by a Yα probe. This is a remarkable result. In cells growing at 30°C, *MAT* switching requires approximately 60 minutes. Similar results have been obtained by D. Reveh and J. Strathern (personal communication). As we discuss later (Section III,C), this very slow process appears to involve at least two very slow steps.

By following *MAT* switching in synchronized cells, Connolly *et al.* (*90*) demonstrated that switching can occur at any stage of the cell cycle, with the same kinetics. Moreover, in experiments where *HO* is

A

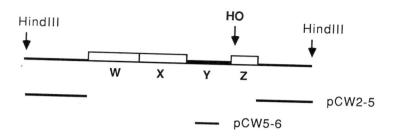

B

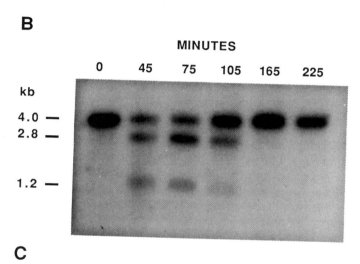

C

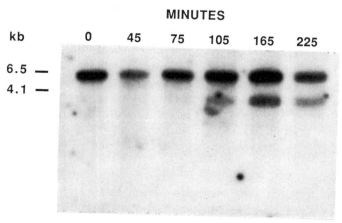

induced continually, we find evidence that more than a single switching event can occur within a single cell cycle.

C. Intermediates of *MAT* Switching

The ability to induce *HO* to initiate a synchronous switching event in a large population of cells makes it possible to look for transient intermediates of switching. Two laboratories have been pursuing this approach. In both cases, DNA taken at intervals after *HO* induction was probed with strand-specific probes to look for events leading to the completion of the switch. For example, J. Strathern *et al.* (personal communication) have looked for strand-specific exonucleolytic removal of DNA sequences after *HO* endonuclease cutting; to date they have not found the removal of any significant extent of sequences adjacent to the cut site. They also have been using oligonucleotides as primers for dideoxynucleotide sequencing of genomic DNA, to look for novel products during switching. For example, one might expect to find the joining of the *MAT* Z1 region to the donor Y sequence. C. I. White, B. Connolly and J. E. Haber (unpublished) used similar approaches to look for intermediates of switching. Hybridization of strand-specific probes complementary to sequences immediately adjacent to *MAT* revealed the appearance of an apparent 9-kb switching intermediate that appears 30 minutes after *HO* endonuclease cleavage of *MAT* and approximately 30 minutes before *MAT* switching is completed (Fig. 14). The appearance and disappearance of this novel *Hind*III fragment are consistent with its being a quasistable intermediate of switching, but does not prove that it is an obligate step during *MAT* conversion. This novel species is found on both native and denaturing agarose gels.

A detailed hybridization analysis of this novel 9-kb fragment shows that it does not have the structure we would predict for any of

FIG. 13. Kinetics of *MAT* switching. Cells of the *MATa HMLα hmrΔ* strain R166, carrying the *GAL10::HO* plasmid, and containing the *HO* gene fused to a galactose-inducible promoter, were synchronized by the addition of α-factor. The G_1-arrested cells were then released and *HO* induced for 45 minutes, at which time cells were transferred to glucose-containing medium to shut off *HO* expression. A Southern blot of *Hind*III restriction fragments at intervals after induction is shown. (A) A diagram of the *MAT* locus, with the location of probes that hybridize to *MAT*-specific sequences surrounding *MAT* (pCW2-5) and to Yα (pCW5-6). (B) The blot was probed with labeled pCW2-5, homologous to regions immediately proximal and distal to *MAT*. Two *HO*-cleaved fragments of 2.8 and 1.2 kb are seen at 45 minutes. (C) When the same blot was probed with Yα-specific probe, the appearance of *MATα* (the product of switching from *MATa* to *MATα*) was not seen until 105 minutes. The Yα probe also hybridizes to *HMLα*.

246

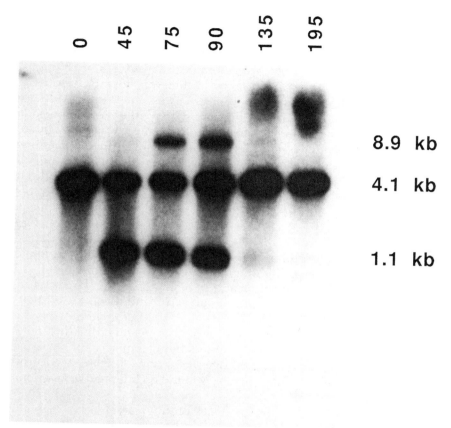

minutes

0   45   75   90   135   195

8.9 kb

4.1 kb

1.1 kb

FIG. 14. Appearance of a possible 9-kb intermediate in *MAT* switching. *Hind*II-digested DNA, extracted at intervals after induction of the *HO* endonuclease in a synchronized culture of cells, was hybridized with a radioactive strand-specific RNA probe complementary to the "bottom" strand that ends 3′ at the *HO* endonuclease cut site. Thirty minutes after induction, there is cleavage of *MAT* to yield 2.8- and 1.1-kb fragments. Approximately 30 minutes later, the relative abundance of the 1.1-kb fragment decreases relative to the 2.8-kb fragment. At the same time, a 9-kb fragment appears. This fragment is complementary to a bottom-strand-specific probe of the region distal to *MAT*, but does not hybridize to a probe complementary to the top strand.

the steps illustrated in molecular models, such as that in Fig. 11 or its variants. The band hybridizes to probes complementary to the *MAT*-Z region and to the region distal to *MAT*. This band does not hybridize with probes homologous to the W, X, Ya, or Yα regions shared by *MAT* and its donors, nor with the region immediately proximal to *MAT*. In fact, the band is homologous to probes for only one of the two strands distal to *MAT*: the strand that ends 3' at the *HO* cut site. This suggests that the novel fragment is partially single-stranded over more than 1 kb, extending beyond the first *Hin*dIII site. The large size of the intermediate is explained by the fact that *Hin*dIII fails to cleave single-stranded DNA and that the next *Hin*dIII site (which is still double-stranded) is more than 6 kb away. Thus, one of the two strands distal to the cut site has been degraded; surprisingly this process removes DNA more than 800 bp from the end of the *MAT* Z2 region (i.e., beyond the end of the region that can be repaired by homolgous recombination). The creation of such a long single-stranded region with a 3' end may be an essential step in promoting strand invasion into an intact, double-stranded donor.

D. Analysis of *MAT* Switching in the Presence of Mutations or Inhibitors of Cell Growth

As with our analysis of meiotic recombination, one can analyze *MAT* switching when the cells are arrested in growth or carry mutations that cause lethality in *HO* strains. For example, the *rad52* mutation is lethal to cells that attempt to switch *MAT* (23, 83). When *rad52* cells are induced for *HO*, we find that *HO* cleavage of the *MAT* occurs, and that the 9-kb intermediate also accumulates. There is no evidence of any of the subsequent steps expected in *MAT* switching (C. I. White and J. E. Haber, unpublished). Similarly, we have shown that arresting cells with the DNA synthesis inhibitor, hydroxyurea, also leads to *HO* cutting and the accumulation of the unusual 8-kb band, but prevents the completion of switching (Fig. 15). One striking observation from these experiments is that the cut ends of the *MAT* locus are stable even after 4 hours of hydroxyurea arrest. This implies that there is no rampant exonucleolytic activity that removes the *MAT* Y region, though it is clear that this region must be replaced during the switching process. The ends are, in fact, intact, as switching can be completed 70 minutes after hydroxyurea is removed (Fig. 15, lane 7).

Finally, we can begin to explore why *MAT* switching takes 60 minutes from the time *HO*-induced cutting can be seen. One possible explanation is that the *HO*-induced cut at *MAT* (or the *HO* protein itself) induces other DNA repair functions needed to complete

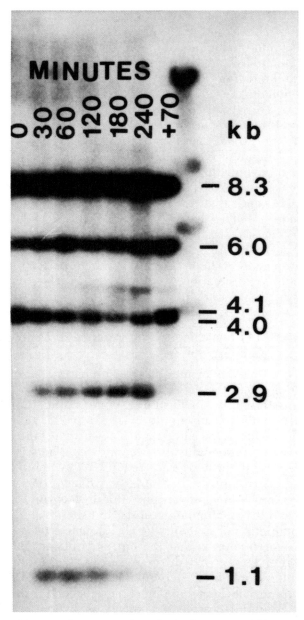

FIG. 15. Inhibition of *MAT* switching by hydroxyurea. Cells were incubated in 0.15 M hydroxyurea for 3 hours, until cells were arrested as large, budded cells. *MAT* switching was initiated by adding galactose to induce *HO* endonuclease from a plasmid containing the *GAL10::HO* fusion. After 30 minutes, cleavage of MAT is observed. The two *Hind*III fragments created by *HO* endonuclease and the 9-kb apparent intermediate remain undegraded for more than 3 hours under these conditions. When the cells are washed and resuspended in fresh YEPD medium, lacking galactose, switching is completed within 70 minutes.

switching. Indeed, this may be case, as switching is blocked if cyclo-heximide is added 45 minutes after *HO* endonuclease is induced by galactose (N. Rudin, B. Connolly and J. E. Haber, unpublished).

E. Analysis of Other *HO*-Induced Mitotic Recombination Events

1. AN *HO*-INDUCED CHROMOSOMAL DELETION

In a strain deleted for *HML* and *HMR*, *HO* cutting at *MAT* leads to cell death (78). However, if the *MAT* locus is inserted between two flanking homologous sequences (as when a pBR322-*MAT-URA3* plasmid is integrated at *ura3-52*), *HO*-induced cutting does not lead to death, but rather to the efficient recombination of the flanking homologous regions, which may be more than 4 kb from the cut site (Fig. 16A) (N. Rudin and J. E. Haber, unpublished). They have also examined the kinetics of this simpler recombination system, which does not depend on long-range interactions between *MAT* and its donor. Our conclusions are remarkably similar to what we have seen with *MAT* switching: from the time of *HO*-cutting of DNA to the comple-

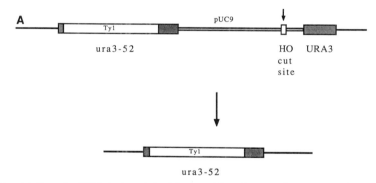

FIG. 16. Repair of HO-induced double-strand breaks on a chromosome, by recombination between well-separated, flanking homologous regions. (A) The 117-bp *BglII–HincII* fragment containing the *HO* endonuclease cutting site from *MATa* was cloned into the vector pUC9 also containing *URA3*. This construct was integrated into a chromosome at the *ura3-52* locus (*ura3-52* contains an insertion of the yeast transposable element, TY1). When *HO* endonuclease cleaves this cutting site, the broken chromosome is repaired by recombination between the flanking *ura3-52* and *URA3* loci, usually yielding a *ura3-52* product. (B) A time-course of *Bam*HI-digested DNA showing the *HO*-induced cleavage and subsequent repair of a chromosomal break. Thirty minutes after induction of *GAL10::HO*, the 15.5-kb fragment containing the *URA3* duplication, pUC9, and the *HO* cut site is cleaved into 13.8- and 1.7-kb fragments. After 90 minutes, an 11.5-kb band, formed by recombination between *ura3-52* and *URA3*, appears. The two bands present in all lanes are derived from the *GAL10::HO* plasmid.

B minutes

0 30 60 90 120 150 180 210 240

15.5 kb
13.8 kb
11.5 kb

1.7 kb

FIG. 16B.

tion of the DNA repair event takes about 60 minutes (Fig. 16B). Furthermore, adding cycloheximide after induction of *HO*, but prior to completing the deletion, also prevented the completion of this deletion event. It should be possible to follow this reaction in great detail, to look for molecular intermediates.

The stimulation of recombination at some distance by the creation of a double-strand break is reminiscent of the stimulation of recombination in *E. coli* by the recBC enzyme complex. Creating a double-strand break in phage λ, *in vivo*, with *Eco*RI, leads to the stimulation of events that is best explained by the entry of the recBCD enzyme complex onto the DNA at the site of a double-strand break and its subsequent movement down the DNA (*84, 84a, 85*). We are interested in determining if the DNA near the break-point is degraded or if a recBC-like activity in yeast moves down the DNA, unwinding but not degrading it, until homologous recombination occurs.

2. *HO*-INDUCED GENE CONVERSION OF *LACZ* SEQUENCES

Another approach to study *HO*-induced events involves an *HO*-dependent recombination system in which the expressed and unexpressed donor sequences are *E. coli* galactosidase (*LACZ*) sequences (Fig. 17) (N. Rudin and J. E. Haber, unpublished). In these constructs, a copy of *LACZ* containing a functional promoter is disrupted by the insertion of a 117-bp fragment carrying the *MAT*a *HO* cut site. The plasmids also carry a promoterless, intact *LACZ* segment, inserted either in the same or opposite orientation. The plasmids also carry a *CEN* (centromere) sequence to maintain the plasmid in a low (1 or 2) copy number. Expression of β-galactosidase occurs when *HO* endonuclease induces gene conversion of *LACZ*::*cut site* by the unexpressed copy of *LACZ*, to restore a functional *LACZ* gene. Such events are easily detected in yeast by the cleavage of the substrate X-Gal to produce a blue color.

The same authors have examined the conversion of this plasmid in cells containing the galactose-inducible *HO* gene. One such time-course is shown in Fig. 18A. An initially supercoiled plasmid is cleaved approximately 15–30 minutes after induction of *HO*. After another 30 minutes, several minor bands appear; these may be intermediates of the *LACZ* conversion process. After approximately 1 hour, the switched products are evident. Surprisingly, at least 50% of the switching events are accompanied by crossing-over; in the case where *LACZ*::*cut site* and the silent *LACZ* are in direct orientation, nearly 80% result in the deletion expected for an exchange accompanying gene conversion. In contrast, in a similar *CEN* plasmid containing

---

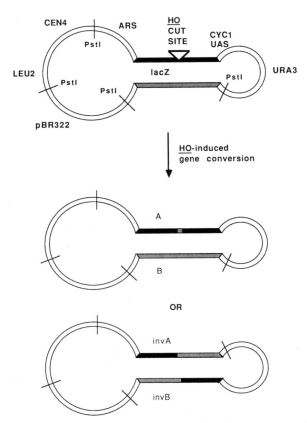

FIG. 17. A plasmid system to study *HO*-induced gene conversion of *LACZ* sequences. The centromere-containing plasmid, pNR17, contains a transcribed *CYC1::LEU2::LACZ* gene that is interrupted at the *Bcl*I site by the insertion of two 117-bp *Bgl*II–*Hinc*II *HO* endonuclease cutting sites from *MAT*a. The plasmid also contains a second, untranscribed copy of *LACZ*, in opposite orientation. In yeast, *HO*-induced cleavage of the cutting site results in repair of the transcribed *LACZ* region, yielding a plasmid that expresses β-galactosidase; consequently cells grown on X-Gal plates turn blue. In approximately 50% of the gene conversion events, there is an associated crossing-over that results in the inversion within the plasmid.

*MAT*α and *HMR*a,* only 5% of the switches are associated with crossing-over (H. Friesen, B. Andrews, J. Haber and P. Sadowski, unpublished). We believe the difference reflects the presence of "pairing sites" that both facilitate pairing between *MAT* and a donor, and apparently constrain the repair event.

* HMR = homothallism donor, right arm of chromosome III.

hours

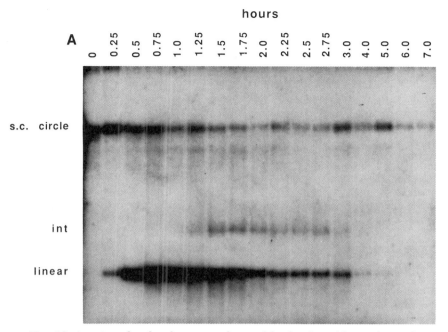

A

| 0 | 0.25 | 0.5 | 0.75 | 1.0 | 1.25 | 1.5 | 1.75 | 2.0 | 2.25 | 2.5 | 2.75 | 3.0 | 4.0 | 5.0 | 6.0 | 7.0 |

s.c. circle

int

linear

FIG. 18. A series of molecular events detected by Southern blot analysis of *HO*-induced gene conversion of the *LACZ* sequences in plasmid pNR17. *HO*-induced recombination of the *LACZ* plasmid was initiated by adding galactose to cells grown in YEP-lactate. (A) A Southern blot of undigested DNA taken at intervals after galactose induction. Supercoiled NR17 plasmid DNA is cleaved by *HO* endonuclease to a linear form 30 minutes after induction. An apparent intermediate (int) appears and subsequently disappears before the plasmid is apparently repaired back to a closed circular form. Because some cells have lost the plasmid carrying the *GAL10::HO* construct, some of the plasmid DNA is never cleaved; consequently one cannot unequivocally see the conversion of cut DNA back to supercoiled plasmid lacking the *HO* cut site. (B) The Southern blot shown is of *Pst*I-digested DNA extracted at intervals and probed with ^{32}P-labeled *LACZ* DNA. Induction of the *HO* endonuclease results in the cutting of both 117-bp cutting sites inserted in *LACZ*. Cleavage of both recognition sites yields fragments labeled A-CS″ and A-CS′; cleavage of only one of the two sites produces two additional fragments, A-CS$_2$″ and A-CS$_2$′. Subsequently, there is the appearance of the two restriction fragments (designated invA and invB) resulting from crossing-over associated with the repair of the cut *LACZ* region. In addition, another restriction fragment, consistent with the repair of the *LACZ* region, and lacking the cut site (designated A), appears. It is evident that the invB product appears significantly earlier than the reciprocal invA product.

hours

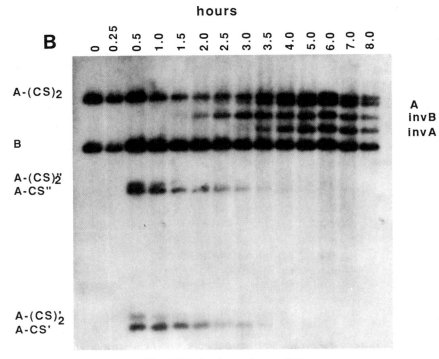

FIG. 18B. See legend on p. 253.

Southern blot analysis of *Pst*I-digested DNA reveals a remarkably detailed sequence of events (Fig. 18B). After 30 minutes of induction of *HO*, one sees the appearance of the expected *HO* endonuclease-cut restriction fragments. In the construct used in these experiments, the *LACZ* :: *cut site* actually contained two cut sites in direct orientation. Cleavage at only one site yields either bands A-(CS)$_2''$ and A-CS' or bands A-CS'' and A-(CS)$_2'$. Cleavage of both sites yields bands A-CS'' and A-CS'. Most of the plasmids appear to have enjoyed cutting at both sites, as these two bands predominate. Approximately 30 minutes after the cleavage of the *LACZ* :: *cut site*, one sees the appearance of one of the two expected products of crossing-over between one cut (recombinogenic) end of *LACZ* with its "silent" *LACZ* homologue. The preferred strand invasion is the one that involves the 3' end in the *MAT-Z* region; the 3' end derived from Ya sequences is apparently unable to recombine with homologous sequences as efficiently. Later, about 60 minutes after the *HO*-induced cleavage of *LACZ* :: *cut site*, one sees the pair of bands expected for the inverted, recombined $LACZ^+$ plasmid. At this time, too, one sees the appearance of another fragment approximately 200 bp smaller than the original $LACZ::cut\ site$. This band is consistent with the size expected for the formation of $LACZ^+$ (lacking the pair of 117-bp cut sites) if there was no exchange of flanking markers. Thus we can see a series of events leading to the expected products.

The use of this $LACZ$ model system should allow us to explore a number of questions: (1) Is the segment adjacent to the cut site degraded to include a long single-stranded region? (2) Will inverting the orientation of the cut site also change which of the two expected recombination products appears before the other? (3) What DNA sequences within or adjacent to MAT prevent fragment crossing-over between the donor and recipient sequences? Further analysis of $LACZ$ switching should also provide an opportunity to look for Holliday structures accompanying this mitotic recombination event.

IV. Physical Analysis of Other Mitotic Recombination Events

A. 2μ-DNA and *FLP*

The yeast plasmid, 2μ-DNA, is a naturally occurring, autonomously replicating yeast plasmid with no known function. The 6.3-kb plasmid carries a pair of 599-bp homologous regions in inverted orientation (86). Recombination between these two regions inverts one unique region relative to the other and yields two forms, designated A and B. Although "flipping" from one form to the other can occur at low frequency by homologous recombination, isomerization of 2μ-DNA occurs at high frequency via a site-specific recombination event catalyzed by the *FLP* protein, which is encoded on 2μ-DNA. This reaction has been studied extensively *in vitro* (51, 52). The reaction is extremely fast *in vitro;* in essence, it is complete within 1 minute after adding purified *FLP* protein to its substrate. The kinetics of this reaction can also be studied *in vivo*. When the *FLP* protein is placed under the control of a galactose-inducible promoter, to induce the *FLP* reaction *in vivo*, flipping occurs very rapidly after galactose induction (87). This makes the slowness of the *HO*-induced switching and related events even more striking.

B. *LOX/CRE**

A similar approach (88), in collaboration with several others, is to follow another site-specific recombination reaction in yeast. The

---

* LOX = locus of crossing-over; CRE = creates recombination.

LOX/CRE recombination system of bacteriophage P1 has been introduced into yeast. The *CRE* gene encodes an enzyme that catalyzes site-specific recombination between a pair of 34-bp *LOX* sites. The *CRE* gene has recently been cloned behind a galactose-inducible promoter (88). The site-specific recombination can be seen in Southern blots of DNA taken at intervals after galactose induction (J. Bilski, B. Sauer and N. Cozarelli, personal communication). The effect of various mutants, including those affecting topoisomerases, is currently under investigation.

V. Closing Thoughts

Genetic analysis of gene conversions and their associated exchanges of flanking markers has provided a wealth of data from which to construct molecular models of recombination. It should be clear from this review of recent work that recombinant DNA methods of site-directed mutagenesis and gene-replacement have made it possible to construct strains ideally suited to test the predictions of different molecular models. Already there have been surprises. For example, the effect of multiple heterozygosities on meiotic recombination has provided evidence of a repair-induced recombination system in meiotic cells. In addition, similar studies have shown that a significant proportion of crossover events in a centromere-adjacent interval actually occurs very close to the centromere. Similarly, physical monitoring of *MAT* switching has led to the discovery that this site-specific gene conversion event is a surprisingly slow event with the accumulation of unexpected intermediates. A detailed description of molecular events during recombination will in turn stimulate a search at the biochemical level for such enzymatic activities. The development of an *in vitro* recombination system from yeast (89) provides an essential step in purifying the individual biochemical activities required for this complex process.

A complete description of the molecular events in recombination clearly demands that we be able to visualize molecules undergoing recombination. With synchronized cells and the use of strand-specific probes and novel gel electrophoresis conditions we can begin to "capture" and characterize intermediates in recombination. Only a few years ago, the idea that we could visualize genomic events at this level of resolution seemed far in the future. What will be discovered in the next few years will undoubtedly be equally astonishing.

ACKNOWLEDGMENTS

We are grateful to Elissa Sena for providing Fig. 7, and to J. Strathern, L. Symington, T. Petes, J. Game, R. Mortimer, R. Malone, B. Brewer, W. Fangman, J. Huberman, R. Butow, and N. Cozarelli for communicating unpublished data. Work from this laboratory was funded by NIH Grants GM20056 and GM29736, NSF Grant DCB8409086, and Grant 1-968 from the March of Dimes Birth Defects Foundation.

REFERENCES

1. H. B. Creighton and B. McClintock, *PNAS* **10**, 403 (1931).
2. C. Stern, *Biol. Zentralbl.* **51**, 547 (1931).
3. S. Fogel, R. K. Mortimer, K. Lusnak and F. Tavares, *CSHSQB* **43**, 1325 (1978).
4. M. S. Esposito and J. E. Wagstaff, in "The Molecular Biology of the Yeast *Saccharomyces*" (J. N. Strathern, E. W. Jones and J. R. Broach, eds.), p. 341. Cold Spring Harbor Laboratory, Cold Spring Harbor, New York, 1981.
5. R. E. Esposito and S. Klapholz, in "The Molecular Biology of the Yeast *Saccharomyces*" (J. N. Strathern, E. W. Jones and J. R. Broach, eds.), p. 211. Cold Spring Harbor Laboratory, Cold Spring Harbor, New York, 1981.
6. M. S. Esposito, in "Controlling Events in Meiosis (Symposium of the Society for Experimental Biology)" (C. W. Evans and H. G. Dickinson, eds.), p. 123. The Company of Biologists Ltd., Sarborough, 1984.
7. M. A. Resnick, A. Sugino, J. Nitiss and T. Chow, *MCBiol* **4**, 2811 (1984).
8. M. A. Resnick, J. Nitiss, C. Edwards and R. E. Malone, *Genetics* **113**, 531 (1986).
9. R. H. Borts, M. Lichten, L. Davidow, M. Hearn and J. E. Haber, *CSHSQB* **49**, 67 (1984).
10. R. H. Borts, M. Lichten and J. E. Haber, *Genetics* **115**, 233 (1986).
11. F. Sherman and H. Roman, *Genetics* **48**, 255 (1963).
12. R. E. Esposito and M. S. Esposito, *PNAS* **71**, 3172 (1974).
13. C. Newlon, R. P. Green, K. J. Hardeman, K. E. Kim, L. R. Lipchitz, P. G. Plzkill, S. Synn and S. T. Woody, *UCLA Symp. Mol. Cell Biol.* **33**, 211 (1985).
14. M. Lichten, R. H. Borts and J. E. Haber, *Genetics* **225**, 233 (1987).
15. G. F. Carle and M. V. Olson, *NARes* **12**, 5647 (1984).
16. J. E. Haber, P. C. Thorurn and D. Rogers, *Genetics* **106**, 185 (1984).
17. J. E. Haber and P. C. Thorburn, *Genetics* **106**, 207 (1984).
18. S. Jinks-Robertson and T. D. Petes, *PNAS* **82**, 3350 (1985).
19. S. Jinks-Robertson and T. D. Petes, *Genetics* **114**, 731 (1986).
20. J. A. Jackson and G. R. Fink, *Genetics* **111**, 303 (1985).
21. H. L. Klein, *Nature* **310**, 748 (1984).
22. H. L. Klein and T. D. Petes, *Nature* **289**, 144 (1981).
23. R. E. Malone and R. E. Esposito, *PNAS* **77**, 503 (1980).
24. R. E. Malone, *Genetics* **109**, 405 (1983).
25. S. Klapholz, C. S. Waddell and R. E. Esposito, *Genetics* **110**, 187 (1985).
26. M. A. Resnick, J. N. Kasimos, J. C. Game, R. J. Braun and R. M. Roth, *Science* **212**, 543 (1981).
27. D. Hurst, S. Fogel and R. K. Mortimer, *PNAS* **69**, 101 (1972).
28. R. K. Mortimer and D. Schild, *Microbiol. Rev.* **49**, 181 (1985).
29. J. E. Haber and M. Hearn, *Genetics* **111**, 7 (1985).
30. E. J. Lambie and G. S. Roeder, *Genetics* **114**, 769 (1986).
31. J. H. White, K. Lusnak and S. Fogel, *Nature* **315**, 350 (1985).

32. E. A. Savage and P. J. Hastings, *Curr. Genet.* 3, 37 (1983).
33. M. S. Meselson and C. M. Radding, *PNAS* 72, 358 (1975).
34. J. W. Szostak, T. L. Orr-Weaver, R. J. Rothstein and F. W. Stahl, *Cell* 33, 25 (1983).
35. F. W. Stahl, M. M. Stahl, R. E. Malone and J. M. Crasemann, *Genetics* 94, 235 (1980).
36. F. W. Stahl, M. Lieb and M. M. Stahl, *Genetics* 103, 795 (1984).
37. A. S. Ponticelli, D. W. Schultz, A. F. Taylor and G. F. Smith, *Cell* 41, 145 (1985).
38. A. F. Taylor, D. W. Schultz, A. S. Ponticelli and G. R. Smith, *Cell* 41, 153 (1985).
39. H. Gutz, *Genetics* 69, 317 (1971).
40. F. W. Stahl "Genetic Recombination: Thinking About it in Phage and Fungi." Freeman, San Francisco, California, 1979.
41. J. H. Wilson, *PNAS* 76, 3641 (1979).
42. S. McGavin, *Heredity* 39, 15 (1977).
43. A. L. Kolodkin, A. J. S. Klar and F. W. Stahl, *Cell* 46, 733 (1986).
44. P. J. Hastings, *CSHSQB* 49, 49 (1984).
45. M. Lichten and M. Fox, *NARes* 11, 3959 (1983).
46. G. R. Fink and C. Styles, *Genetics* 77, 231 (1974).
47. R. M. Myers, L. Lehrman and T. Maniatis, *Science* 230, 1242 (1985).
48. M. S. Williamson, J. C. Game and S. Fogel, *Genetics* 110, 187 (1985).
49. R. Holliday, *Genet. Res.* 5, 282 (1964).
50. L. Bell and B. Byers, *PNAS* 76, 3445 (1979).
51. D. Vetter, B. J. Andrews, L. Roberts-Beatty and P. Sadowski, *PNAS* 80, 7284 (1983).
52. M. M. Cox, *PNAS* 80, 4223 (1983).
53. R. A. Young and R. W. Davis, *PNAS* 80, 1194 (1983).
54. D. Shortle, J. E. Haber and D. Botstein, *Science* 217, 371 (1982).
55. R. J. Rothstein, *Methods Enzymol.* 101, 202 (1983).
56. J. D. Boeke, F. LaCroute and G. R. Fink, *MGG* 197, 345 (1984).
57. R. H. Borts and J. E. Haber, *Science* 237, 1459 (1987).
58. R. K. Mortimer and S. Fogel, *in* "Mechanisms of Recombination" (R. F. Grell, ed.), p. 263. Plenum, New York, 1974.
59. A. T. C. Carpenter, *CSHSQB* 49, 23 (1984).
60. J. L. Rossignol, A. Nicolas, H. Hamza and T. Langin, *CSHSQB* 49, 13 (1984).
61. B. T. Ahn and D. Livingston, *MCBiol* 6, 3685 (1986).
62. B. Dujon, *in* "The Molecular Biology of the Yeast *Saccharomyces*" (J. N. Strathern, E. W. Jones and J. R. Broach, eds.), p. 505. Cold Spring Harbor Laboratory, Cold Spring Harbor, New York, 1981.
63. B. Dujon, *Cell* 20, 185 (1980).
64. I. G. Macreadie, R. M. Scott, A. R. Zinn and R. A. Butow, *Cell* 41, 395 (1985).
65. A. R. Zinn and R. A. Butow, *CSHSQB* 49, 115 (1984).
66. A. R. Zinn and R. A. Butow, *Cell* 40, 887 (1985).
67. A. Jacquier and B. Dujon, *Cell* 41, 383 (1985).
68. L. Colleaux, L. D'Auriol, M. Betermier, G. Cottarel, A. Jacquier, F. Galibert and B. Dujon, *Cell* 44, 521 (1986).
69. R. H. Butow and A. R. Zinn, *in* "Extrachromosomal Elements in Lower Eucaryotes" (R. B. Wickner, A. Hinnebusch, I. C. Gunsalus and A. Hollaender, eds.), p. 29. Plenum, New York, 1986.
70. D. Morisato and N. Kleckner, *Cell* 39, 181 (1984).
71. A. R. Zinn, J. K. Pohlman, P. S. Perlman and R. A. Butow, *Plasmid* 17 (in press).
72. J. E. Haber, *in* "Mobile Genetic Elements" (J. S. Shapiro, ed.), p. 591. Academic Press, New York, 1983.

73. K. A. Nasmyth, *ARGen* **16**, 439 (1983).
74. A. J. S. Klar, J. N. Strathern and J. B. Hicks, *in* "Microbial Development" (R. Losick and L. Shapiro, eds.), p. 151. Cold Spring Harbor Laboratory, Cold Spring Harbor, New York, 1984.
75. J. N. Strathern, A. J. S. Klar, J. B. Hicks, J. A. Abraham, I. M. Ivy, K. A. Nasmyth and C. McGill, *Cell* **31**, 183 (1982).
76. R. Kostriken, J. N. Strathern, A. J. S. Klar, J. B. Hicks and F. Heffron, *Cell* **35**, 167 (1983).
77. B. Weiffenbach and J. E. Haber, *MCBiol* **5**, 2154 (1985).
78. Y. Oshima and I. Takano, *Genetics* **94**, 841 (1980).
79. D. W. Mascioli and J. E. Haber, *Genetics* **94**, 341 (1980).
80. R. Jensen and I. Herskowitz, *CSHSQB* **49**, 97 (1984).
81. A. J. S. Klar, J. McIndoo, J. Strathern and J. B. Hicks, *Cell* **22**, 291 (1980).
82. K. A. Nasmyth, *Nature* **302**, 670 (1983).
83. B. Weiffenbach and J. E. Haber, *MCBiol* **1**, 522 (1981).
84. M. M. Stahl, I. Kobayashi, F. W. Stahl and S. K. Huntington, *PNAS* **80**, 2310 (1983).
84a. D. S. Thaler, M. M. Stahl and F. W. Stahl, *JMB* **195**, 75 (1987).
85. D. S. Thaler, M. M. Stahl and F. W. Stahl, *Genetics* **116**, 501 (1987).
86. J. R. Broach, *in* "The Molecular Biology of the Yeast *Saccharomyces*" (J. N. Strathern, E. W. Jones and J. R. Broach, eds.), p. 445. Cold Spring Harbor Laboratory, Cold Spring Harbor, New York, 1981.
87. F. C. Volkert and J. R. Broach, *Cell* **46**, 541 (1986).
88. B. Sauer, *MCBiol* **7**, 2087 (1987).
89. L. S. Symington, L. M. Fogarty and R. Kolodner, *Cell* **35**, 805 (1983).
90. B. Connolly, C. I. White and J. E. Haber, *MCBiol* **8** (in press).
91. B. J. Brewer and W. Fangman, *Cell* **51**, 463 (1987).
92. J. A. Huberman, L. D. Spotila, K. A. Nawotka, S. M. El-Assouli and L. R. Davis, *Cell* **51**, 473 (1987).
93. L. S. Symington and T. D. Petes, *Cell* **52**, 237 (1988).
94. L. S. Symington and T. D. Petes, *MCBiol* **8** (in press).

Early Signals Underlying the Induction of the c-*fos* and c-*myc* Genes in Quiescent Fibroblasts: Studies with Bombesin and Other Growth Factors

ENRIQUE ROZENGURT AND
JAMES SINNETT-SMITH

Imperial Cancer Research Fund
Lincoln's Inn Fields
London WC2A 3PX, England

The cells of many tissues and organs exist in a nonproliferating state in the G_0/G_1 phase of the cell cycle in which they remain viable and metabolically active. They retain the capacity of responding to extracellular signals such as polypeptide growth factors, hormones, and antigens by increasing their rate of proliferation. Features of the stimulation of cell proliferation can be studied in cell culture. In recent years, a remarkable advance has been made toward the elucidation of the nature and mechanism of action of the diverse extracellular factors that control the growth of cells in culture. With the purification and identification of various polypeptide growth factors (for review, see *1–7*) and with the availability of nutrient media that render possible the study of mitogen action under chemically defined conditions (8, 9), it has become apparent that the proliferation of cultured cells

Progress in Nucleic Acid Research
and Molecular Biology, Vol. 35

can be regulated by a variety of mitogenic factors. A recent development is the discovery that small regulatory peptides that behave as local hormones or neurotransmitters, acting in a paracrine or autocrine* fashion on adjacent cells (10–13), can also act as mitogens for cells in culture. For example, the neurohypophyseal peptide vasopressin and the amphibian tetradecapeptide bombesin are potent mitogens for Swiss 3T3 cells (14–16).

The marked reduction in the dependence of many tumor cell lines on serum or exogenous growth factors and their ability to produce growth factors led to the hypothesis that the production of growth factors by malignant cells results in the establishment of an autocrine growth loop that will sustain the abnormal proliferation of such cells (2, 5, 17, 18). The concept that growth factors, which presumably play an essential role in the function of normal differentiated cells, may also play a fundamental role in tumorigenesis has been strikingly reinforced by the discovery of an important link between growth factors and their receptors and oncogene products (5, 19–23). All these findings suggest that growth factors play a critical role in modulating both normal and abnormal cell proliferation.

Many studies directed toward understanding the mechanisms by which these diverse external ligands regulate cell proliferation have utilized cultured fibroblasts, and in particular Swiss 3T3 cells, as a model system. These cells cease to proliferate and become arrested in the G_0/G_1 phase of the cell cycle when they deplete the medium of its growth-promoting activity. Such quiescent cells can be stimulated to reinitiate DNA synthesis and cell division not only by replenishing the medium with fresh serum, but also by the addition of defined growth-promoting agents in a serum-free medium (1–3).

Studies performed with combinations of defined growth-promoting factors reveal an important aspect of their action: the existence of potent and specific synergistic interactions (1, 24). This finding suggests that extracellular factors bind to different receptors, and generate multiple complementary intracellular signals that interact synergistically to initiate a proliferative response (1, 24, 25). In accord with this, considerable attention has been focused on the initial cellular responses that follow the interaction of mitogenic factors with specific surface receptors in the expectation that the early events will provide clues to primary regulatory mechanisms (24).

---

* Paracrine: production of a cell-growth regulator by an adjacent cell. Autocrine: production of a cell-growth regulator by the same cell, which has functional receptors [Eds.].

The early molecular events in the membrane and cytosol implicated in mitogenesis include changes in the transmembrane flux of ions (26), alterations in the level of cyclic nucleotides (3, 27), activation of protein kinases (28), and modifications of the properties of the receptors themselves (29). An early response in the nucleus that has been the focus of considerable interest in recent years is the rapid increase in the expression of the protooncogenes c-*fos* and c-*myc*.* Other cellular genes such as those for β-actin (30), ornithine decarboxylase (31), and other unidentified genes revealed by differential screening of cDNA libraries (32) are also rapidly induced by addition of serum or growth factors.

Since the first step in the action of polypeptide growth factors is to bind to specific receptors located at the cell surface, a central problem in understanding their mechanism of action is to identify which early events in the membrane and cytosol may play roles in transmitting the mitogenic signal to the nucleus. In the present article, we concentrate on recent developments that have improved our understanding of the molecular signals underlying the induction of c-*fos* and c-*myc*. Special emphasis will be placed upon novel effects of peptides of the bombesin family and on the role of protein kinase C in mediating the expression of these genes.

I. Early Protooncogene Expression

In addition to rapid events in the membrane and cytosol, serum and growth factors transiently induce the expression of the protooncogenes c-*fos* and c-*myc* (30, 33–36). Protooncogenes represent the cellular counterparts of transforming DNA sequences initially isolated from acutely transforming retroviruses. Since these cellular genes are highly conserved during evolution and because many protooncogenes are expressed in developing embryonic tissues, it is widely thought that they may play a role in the regulation of normal growth and differentiation. Indeed, expression of a transfected *myc* gene (37–39) or microinjection of the c-*myc* protein into quiescent 3T3 cells (40) stimulates entry into DNA synthesis in the presence of other growth factors. Transfection of fibroblasts with the c-*fos* gene can also lead to transformation when the gene is linked to a viral long terminal repeat to enhance transcription, or by the removal of sequences at the 3' end

---

* c-*fos* and c-*myc* are the normal cellular (c) homologues of the transforming genes of the FBJ osteosarcoma (*fos*) and avian myelocytomatosis (*myc*) viruses, respectively [Eds.].

(reviewed in *41*). The function(s) of the products of the c-*fos* and c-*myc* protooncogenes is (are) unknown. Since these genes encode nuclear proteins (*41–45*) it is plausible that their transient expression in early G_1 may play a role in the transduction of the mitogenic signal in the nucleus.

In 3T3 cells stimulated to proliferate by serum, the rate of c-*fos* transcription (*30*) and the level of c-*fos* mRNA are increased within minutes (*34–36*). Platelet-derived growth factor (PDGF)* is considerably more effective than epidermal growth factor (EGF) in promoting the increase in c-*fos* mRNA levels. It is becoming increasingly recognized that inducible gene expression involves specific transcription factors that interact with cis-acting DNA sequences (*46*). A short sequence located in the 5′ flanking region of the c-*fos* gene is required for efficient transcriptional activation (*47*). Specific DNA-binding proteins in crude nuclear extracts that interact selectively with this sequence in the 5′ flanking region of the c-*fos* gene have been identified and subsequently purified (*48, 49, 49a*). Treatment with serum has no effect on the binding activity or abundance of this factor (*48, 49*). Recently, a factor that binds to a different sequence of the c-*fos* 5′ flanking region has been detected in extracts from 3T3 cells treated with PDGF (*50*). Modulation of c-*fos* transcription may involve both positive and negative transcription factors (*51*). These results imply that the increase in c-*fos* transcription might be mediated by multiple cis-acting sequences and transcription factors.

The induction of c-*fos* mRNA is rapidly followed by the transient expression of high levels of c-*fos* protein (*34, 35*) which undergoes extensive posttranslational modification (*41*), including phosphorylation (*52*). The transient induction of c-*fos* mRNA and protein suggests that additional control occurs at the level of turnover. The half-life of c-*fos* mRNA is only 9 minutes and a sequence at the 3′ end of the c-*fos* mRNA molecule is involved in its low stability (*53*). It has been suggested that an (A + T)-rich sequence in the 3′-untranslated region of several unstable RNAs is responsible for rapid turnover (*54*).

A significant increase in c-*myc* mRNA appears 30 minutes after mitogenic stimulation; the maximum increase occurs after 3 hours of stimulation (*30, 33, 34, 55, 56*). Similar results have been obtained by different investigators, although the precise timing and magnitude of the response depend on the cell line used, the assay employed, and

---

* Abbreviations used: GRP, gastrin-releasing peptide; PDGF, platelet-derived growth factor; FDGF, fibroblast-derived growth factor; EGF, epidermal growth factor; AP1, a transcription factor designated "activator protein 1."

the mitogen added. In contrast to the transcriptional activation seen with c-*fos*, posttranscriptional modification at the level of RNA turnover appears to account for much of the increase in c-*myc* mRNA level after mitogenic stimulation (57).

The increase in c-*fos* and c-*myc* mRNA levels is not prevented by inhibitors of protein synthesis (33, 58). In fact, these genes were overexpressed when growth factors were added together with drugs such as cycloheximide or anisomycin (33, 58). These findings indicate that the increase in c-*fos* and c-*myc* mRNA levels is not secondary to the growth response. On the contrary, it is logical to assume that the cellular machinery leading to the induction of these genes is inactive in quiescent cells but poised to respond to specific signals generated in response to receptor occupancy.

In view of these considerations it is important to determine whether any early event in the membrane and cytosol evoked by growth factors is causally linked to the increased expression of these genes. The analysis of these cause–effect relationships requires the use of defined extracellular factors. We reported that the amphibian tetradecapeptide bombesin stimulates Swiss 3T3 cells to recommence DNA synthesis and cell division (*16*). This peptide which, like PDGF, is a mitogen in the absence of other grow&h-promoting agents, exists in a number of closely related molecular forms in both normal and abnormal mammalian tissues. These bombesin-related peptides are also potent mitogens for Swiss 3T3 cells, and their mitogenic effects are mediated by specific, high-affinity receptors that do not recognize other growth factors for these cells, including PDGF and EGF; both mitogenesis and receptor binding are selectively and reversibly inhibited by a bombesin antagonist (ref. in Section III). All these findings indicate that this family of novel mitogenic peptides may provide a new and attractive model with which to elucidate the mechanism(s) leading to an increase in protooncogene expression.

II. Bombesin

A. Bombesin: Biological Effects and Distribution

A large number of new regulatory peptides have been identified in the brain, gastrointestinal tract, and other tissues (*10–13*). These peptides, which elicit a multiplicity of biological responses, appear to behave as local hormones or neurotransmitters acting in a paracrine or autocrine fashion on adjacent cells. Bombesin was originally isolated from amphibian skin (59). It has a number of potent pharmacological effects in animals (60–64), and is immunologically related to several endogenous mammalian peptides (65–67). The first bombesin-like peptides to be characterized in mammals was gastrin-releasing peptide (GRP), a 27-amino-acid peptide originally isolated from porcine gut (68) and subsequently found in the brain (69) and in adult and fetal human lung (70, 71). The neuromedins are another class of bombesin-related peptides identified in the brain and spinal cord (72–74). These peptides are found in central and peripheral neurons and neuroendocrine cells (64). High concentrations of bombesin-like peptides have been found in human pulmonary (75–80) and thyroid (81) carcinomas. Both GRP and the neuromedins exhibit striking sequence homology with the bombesin molecule; in particular the carboxyl terminal heptapeptide has been strongly conserved in all the members of this family of peptides.

B. Mitogenic Response of Swiss 3T3 Cells to Bombesin

Bombesin is a potent mitogen for Swiss 3T3 cells (16). At nanomolar concentrations, this peptide markedly enhances the ability of fresh serum to stimulate DNA synthesis in confluent and quiescent cultures of these cells. In a low concentration of serum (3.5%), bombesin stimulates 3T3 cell proliferation. In serum-free media, bombesin induces DNA synthesis in the absence of any other growth-promoting agents with a half-maximal effect at a concentration of 1 nM (Fig. 1). The ability of bombesin, like platelet-derived growth factor (PDGF) and the PDGF-like fibroblast-derived growth factor (FDGF) (82–86), to act as a sole mitogen for Swiss 3T3 cells is in striking contrast to other modulators of cell growth, which are mitogenically active only in synergistic combinations (16, 24).

The stimulation of DNA synthesis by bombesin is markedly potentiated by a variety of other extracellular factors including insulin, colchicine, PDGF, and FDGF. These mitogens both increase the maximal response elicited by bombesin and decrease the bombesin concentration required to produce a half-maximal response (Fig. 1). Other mitogenic agents, including the tumor promoters of the phorbol ester family, vasopressin, and cyclic AMP elevating agents fail to enhance bombesin-induced mitogenesis, suggesting a convergence in their mechanism of action (24).

Endogenous mammalian analogues of bombesin, including GRP and the neuromedins, act as functional agonists in the stimulation of DNA synthesis (87), thus pointing to a possible role for bombesin-like peptides in cell growth regulation *in vivo*. As mentioned previously

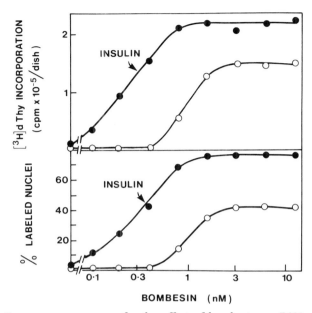

FIG. 1. Dose–response curves for the effect of bombesin on DNA synthesis by quiescent cultures of Swiss 3T3 cells in the absence (open circles) or in the presence (closed circles) of insulin at 1 μg/ml. The peptide was added to confluent and quiescent cultures in 2 ml of Dulbecco's modified Eagle's medium (DMEM) containing [³H]thymidine. DNA synthesis was assessed either by incorporation into acid-insoluble material (upper) or by autoradiography (lower) at 40 hours after continuous exposure to radioactive thymidine (see 16 for other experimental details).

(2, 5, 17, 18), there is now intense interest in tumor-derived growth factors that play a role in sustaining abnormal cell proliferation by an autocrine growth mechanism. In view of the potent mitogenic effects of bombesin we suggested (16) that the ectopic production of mammalian forms of this peptide by small cell carcinoma of the lung (SCCL) may play an important role as part of such an autocrine growth circuit. This suggestion has been supported by the recent reports of a growth-promoting activity for bombesin and GRP, in both normal human bronchial epithelial (88) and SCCL cells (89, 90), and the finding that anti-bombesin and anti-GRP monoclonal antibodies inhibit the growth of these cells both *in vitro* and *in vivo* (80, 91). In the light of these recent findings, the use of peptides of the bombesin family as model mitogens for the elucidation of the mechanism(s) underlying cell proliferation assumes an added significance.

C. The Mitogenic Effects of Peptides of the Bombesin Family Are Mediated by Specific High-Affinity Receptors

An important step in the elucidation of the mechanism of bombesin-stimulated mitogenesis is to determine the presence of specific receptors for this peptide in Swiss 3T3 cells. We found that GRP binds to intact, quiescent Swiss 3T3 cells in a specific, saturable, and reversible manner (87). Scatchard analysis indicates the presence of a single class of high-affinity sites of K_d about 1 nM and a value for the number of binding sites per cell of approximately 1.25×10^5 (87). Specific binding of [Tyr^4]bombesin has been demonstrated in pancreatic acinar cells (92), rat brain membranes (93), and pituitary cells (94). A comparison of the results of these studies with our own shows close agreement for the affinities of the receptors, although Swiss 3T3 cells appear to possess considerably more receptors than either pancreatic acinar or pituitary cells.

GRP binding to Swiss 3T3 cells was not inhibited by other mitogens, including PDGF, FDGF (82, 86), EGF (95), vasopressin (14, 15), phorbol 12,13-dibutyrate (PBt$_2$) (96), insulin (95), and two neuropeptides—a vasoactive intestinal peptide and substance P (SP)*—which exhibit a slight C-terminal homology with peptides of the bombesin family (87). This result strongly suggests that peptides of the bombesin family interact with receptors differing from those recognizing other mitogens for Swiss 3T3 cells.

An important aspect in the study of hormone receptors is the comparison between the ability of hormonal agonists and antagonists to bind to high-affinity sites and their relative potency in either eliciting or inhibiting a characteristic biological response (97). Structure–activity studies, using a range of peptides structurally related to bombesin and GRP, demonstrate a striking parallelism between the ability of these analogues to inhibit binding and their relative mitogenic potency (87).

An analogue of substance P, [DArg^1,DPro^2,DTrp^{7,9},Leu^{11}]SP, is the first bombesin antagonist reported (98, 99). It causes a marked reduction in GRP binding and inhibits both bombesin and GRP-induced mitogenesis (87, 100). In contrast, it has no significant effect on the stimulation of DNA synthesis by a variety of other mitogens, including PDGF (87).

---

* Substance P is a tachykinin, an undecapeptide of known structure, abbreviated here SP [Eds.].

To gain information concerning the basic physical properties of the bombesin/GRP receptor, we used affinity-labeling to identify surface components of Swiss 3T3 cells that specifically recognize GRP. Homobifunctional disuccinimidyl cross-linking agents have been successfully employed to identify receptors for other peptide mitogens, including those for EGF and PDGF. Analysis of extracts of cells incubated with labeled GRP and subsequently treated with a variety of disuccinimidyl cross-linking reagents revealed the presence of a major band migrating with an apparent molecular weight of 75,000–85,000 (101). Several lines of evidence, including specificity and dose–response relationships, support the conclusion that this protein is a component of the receptor for peptides of the bombesin family in these cells (101, 102). All these studies indicate that the mitogenic response of Swiss 3T3 cells to peptides of the bombesin family is mediated by a novel mitogenic receptor.

D. Induction of c-*fos* and c-*myc* by Bombesin

The fact that bombesin-related peptides interact with receptors distinct from those of other mitogens, including PDGF, makes this family of peptides an attractive model with which to explore the mechanism(s) underlying early protooncogene induction. Moreover, the striking similarity observed between bombesin and PDGF in their ability to stimulate mitogenesis in the absence of other growth factors, suggested that bombesin might elicit a similar array of early biological responses (24), including the induction of the cellular oncogenes c-*fos* and c-*myc*. In accord with this, we have made a detailed study of the effect of bombesin and structurally related peptides on the c-*fos* and c-*myc* mRNA levels in Swiss 3T3 cells.

Quiescent cultures of Swiss 3T3 cells were treated with bombesin at 6 nM, a saturating concentration, to elicit early responses and mitogenesis in this cell line (16, 87, 100). The 2.2-kilobase c-*fos* mRNA which is at the limit of detection in quiescent cells is markedly increased by bombesin. Figure 2 shows that c-*fos* RNA was detected as early as 10 minutes after bombesin addition, was maximally increased after 30 minutes, and decreased thereafter. Densitomer tracing of the autoradiograms indicated that bombesin increased the level of c-*fos* mRNA in the 30 minute samples by 122 ± 14-fold (103). The addition of bombesin to quiescent cultures of Swiss 3T3 cells also increased the c-*myc* mRNA level. In contrast to the rapid induction of c-*fos*, the 2.4-kilobase c-*myc* mRNA was detectable within 30 minutes after

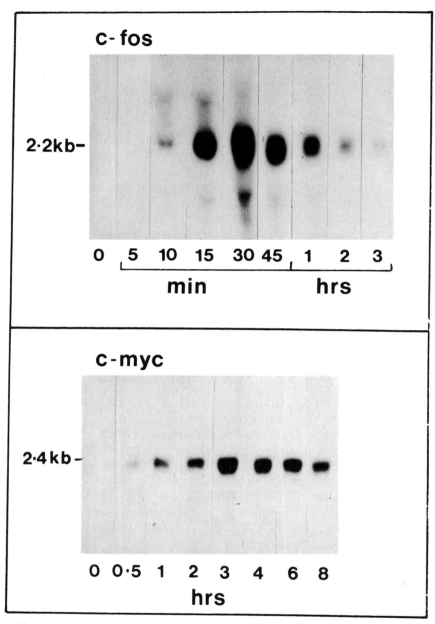

FIG. 2. Time-course of c-*fos* and c-*myc* induction by bombesin. Quiescent cultures of Swiss 3T3 cells grown in 175-cm^2 Nunc flasks were washed and incubated with DMEM containing bombesin (6.2 nM) for the indicated times. Total RNA was extracted, fractionated on a 1% agarose/6% formaldehyde gel, and analyzed for c-*fos* and c-*myc* mRNA (Northern blotting) as described in *103*.

bombesin addition, and the maximum increase (82 ± 16-fold; $n = 13$) occurred after 3 hours of stimulation. A typical experiment is shown in Fig. 2. The peak levels of c-*fos* and c-*myc* mRNAs induced by bombesin were comparable to those promoted by addition of PDGF to parallel cultures (*103*). In contrast, the mRNA levels of the protooncogene c-Harvey-*ras* (c-*ras*[H]), varied little during the time-course examined. Similar results have been reported by other investigators (*104–107*).

The dependence of c-*fos* and c-*myc* induction on bombesin concentration is shown in Fig. 3. The concentration of peptide required for half-maximal increase in the level of c-*fos* mRNA was 1 nM. Half-maximal increase in c-*myc* mRNA content occurred at 0.9 nM. These concentrations are virtually identical to the concentration (1 nM) required for the half-maximal stimulation of DNA synthesis by this peptide in serum-free medium (*16, 103*).

The mitogenic response to bombesin and related peptides depends upon their binding to specific high-affinity receptors that are distinguishable from those of other growth factors for these cells, including PDGF (*87*). As previously mentioned, the peptide [DArg[1],DPro[2],DTrp[7,9],Leu[11]]SP inhibits the binding of bombesin to its receptor and bombesin-stimulated DNA synthesis in Swiss 3T3 cells. Figure 4 shows that this inhibitor prevents the increase in c-*fos* and c-*myc* RNA levels promoted by bombesin. In contrast, the antagonist had only a slight effect on the c-*fos* and c-*myc* induction caused by PDGF. Gastrin-releasing peptide (GRP) and neuromedin B, which exhibit striking sequence homology with the highly conserved carboxyl-terminal heptapeptide of bombesin, also increased c-*fos* mRNA levels whereas the amino-terminal fragment of GRP, which has no homology with bombesin, did not increase the c-*fos* mRNA level, even at 500 nM.

The findings discussed in this section demonstrate that additions of regulatory peptides of the bombesin family to quiescent cultures of Swiss 3T3 cells cause a striking increase in c-*fos* and c-*myc* mRNA levels. These results strongly suggest that the peptides of the bombesin family promote early protooncogene induction through their own receptors. The time-course and magnitude of these effects are comparable to those induced by PDGF added at saturating concentrations for eliciting mitogenesis. Since bombesin and PDGF bind to different receptors in the cell membrane, a fundamental question is to determine whether any of the early signals in the membrane and cytosol evoked by bombesin and PDGF (*24*) play a role in increasing the expression of c-*fos* and c-*myc*.

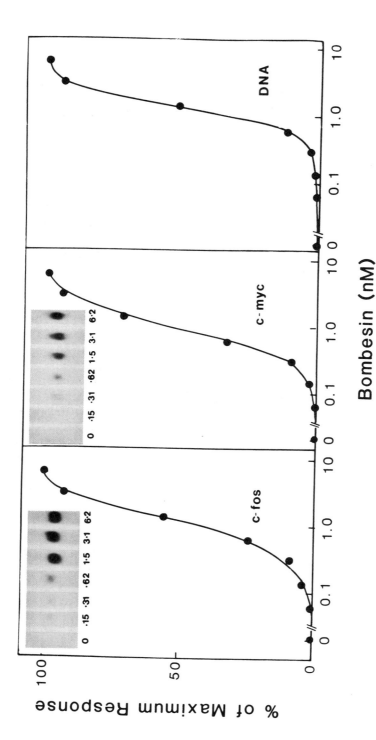

FIG. 3. Effect of varying concentrations of bombesin on the levels of *c-fos* and *c-myc* mRNAs and on DNA synthesis in Swiss 3T3 cells. Quiescent cultures of Swiss 3T3 cells were stimulated with bombesin at the indicated concentrations. Total RNA, extracted after 30 minutes for *c-fos* and 3 hours for *c-myc*, was analyzed by Northern blotting (103). [³H]Thymidine incorporation was measured after 30 hours of incubation. The *c-fos* and *c-myc* levels were measured by scanning densitometry and the values are expressed as a percentage of the maximum level.

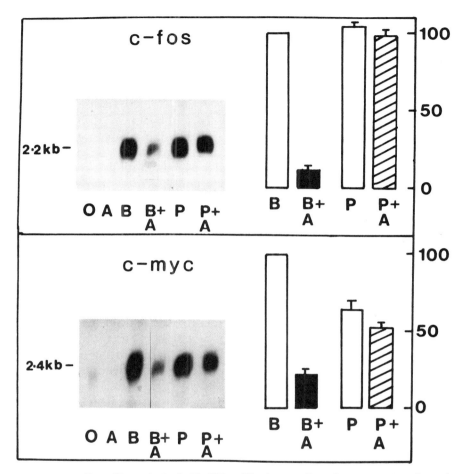

FIG. 4. Effect of [DArg¹,DPro²,DTrp⁷,⁹,Leu¹¹] substance P on the increase in c-*fos* and c-*myc* mRNA levels promoted by bombesin or PDGF. Quiescent cultures of Swiss 3T3 cells were incubated with DMEM without (O) or with either 1.6 nM bombesin (B) or 0.75 nM PDGF (P) in the absence (open bars) or presence (closed bars) of [DArg¹,DPro²,DTrp⁷,⁹,Leu¹¹] substance P (A). Total RNA was extracted after 30 minutes for c-*fos* and 3 hours for c-*myc*. Left: Autoradiograms of Northern blots of representative experiments for c-*fos* and c-*myc*. Right: Levels of c-*fos* and c-*myc* mRNAs measured by scanning densitometry. The values (mean ±, $n = 4$) are expressed as the percentage of the maximum level obtained in each experiment.

III. Protein Kinase C, Cytosolic Calcium Ion, and Cyclic Adenylate

A. The Role of Protein Kinase C in Mitogenic Signaling

One of the major signal transduction pathways defined recently involves the enzyme protein kinase C, a widely distributed cyclic nucleotide- and calmodulin-independent phosphotransferase that is activated by unsaturated diacylglycerols in the presence of phospholipids and physiological concentrations of calcium ion (108, 109). These kinetic properties were established using highly purified preparations of the enzyme. The complete amino-acid sequences of several forms of protein kinase C from bovine (110) and rat brain (111) have been deduced from cDNA clones. These studies revealed the existence of several domains; the catalytic domain at the carboxyl terminal shows substantial homology to sequences of other protein kinases (110). The existence of at least three different forms of the enzyme (112) raises the possibility that they are involved in different signal transduction pathways, a proposition that warrants much more experimental work.

Although diacylglycerols are normally absent from plasma membranes, the occupancy of a variety of receptors triggers phospholipid turnover, thereby generating diacylglycerol, which is thought then to act as a "second messenger" responsible for the activation of protein kinase C (109). Diacylglycerols may result from the phosphodiesterase cleavage of phosphatidylinositol 4,5-bisphosphate (109), but other sources of diacylglycerol have also been described (113). Studies with both cell-free preparations (114–117) and intact fibroblasts (118) show that tumor promoters of the phorbol ester family can substitute for diacylglycerol in the activation of protein kinase C (108). Further studies have shown that homogeneous preparations of protein kinase C from rat brain bind phorbol 12,13-dibutyrate (PBt$_2$) (119, 120) and that 1,2-diacylglycerols compete with this ligand for common binding sites (121). It is increasingly recognized that the specific high-affinity receptor for phorbol ester detected in a wide variety of cells and tissues (96, 122–126) is a tertiary complex formed between protein kinase C, calcium, and membrane phospholipids, and that unsaturated diacylglycerols generated by phospholipid breakdown may represent the endogenous analogues of the phorbol esters and structurally related plant diterpenes (108, 109, 127–129).

Protein kinase C has been implicated in the signal transduction for the activation of many short-term cellular responses (reviewed in

109). Of particular interest in the context of this article is the evidence implicating protein kinase C in mediating long-term responses. Phorbol esters stimulate DNA synthesis and cell division in quiescent cells in synergy with other growth factors (*95, 96, 127*). The mitogenic effect is mediated by high-affinity binding sites (*96*) that have been identified as protein kinase C (see above). As discussed in the following section, activation of protein kinase C is one of the earliest responses elicited by the addition of serum (*130*) and the mitogens PDGF (*118, 130*), vasopressin (*131*), and bombesin (*132*) to intact quiescent Swiss 3T3 cells. Hence, protein kinase C may not only mediate the diverse biological actions of phorbol esters, but could also play a fundamental role in the regulation of cell proliferation (*28*).

An important step for testing this hypothesis was to demonstrate that exogenously added diacylglycerols could mimic the action of phorbol esters in stimulating the reinitiation of DNA synthesis and cell division in quiescent cells. The addition of the synthetic diacylglycerol 1-oleoyl-2-acetylglycerol (OAG), which directly competes with PBt_2 for binding to specific receptors in intact Swiss 3T3 cells and rapidly stimulates protein kinase C in these cells (*129*), is a potent mitogen acting synergistically with such other growth factors as insulin. Indeed, several lines of evidence indicate that exogenously added synthetic diacylglycerol shares with phorbol ester a common pathway of mitogenic action via the stimulation of protein kinase C activity in intact 3T3 cells (*28, 129*). These results provide support for the hypothesis that this phosphotransferase system is of importance in the control of cellular proliferation.

B. Peptides of the Bombesin Family Activate Protein Kinase C

We have proposed that a rapid increase in the phosphorylation of an 80,000 M_r cellular protein (termed 80K) by biologically active phorbol esters (*118*) or diacylglycerols either exogenously added (*129*) or generated endogenously by addition of phospholipase C (*118*) reflects the activation of protein kinase C. In contrast, both insulin and EGF, neither of which stimulates endogenous phospholipase C activity in 3T3 cells, failed to increase 80K phosphorylation (*28*). Further, prolonged exposure of 3T3 cells to saturating concentrations (0.8 μM) of PBt_2, which leads to both a marked reduction in the number of specific PBt_2-binding sites in these cells (*96, 97, 134, 135*) and to the disappearance of protein kinase C activity in cell-free preparations (*136–142*), abolishes the 80K phosphoprotein generated in response to phorbol esters and exogenous or endogenous diacylglycerol (*118,*

129, 130). There is direct evidence supporting this conclusion: The same 80K phosphorylation can be generated in cell-free extracts by activation of protein kinase C (i.e., by addition of phosphatidylserine, Ca^{2+}, PBt$_2$, and ATP), or by addition of the purified enzyme (*139, 140*). All these findings taken together demonstrate that the phosphorylation of 80K is mediated by the activation of protein kinase C in intact cells. Although the nature and role of the 80K protein remain to be elucidated, changes in its phosphorylation state provide a specific marker for assessing which mitogenic agents activate protein kinase C in intact cells.

In the course of studies designed to determine which extracellular agents activate this phosphotransferase system in intact and quiescent 3T3 cells, we found that the addition of bombesin causes a potent and rapid increase in 80K phosphorylation (*132*). An enhancement in phosphorylation can be detected as early as 15 seconds after the addition of bombesin, and maximal phosphorylation is obtained in less than 60. Thus, the time-course for bombesin-stimulated 80K phosphorylation is very similar to that for phorbol esters (*118*). The increase in 80K phosphorylation produced by bombesin is concentration-dependent; the half-maximal effect is seen at a concentration (1.5 nM) close to that for bombesin stimulation of DNA synthesis (1 nM).

The 80K phosphoproteins generated in response to the addition of either bombesin or PBt$_2$ comigrate in one- and two-dimensional polyacrylamide gel electrophoresis. Further, peptide mapping of the 80K phosphoprotein bands generated by bombesin and PBt$_2$ excised from one-dimensional polyacrylamide gel electrophoresis showed the presence of similar phosphopeptide fragments (*132*). Although these findings indicate that bombesin and PBt$_2$ stimulate the phosphorylation of an identical 80K protein, it is plausible that the phosphorylation of 80K seen in response to bombesin is caused by the activation of a phosphotransferse system other than protein kinase C. To test this possibility, cultures of Swiss 3T3 cells were treated with a saturating concentration of PBt$_2$ for 40 hours.

As discussed below, this treatment causes a striking down-regulation of protein kinase C in quiescent Swiss 3T3 cells. It also prevents the increase in 80K phosphorylation elicited by subsequent addition of phorbol esters, phospholipase C, or oleoylacetylglycerol (*118, 129, 130, 137*). Prolonged preliminary treatment with PBt$_2$ completely abolishes the effect of bombesin on 80K phosphorylation (*132*). These findings strongly suggest that addition of bombesin causes a rapid stimulation of protein kinase C activity in intact Swiss 3T3 cells. Others have reached a similar conclusion (*143*).

To determine whether the stimulation of 80K phosphorylation by peptides of the bombesin family is mediated by specific, high-affinity receptors for these peptides, we tested the ability of the bombesin-related peptides to enhance the phosphorylation of 80K. There is a close correspondence between the ability of bombesin agonists to stimulate 80K phosphorylation and both their relative mitogenic potency and capacity to inhibit specific GRP binding (132). Further, the antagonist [$_D$Arg^1,$_D$Pro^2,$_D$Trp^{7,9},Leu^{11}]SP abolishes the increase in 80K phosphorylation induced by bombesin and GRP (132) at a concentration similar to that required to block both mitogenesis and receptor binding (87, 100). These structure–activity relationships strongly suggest that the activation of protein kinase C by bombesin-related peptides is mediated by the specific high-affinity receptors we have described for these peptides in Swiss 3T3 cells (87, 101, 102).

C. The Role of Protein Kinase C in Mediating the Induction of c-*fos* and c-*myc* mRNA in Quiescent Cells

Addition of phorbol esters to quiescent cells causes a marked increase in c-*fos* and c-*myc* mRNA levels (33, 103, 107, 141, 144, 145). This implies that activation of protein kinase C, a major receptor of the tumor promoters, leads to c-*fos* and c-*myc* induction. This interpretation is substantiated by the finding that the addition of oleoylacetylglycerol or phospholipase C, which activates protein kinase C in intact cells, also increases c-*fos* expression in quiescent cells (145). This raises the possibility that activation of protein kinase C may represent one of the molecular steps in the sequence of events linking receptor occupancy and protooncogene expression.

As described in the preceding section, bombesin and structurally related peptides rapidly increase the phosphorylation of an acidic 80-kDa cellular protein (80K), which reflects the activation of protein kinase C in intact and quiescent 3T3 cells. To determine the contribution of protein kinase C activation to the increase in c-*fos* and c-*myc* mRNA levels by bombesin, we exploited the selective down-modulation of protein kinase C achieved by long-term treatment with phorbol esters. Chronic exposure to phorbol esters leads to a marked decrease in the number of specific phorbol ester-binding sites in intact cells (96, 135) and to the disappearance of measurable protein kinase C activity in cell-free preparations (136–142). This long-term exposure to PBt$_2$ also prevents the increase in the phosphorylation of the 80-kDa cellular protein elicited by subsequent addition of direct activators of protein kinase C (i.e., phorbol esters or diacylglycerols) or bombesin (132). In parallel with this loss of protein kinase C activity,

278   ENRIQUE ROZENGURT AND JAMES SINNETT-SMITH

the cells become desensitized to further biological effects elicited by either phorbol esters (96, 135, 138, 141, 144, 144a) or exogenous diacylglycerols (129, 146).

If the action of bombesin on c-fos and c-myc mRNA levels is mediated through activation of protein kinase C, long-term exposure to PBt₂ should block the increase in the expression of these cellular oncogenes caused by a subsequent challenge with bombesin. To test this possibility quiescent cultures of 3T3 cells were treated with PBt₂ at a saturating concentration (0.8 μM). After 40 hours, control and treated cultures were washed extensively to remove residual PBt₂ (147) and then transferred to medium containing PBt₂, bombesin, or PDGF. As shown in Fig. 5 prolonged exposure to 3T3 cells to PBt₂ completely abolished the increase in c-fos mRNA induced by a subsequent addition of PBt₂. Down-regulation of protein kinase C markedly decreased but did not abolish the induction of c-fos promoted by bombesin and PDGF (Fig. 5).

These experiments were extended by studying the effects of various concentrations of bombesin in control cells and cells down-regulated by protein kinase C. The levels of c-fos and c-myc mRNAs and cellular DNA synthesis were measured after 30 minutes, 3 hours, and 40 hours of incubation, respectively. The results (shown in Fig. 6) demonstrate that desensitization of the protein kinase C pathway markedly decreased c-fos and c-myc induction promoted by a subsequent addition of bombesin. Significantly, long-term treatment with PBt₂ also blocked the stimulation of DNA synthesis induced by bombesin in serum-free medium (Fig. 6; 103). Similar conclusions have been reached by others (106, 107). Thus, activation of protein kinase C may play an important role in mediating the early protooncogene induction and the proliferative response elicited by bombesin and structurally related peptides in Swiss 3T3 cells.

There are several important controls concerning the experiment discussed above. Long-term exposure to PBt₂ does not impair the induction of c-fos by a growth factor that does not activate protein kinase C (e.g., EGF). This finding strongly suggests that the prolonged incubation with PBt₂ does not damage the inducibility of the c-fos gene. In addition, prolonged treatment with PBt₂ neither alters the binding of bombesin to its receptor (I. Zachary and E. Rozengurt, unpublished results) nor prevents the mobilization of intracellular Ca²⁺ caused by bombesin (148). All these findings suggest that long-term exposure to PBt₂ decreases c-fos and c-myc induction by bombesin acting through protein kinase C rather than by reducing the functional capacity of bombesin receptors. Protein kinase C activation

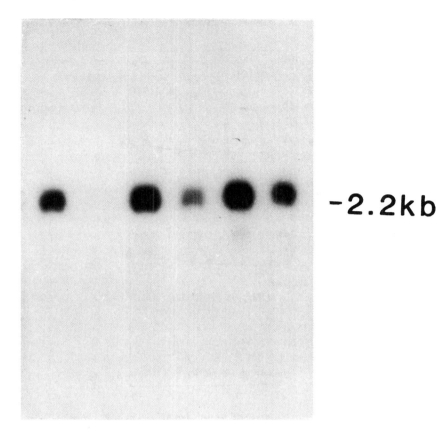

-2.2kb

− pt − pt − pt

PBt₂   BOM   PDGF

FIG. 5. Effect of treatment of 3T3 cells with phorbol dibutyrate (PBt₂) on the induction of c-*fos* promoted by subsequent addition of PBt₂, bombesin, or PDGF. Quiescent cultures of Swiss 3T3 cells were incubated for 40 hours in conditioned medium in the absence (−) or presence (pt) of Bt₂phorbol (PBt₂) (800 nM). At the end of the incubation period all cultures were washed with DMEM containing 1 mg/ml bovine serum albumin and incubated in this medium for 20 minutes at 37°C before two additional washes with the same medium. This procedure was shown previously to remove any residual PBt₂. The cultures were then incubated with PBt₂ at 200 nM, bombesin (BOM) at 6 nM, or PDGF at 2 nM. Total RNA was extracted after 30 minutes of incubation and analyzed for c-*fos* by Northern blotting as described (*103*). The radioactivity was visualized by autoradiography.

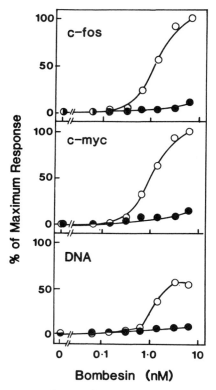

Fɪɢ. 6. Effect of treatment of 3T3 cells with PBt₂ on the increase in c-*fos* and c-*myc* mRNA levels and on the stimulation of [³H]thymidine incorporation promoted by varying concentrations of bombesin. Quiescent cultures of Swiss 3T3 cells were incubated for 40 hours in their own conditioned medium in the absence (open symbols) or presence (closed symbols) of PBt₂ (800 nM). At this time, the cells were washed as described in Fig. 5 and incubated with bombesin at the indicated concentrations. Upper and middle panels: the values expressed as percentage of maximum level were obtained by scanning densitometry of Northern blots of total RNA. Lower panel: [³H]Thymidine incorporation into acid-precipitable material was measured after 40 hours of incubation; the values shown represent the percentage of maximum stimulation produced by addition of DMEM containing 10% (v/v) fetal bovine serum.

is also implicated in the pathway(s) leading to increased expression of c-*myc* (*141, 144*). The molecular mechanisms by which activation of protein kinase C enhances gene expression remain unknown. A short nucleotide sequence may play a crucial role in the transcriptional activation by phorbol esters of several genes; this sequence is the binding site for the transcription factor "activated protein 1" (AP1)

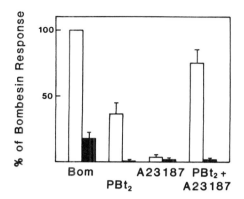

FIG. 7. Effect of bombesin, PBt₂, and A23187 on c-*fos* mRNA levels. Quiescent cultures of Swiss 3T3 cells were incubated for 40 hours in conditioned medium in the absence (open bars) or presence (closed bars) of PBt₂ (800 nM). The cultures were then washed as described in Fig. 5 and incubated at 37°C for 30 min in the presence of bombesin (6.2 nM), PBt₂ (200 nM), A23187 (50 nM), and PBt₂ + A32187 (200 and 50 nM). The values are expressed as a percentage of the maximum level in each experiment and were obtained by scanning densitometry of Northern blots of total RNA. The results shown represent the mean ± SEM of 4 independent experiments. Other experimental details were as described in *103*.

(*149, 150*). The elucidation of the role of this factor in the induction of c-*fos* and c-*myc* by phorbol esters and growth factors and the relationships of AP1 to other transcription factors apparently involved in the induction of c-*fos* (*48–50, 151*) require further experimental work.

D. Calcium Ion Flux and Induction of c-*fos* and c-*myc*

While the findings discussed in the preceding section implicate protein kinase C activation in the sequence of events leading to c-*fos* and c-*myc* induction it is also clear that activation of protein kinase C is not sufficient to elicit a maximal induction of c-*fos* and c-*myc*. For example, direct activation of protein kinase C by dibutyryl phorbol (PBt₂) at saturating concentrations (*96, 118, 127*) increased c-*fos* and c-*myc* mRNA levels producing $36 \pm 7\%$ ($n = 9$) and $52 \pm 6\%$ ($n = 7$) of the maximal induction promoted by bombesin (*103*, Fig. 7). Thus, activation of protein kinase C is not sufficient to evoke a maximal response. A similar conclusion was reached in other studies. It is therefore likely that other early signals may also enhance the expression of c-*fos* and c-*myc*.

One of the earliest events elicited by bombesin and related peptides in Swiss 3T3 cells is a mobilization of calcium from intracellular stores thereby leading to a decrease in the total calcium content of the cells (148, 152). The finding that bombesin causes a rapid threefold transient increase in cytosolic calcium as measured by the fluorescent calcium-binding indicators quin-2 and fura-2 (148, 153) suggests that release from intracellular stores promotes calcium efflux by activation of the plasma membrane calcium-dependent (transporting) adenosinetriphosphatase (Ca^{2+}-ATPase, EC 3.6.1.38). The mobilization of calcium may be mediated by inositol 1,4,5-trisphosphate ($InsP_3$), which has been proposed as a second messenger in the action of many ligands that induce receptor-mediated inositol lipid turnover and calcium efflux (154, 155). $InsP_3$ is formed as a result of increased hydrolysis of phosphatidylinositol 4,5-bisphosphate ($PtdInsP_2$) in the plasma membrane, a process that also generates 1,2-diacylglycerols (DAG). Bombesin induces a marked increase in $InsP_3$ production in Swiss 3T3 cells (148, 153, 156).

Since bombesin induces mobilization of calcium from an intracellular store and increases cytosolic calcium ion concentration in 3T3 cells, we tested the effect of the calcium ionophore A23187 on c-*fos* and c-*myc* induction. Addition of A23187 at 50 nM, a concentration that causes an increase in cytosolic calcium ion comparable to that induced by a saturating concentration of bombesin (148), has only a slight effect on c-*fos* (Fig. 7) and c-*myc* (103) mRNA levels. The calcium ionophore, however, markedly enhanced c-*fos* and c-*myc* induction promoted by PBt_2 (Fig. 7). It should be mentioned that PBt_2 does not induce calcium mobilization in Swiss 3T3 cells (25, 157, 158) and that A23187 at 50 nM does not activate protein kinase C in intact 3T3 cells, as monitored by the phosphorylation of the 80-kDa cellular protein (A. Rodriguez-Pena and E. Rozengurt, unpublished results).

Because bombesin causes a marked increase in cytosolic calcium ion (148), and since elevation of calcium by addition of the ionophore A23187 enhances c-*fos* and c-*myc* induction by PBt_2 (Fig. 7), it is likely that the induction of these cellular oncogenes by bombesin is mediated by the coordinated effects of calcium mobilization and activation of protein kinase C. This interpretation is further substantiated by studies with the neurohypophyseal peptide vasopressin, which is also a potent synergistic mitogen for Swiss 3T3 cells (14, 15, 127), acting via specific receptors (159). Vasopressin rapidly mobilizes calcium (157, 158, 160), activates protein kinase C (131), and induces $InsP_3$ formation (153) in Swiss 3T3 cells. A salient feature is that vasopressin also increases c-*fos* mRNA levels in these cells (Fig. 8). This response is markedly reduced by down-regulation of the protein kinase C pathway. Furthermore, A23187 at concentrations that in-

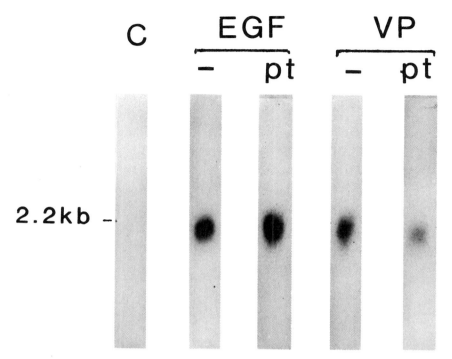

FIG. 8. Effect of EGF or vasopressin (VP) on c-*fos* mRNA levels in control and Swiss 3T3 cells desensitized by protein kinase C. Quiescent cultures were incubated for 40 hours in their own conditioned medium in the absence (−) or presence (pt) of PBt$_2$ (800 nM). At this time the cells were washed as described in the legend to Fig. 4. The cultures were then incubated in the presence of EGF at 5 ng/ml or vasopressin at 20 ng/ml. Parallel cultures were incubated in the absence of peptide (C). Total RNA was extracted after 30 minutes and analyzed by Northern blotting. The radioactivity was visualized by autoradiography.

crease both cystolic calcium and protein kinase C activity causes a striking increase in the level of c-*fos* mRNA in human carcinoma A431 cells (*161*).

E. Cyclic Nucleotides and c-*fos* and c-*myc* Induction

The role of cyclic nucleotides in the control of the proliferative response of quiescent fibroblasts has been the subject of a large and controversial literature (*27*). It is now recognized that a sustained increase in the cellular level of cyclic adenosine 3′,5′-monophosphate (cAMP) constitutes a growth-promoting signal for Swiss 3T3 cells (*162–167*). PDGF induces a striking accumulation of cAMP in quiescent 3T3 cells incubated in the presence of inhibitors of cyclic nucleotide degradation (84). In contrast, other growth-promoting factors (including insulin and EGF) did not increase the level of cAMP.

The alteration of cAMP metabolism by PDGF occurs in an indirect fashion. This mitogen elicits a striking release of arachidonate, which is converted into many biologically active metabolites including stable prostaglandins of the E series. The accumulation of cAMP elicited by PDGF is mediated by increased synthesis of E-type prostaglandins, which in turn leave the cell and stimulate cAMP synthesis through their own receptors (84, 165). Therefore, cAMP may be one of the multiple signals utilized by PDGF to stimulate reinitiation of DNA synthesis in Swiss 3T3 cells. In addition, activation of protein kinase C either by PBt$_2$ or OAG has recently been shown to enhance cAMP accumulation in Swiss 3T3 cells (168). In accord with these findings, bombesin also markedly potentiates the accumulation of cAMP caused by cAMP-elevating agents such as forskolin, an effect mediated at least in part by protein kinase C (J. Millar and E. Rozengurt, unpublished observations).

Since cAMP is one of the early signals that can stimulate mitogenesis in synergy with other growth factors, it is of interest to examine its role in modulating the expression of c-fos and c-myc. Recent studies are not entirely consistent. cAMP-increasing agents appeared not to increase the expression of c-fos in NIH 3T3 cells (107, 145). In contrast, various agents that elevate cAMP stimulated c-fos expression but the effect was only 20% of that promoted by PDGF (169). Finally, cholera toxin did not increase c-fos or c-myc mRNA levels in BALB 3T3 cells but potentiated the effect of EGF on the expression of these genes (170). The differences could be the result of variation in the responsiveness of the cell lines and techniques used to determine mRNA levels. Also, none of the studies included parallel measurements of cAMP levels. Clearly, elucidation of the role of cAMP in the expression of c-fos and c-myc requires further experimental work.

F. Additional Pathways of c-fos Induction

The results discussed in the preceding sections strongly suggest that activation of protein kinase C and calcium ion fluxes act synergistically in inducing the expression of the c-fos and c-myc protooncogenes. It is, however, important to point out that several lines of evidence suggest the existence of additional, as yet not identified, pathways. (1) As can be seen in Fig. 7 the addition of PBt$_2$ and a calcium ionophore to quiescent 3T3 cells is not sufficient to evoke a response equivalent to that elicited by bombesin and PDGF. (2) Down-regulation of the protein kinase C pathway completely blocks the induction of c-*fos* produced either by addition of PBt$_2$ or by the simultaneous addition of PBt$_2$ and calcium ionophore (Fig. 7). In contrast, the prolonged pretreatment with PBt$_2$ does not completely abolish the induction of c-*fos* or c-*myc* promoted by bombesin or PDGF, (Fig. 5 and *103, 107*). (3) The effects of EGF on c-*fos* induction is of special significance. EGF does not activate protein kinase C in intact Swiss 3T3 cells (*118, 133*). Further, the mitogenic effect of this growth factor is not blocked by down-regulation of protein kinase C (*133, 136*). As mentioned before, EGF increases the level of c-*fos* mRNA although it is less potent than either bombesin or PDGF. A salient feature of the results shown in Fig. 8 is that prolonged treatment with PBt$_2$ does not prevent the induction of c-*fos* promoted by EGF. This result points to pathways of control of c-*fos* expression that are completely independent of activation of protein kinase C.

IV. Induction of c-*fos* and c-*myc* Protooncogenes: Significance in the Mitogenic Response

At least two alternative possibilities concerning the role of c-*fos* and c-*myc* induction in fibroblast mitogenesis could be envisaged. The increase in the mRNA levels of these cellular oncogenes could be an obligatory step in the sequence of molecular events leading to initiation of DNA synthesis. Alternatively, the induction of c-*fos* and c-*myc* may be a specific response to one of the signaling pathways activated by bombesin and PDGF, i.e., protein kinase C stimulation and mobilization of calcium pools. The first hypothesis predicts that c-*fos* and c-*myc* induction will occur regardless of the growth factors used to stimulate cell proliferation, while, according to the second, c-*fos* and c-*myc* induction could be dissociated from mitogenesis.

The interaction between bombesin and insulin is useful to distinguish between these alternative possibilities because insulin neither induces Ca^{2+} mobilization (*25, 171*) nor activates protein kinase C in intact Swiss 3T3 cells (*118, 137*), but acts synergistically with bombesin to stimulate DNA synthesis (Fig. 1 and *16*). Insulin increases the maximal response promoted by bombesin and decreases the peptide concentration required to produce a half-maximal effect (from 1.2 to 0.15 nM). If the striking increase in c-*fos* and c-*myc* mRNA levels is an obligatory step in the sequence of events leading to DNA synthesis, insulin should cause a marked shift of the dose–response relationship for the effect of bombesin on the expression of these cellular oncogenes. As shown in Fig. 9, insulin has no effect on c-*fos* and c-*myc* induction by bombesin. Inspection of Fig. 9 reveals that bombesin at

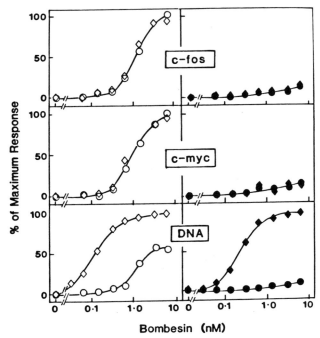

FIG. 9. Effect of different concentrations of bombesin on c-*fos* and c-*myc* mRNA levels and on [³H]thymidine incorporation in the absence (circles) or in the presence (diamonds) of insulin in control (open symbols, left) or protein kinase C-densitized (closed symbols, right) Swiss 3T3 cells. The cultures were treated with 800 nM PBt₂ for 40 hours and subsequently washed as described in the legend to Fig. 5. The cultures were then exposed to different concentrations of bombesin with or without 1 μg/ml insulin. All other experimental details were as described in the legend to Figs. 5 and 6.

low concentrations (0.1–0.3 nM) stimulates DNA synthesis in the presence of insulin, but increases c-*fos* and c-*myc* mRNA levels only slightly. This apparent dissociation was further substantiated in cells with severely down-regulated protein kinase C. In these cells, bombesin at subnanomolar concentrations stimulates DNA synthesis in the presence of insulin but enhances c-*fos* and c-*myc* mRNA levels only slightly (Fig. 9). We conclude that the large induction of c-*fos* and c-*myc* protooncogenes (i.e., 80- to 120-fold) may not be an obligatory event in the stimulation of mitogenesis in 3T3 cells.

Long-term exposure to PBt₂ reduces (by 60%) the induction of c-*myc* by PDGF but does not prevent the mitogenic effect of this growth factor in the presence of insulin (*144*). These results also suggest that c-*myc* induction is not required for the stimulation of mitogenesis.

However, the induction of these genes could be a necessary step in the mitogenic response initiated by ligands that act through protein kinase C, since the stimulation of DNA synthesis by bombesin (in the absence of insulin) is abolished in PBt_2-treated cells. Further experimental work will be required to assess whether the dissociation observed at the level of mRNA expression is maintained at the level of the translation products.

V. Conclusions and Perspectives

In recent years, a remarkable advance has been made in identifying the extracellular factors that control cell proliferation in a variety of cells. These studies opened up experimental avenues to characterize the receptors that both recognize these factors and transmit the mitogenic signal into the cell. Understanding the mechanism of action of growth factors requires the elucidation of the signals generated by receptor occupancy and the identification of the genes that are involved in the transition from G_0 to S Phase.

A logical extension of this approach is to determine which early signals are involved in the control of proliferation-related genes and define the mechanisms by which these genes are regulated. Two major strategies have emerged. On the one hand, recent progress in identifying some of the early signals in the mitogenic response has rendered it possible to establish their contribution in increasing the expression of the early genes, in particular c-*fos* and c-*myc*. Another strategy has been to define the regulatory sequences flanking the coding region of the gene. This information was used for isolating putative transcription factors that could play a crucial role in the flow of information from the receptor to the nucleus. Activation of preexisting transcription factors may involve covalent modification of the protein (e.g., phosphorylation) or an allosteric change in its structure (46). As summarized in the preceding sections and in Fig. 10, the picture that emerges from these complementary approaches is complex. At least three independent signals—activation of protein kinase C, Ca^{2+} mobilization, and cAMP—are involved in the control of c-*fos* and c-*myc* expression. The cause–effect analysis carried out with such factors as EGF that do not elicit these early signals points to additional, unidentified signaling pathways (Fig. 10). Recent results (see Section I) suggest the existence of several cis-acting sequences and transcription factors in the regulation of c-*fos* expression. Whether any of the early signals control directly the activity of the transcription factors remains unknown.

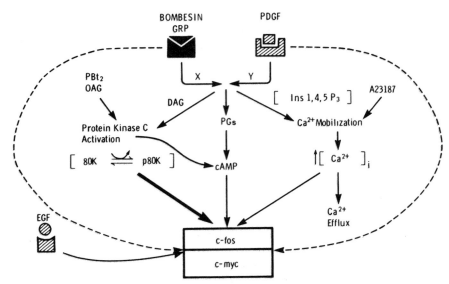

FIG. 10. Early signals in the induction of the protooncogenes c-*fos* and c-*myc*. Bombesin and PDGF activate protein kinase C in quiescent fibroblasts. This effect is mediated by diacylglycerol (DAG), which is formed, at least in part, as a result of the phosphodiesterase cleavage of phosphaditylinositol 4,5-bisphosphate (PtdInsP$_2$). This reaction also generates Ins(1,4,5)P$_3$, another second messenger that triggers the release of Ca^{2+} from intracellular stores and leads to a transient increase in the cytosolic Ca^{2+} concentration. The stimulation of protein kinase C activity in intact cells can be monitored by changes in the phosphorylation of an acidic 80-kDa cellular protein (80K). Activation of protein kinase C can be achieved directly by addition of PBt$_2$ or 1-oleoyl-2-acetylglycerol (OAG). An increase in the cytosolic concentration of calcium ion can be induced by calcium ionophores (e.g., A23187). Protein kinase C can be severely down-regulated by chronic exposure to PBt$_2$. This perturbation can be exploited to identify the cellular responses mediated by protein kinase C (see text). An additional effect promoted by PDGF is a striking increase in the production of prostaglandins, which bind to their own receptors and increase cAMP. All these signals, i.e., protein kinase C activation, Ca^{2+} mobilization (by A23187), and cAMP, are involved in the induction of c-*fos* and c-*myc*. Protein kinase C activation (by PBt$_2$ or OAG) is sufficient to induce c-*fos* and c-*myc*. Calcium mobilization enhances this effect. The binding of EGF to its receptor does not stimulate protein kinase C or increase the cytosolic concentration of calcium in Swiss 3T3 cells. This growth factor is thought to utilize an additional signaling pathway. Furthermore, since down-regulation of the protein kinase C pathways abolishes the induction of c-*fos* and c-*myc* by PBt$_2$ and a calcium ionophore (Fig. 7) but has a partial inhibitory effect on the induction by bombesin or PDGF (Fig. 5), it is postulated that these factors activate other pathways (broken lines). The scheme does not imply that identical mechanisms control the expression of both protooncogenes.

A plausible scenario is based on the fact that all early signals (calcium ion, cAMP, and diacylglycerol) activate protein kinases, which change the biological properties of their target protein by virtue of the phosphorylation of specific residues. Phosphorylation of a transcription factor could enhance or decrease its affinity for the controlling sequence in the gene leading to activation of a positive factor or inactivation of a negative factor, respectively (46). Obviously, these possibilities warrant considerable experimental work.

It is also necessary to point out that there are important post-transcriptional control mechanisms. Indeed, the major control leading to the large increase in the abundance of c-*myc* mRNA appears to be exerted at the level of turnover (Section I). Whether these differences in regulation explain the differences in the time-course of induction of these genes remains unknown. It might be of interest to define whether any of the early signals lead to differential control in the expression of these genes. Finally, little is known about the influence of early signals on the translation of these gene products. The fact that phorbol esters and serum increase the phosphorylation of the c-*fos* protein raises the possibility that the early signals cannot only increase transcription and reduce turnover, but also modify the gene product.

Another area that requires considerable attention is to determine the role of the c-*fos* and c-*myc* products in the proliferative response. First, it will be necessary to clarify whether they play regulatory or obligatory role(s) in the proliferative response. We have proposed that some early events may be crucial in effecting the proliferative response to certain factors, but are not necessary for cell replication in response to others (see 24). Activation of protein kinase C, calcium ion mobilization, and increases in cAMP fall within this class, i.e., they are envisaged as regulatory events. In contrast, other steps will be common in cell replication regardless of the early regulatory signals utilized, i.e., they represent obligatory events. Whether c-*fos* and c-*myc* represent regulatory or obligatory steps in cell multiplication remains unknown. The effect of multiple extracellular factors on gene expression and the use of antisense RNA constructs of c-*fos* (172) may help to clarify this issue. The results obtained with bombesin and insulin strongly suggest that the large induction in c-*fos* and c-*myc* mRNA levels is not necessary for stimulation of DNA synthesis. However, the results cannot rule out that a small increase in these mRNA levels is sufficient to allow a proliferative response in the presence of insulin.

An important conclusion that can be drawn from the preceding considerations is that studies on the identification of the early signals in protooncogene induction as well as the requirements of those genes in the process of reinitiation of cell growth should be conducted with specific growth-promoting factors. In this manner, the contribution of a defined population of receptors and signals in the control of gene expression can be evaluated. The use of serum as a mitogenic stimulus makes it very difficult to define critical cause–effect relationships. In this context, the peptides of the bombesin family, with their multiple agonists and antagonists, defined receptors, and early events provide a valuable model mitogen to further studies on the control of cell proliferation in general and of early gene expression in particular.

ACKNOWLEDGMENTS

We thank Dr. N. Teich for advice and for supplying the c-*fos* probe used throughout, and Mrs. E. Eaton for help in the preparation of the manuscript.

REFERENCES

1. E. Rozengurt, *Curr. Top. Cell. Regul.* 17, 59 (1980).
2. E. Rozengurt, *Mol. Biol. Med.* 1, 169 (1983).
3. E. Rozengurt, in "Molecular Mechanisms of Transmembrane Signalling" (P. Cohen and M. Houslay, eds.), p. 429, Elsevier, Amsterdam, 1985.
4. R. James and R. A. Bradshaw, *ARB* 53 (1984).
5. C. H. Heldin and B. Westermark, *Cell* 37, 9 (1984).
5a. A. B. Roberts and M. B. Sporn, *Cancer Surv.* 4, 683 (1985).
6. A. Baird, F. Esch, P. Mormede, N. Ueno, N. Ling, P. Bohlen, S.-Y. Ying, W. B. Wehrenberg and R. Guillemin, *Recent Prog. Horm. Res.* 42, 143 (1986).
7. G. N. Gill, P. J. Bertics and J. B. Santon, *Mol. Cell. Endocrinol.* 51, 169 (1987).
8. G. D. Shipley and R. G. Ham, *In Vitro* 17, 656 (1981).
9. J. Bottenstein, J. Hayashi, S. Hutchings, H. Masui, J. Mather, D. B. McClure, S. Ohash, A. Rizzino, G. Sato, G. Serrero, R. Wolfe and R. Wu, *Methods Enzymol.* 58, 94 (1979).
10. M. I. Grossman, *FP* 38, 2331 (1979).
11. M. Costa and J. B. Furness, *Br. Med. Bull.* 38, 247 (1982).
12. J. M. Polak and S. R. Bloom, *Br. Med. Bull.* 38, 303 (1982).
13. D. R. Lynch and S. H. Snyder, *ARB* 55, 773 (1986).
14. E. Rozengurt, A. Legg and P. Pettican, *PNAS* 76, 1284 (1979).
15. E. Rozengurt, K. D. Brown and P. Pettican, *JBC* 256, 716 (1981).
16. E. Rozengurt and J. Sinnett-Smith, *PNAS* 80, 2936 (1983).
17. M. B. Sporn and G. T. Todaro, *NEJM* 15, 878 (1980).
18. M. B. Sporn and A. B. Roberts, *Nature* 313, 745 (1985).
19. R. F. Doolittle, M. W. Hunkapiller, L. E. Hood, S. G. Devane, K. C. Robbins, S. A. Aaronson and H. N. Antoniades, *Science* 221, 275 (1983).
20. M. D. Waterfield, G. T. Scrace, N. Whittle, P. Stroobant, A. Johnson, B. Wasteson, B. Westermark, C.-H. Heldin, J. S. Huang and T. F. Deuel, *Nature* 304, 35 (1983).

21. J. Downward, Y. Yarden, E. Mayes, G. Scrace, N. Totty, P. Stockwell, A. Ullrich, J. Schlessinger and M. D. Waterfield, Nature 307, 521 (1984).
22. C. J. Sherr, C. W. Rettenmiew, R. Sacca, M. F. Roussel, A. T. Look and E. R. Stanley, Cell 41, 665 (1985).
23. T. Hunter and J. A. Cooper, ARB 54, 897 (1985).
24. E. Rozengurt, Science 234, 161 (1986).
25. E. Rozengurt and S. A. Mendoza, J. Cell Sci., Suppl. 3, 229 (1985).
26. E. Rozengurt and S. A. Mendoza, Curr. Top. Membr. Transp. 27, 163 (1986).
27. E. Rozengurt, Adv. Cyclic Nucleotide Res. 14, 429 (1981).
28. E. Rozengurt, A. Rodriguez-Pena and J. Sinnett-Smith, Ciba Found. Symp. 116, 66 (1985).
29. I. Zachary and E. Rozengurt, Cancer Surv. 4, 729 (1985).
30. M. E. Greenberg and E. B. Ziff, Nature 311, 433 (1984).
31. C. Kahana and D. Nathans, PNAS 81, 3645 (1984).
32. B. H. Cochran, A. C. Reffel and C. D. Stiles, Cell 33, 939 (1983).
33. K. Kelly, B. H. Cochran, C. D. Stiles and P. Leder, Cell 35, 603 (1983).
34. R. Muller, R. Bravo, J. Burckhardt and T. Curran, Nature 312, 716 (1984).
34a. T. Curran, R. Bravo and R. Muller, Cancer Surv. 4, 655 (1985).
35. W. Kruijer, J. A. Cooper, T. Hunter and I. M. Verma, Nature 312, 711 (1984).
36. B. H. Cochran, J. Zullo, I. M. Verma and C. D. Stiles, Science 226, 1080 (1984).
37. H. A. Armelin, M. C. S. Armelin, K. Kelly, T. Stewart, P. Leder, B. H. Cochran and C. D. Stiles, Nature 310, 655 (1984).
38. E. Mougneau, L. Lemieux, M. Rassoulzadegan and F. Cuzin, PNAS 81, 5758 (1984).
39. V. Sorrentino, V. Drozdoff, M. D. McKinney, L. Zeitz and E. Fleissner, PNAS 83, 8167 (1986).
40. L. Kaczmarek, J. K. Hyland, R. Watt, M. Rosenberg and R. Baserga, Science 228, 1313 (1985).
41. R. Muller, BBA 823, 207 (1986).
42. H. D. Abrams, L. R. Rohrschneider and R. N. Eisenman, Cell 29, 427 (1982).
43. K. Alitalo, G. Ramsey, M. J. Bishop, S. O. Pfeifer, W. W. Colby and A. D. Levison, Cell 36, 259 (1983).
44. T. Curran, A. D. Miller, L. Zokas and I. M. Verma, Cell 36, 259 (1984).
45. H. Persson and P. Leder, Science 225, 718 (1984).
46. T. Maniatis, S. Goodbourn and J. A. Fischer, Science 236, 1237 (1987).
47. R. Treisman, Cell 42, 889 (1985).
48. R. Treisman, Cell 46, 567 (1986).
49. M. Z. Gilman, R. N. Wilson and R. A. Weinberg, MCBiol 6, 4305 (1986).
49a. R. Treisman, EMBO J. 6, 2711 (1987).
50. T. E. Hayes, A. M. Kitchen and B. H. Cochran, PNAS 84, 1272 (1987).
51. P. Sassone-Corsi and I. M. Verma, Nature 326, 507 (1987).
52. J. R. Barber and I. M. Verma, MCBiol 7, 2201 (1987).
53. H. J. Rahmsdorf, A. Schonthal, P. Angel, M. Latfin, U. Ruther and P. Herrlich, NARes 15, 1643 (1987).
54. G. Shaw and R. Kamen, Cell 46, 659 (1986).
55. J. Campisi, H. E. Gray, A. B. Pardee, M. Dean and G. E. Sonenshein, Cell 36, 241 (1984).
56. P. H. Rabbitts, J. V. Watson, A. Lamond, A. Forster, M. A. Stinson, G. Evan, W. Fischer, E. Atherton, R. Sheppard and T. H. Rabbits, EMBO J. 4, 2009 (1985).
57. J.-M. Blanchard, M. Piechaczyk, C. Dani, J.-C. Chambard, A. Franchi, J. Pouysse-gur and P. Jeanteur, Nature 317, 443 (1985).

58. M. E. Greenberg, A. L. Hermanowski and E. B. Ziff, *MCBiol* **6**, 1050 (1986).
59. A. Anastasi, V. Erpsamer and M. Bucci, *Experientia* **27**, 166 (1971).
60. J. E. Rivier and M. R. Brown, *Bchem.* **17**, 1766 (1978).
61. Y. Tache, W. Vale, J. Rivier and M. Brown, *PNAS* **77**, 5515 (1980).
62. J. Gibbs, D. J. Fauser, E. A. Rowe, B. J. Rolls, E. T. Rolls and S. P. Maddison, *Nature* **282**, 208 (1979).
63. S. L. Swope and A. Schonbrunn, *PNAS* **81**, 1822 (1984).
64. P. Panula, *Med. Biol.* **64**, 177 (1986).
65. J. Wharton, J. M. Polak, S. R. Bloom, M. A. Ghatei, E. Solicia, M. R. Brown and A. E. G. Pearse, *Nature* **273**, 769 (1978).
66. J. A. Walsh, H. C. Wong and G. J. Dockray, *FP* **38**, 2315 (1979).
67. T. W. Moody and C. B. Pert, *BBRC* **90**, 7 (1979).
68. T. J. McDonald, H. Jornvall, G. Nilsson, M. Vagne, M. Ghatei, S. R. Bloom and V. Mutt, *BBRC* **90**, 227 (1979).
69. K. A. Roth, C. J. Evans, R. G. Lorenz, E. Weber, J. D. Barchas and J.-K. Chang, *BBRC* **112**, 528 (1983).
70. J. Price, E. Penman, G. L. Bourne and L. H. Rees, *Regul. Pept.* **7**, 315 (1983).
71. K. Yamaguchi, K. Abe, T. Kameya, I. Adachi, S. Taguchi, K. Otsubo, and N. Yanaihara, *Cancer Res.* **43**, 3932 (1983).
72. N. Minamino, K. Kargawa and H. Matsuo, *BBRC* **114**, 541 (1983).
73. N. Minamino, K. Kargawa and H. Matsuo, *BBRC* **119**, 14 (1984).
74. N. Minamino, T. Sudoh, K. Kangawa and H. Matsuo, *BBRC* **130**, 685 (1985).
75. T. W. Moody, C. B. Pert, A. F. Gazdar, D. N. Carney and J. D. Minna, *Science* **214**, 1246 (1981).
76. S. M. Wood, J. R. Wood, M. A. Ghatei, Y. C. Lee, D. O'Shaughnessy and S. R. Bloom, *J. Clin. Endocrinol. Metab.* **53**, 1310 (1981).
77. M. D. Erisman, R. I. Linnoila, O. Hernandez, R. P. DiAugustine and L. H. Lazarus, *PNAS* **79**, 2379 (1982).
78. K. A. Roth, C. J. Evans, E. Weber, J. D. Barchas, D. G. Bostwick and K. G. Bersch, *Cancer Res.* **43**, 5411 (1983).
79. E. A. Sausville, A.-M. Lebacq-Verhayden, E. R. Spindel, F. Cuttitta, A. F. Gazdar and J. F. Battey, *JBC* **261**, 2451 (1986).
80. F. Cuttitta, D. N. Carney, J. Mulshine, T. W. Moody, J. Fedorko, A. Fischler and J. D. Minna, *Nature* **316**, 823 (1985).
81. S. Matsubayashi, C. Yanaihara, M. Ohkubo, S. Fukata, Y. Hayashi, H. Tamai, T. Nakagawa, A. Miyauchi, K. Kuma, K. Abe, T. Suzuki and N. Yanaihara, *Cancer* **53**, 2472 (1984).
82. E. Rozengurt, M. Collins, K. D. Brown and P. Pettican, *JBC* **257**, 3680 (1982).
83. P. Dicker, P. Pohjanpelto, P. Pettican and E. Rozengurt, *Exp. Cell Res.* **135**, 221 (1981).
84. E. Rozengurt, P. Stroobant, M. D. Waterfield, T. F. Deuel and M. Keehan, *Cell* **34**, 265 (1983).
85. P. Stroobant, B. Gullick, M. D. Waterfield and E. Rozengurt, *EMBO J.* **4**, 1945 (1985).
86. A. Lopez-Rivas, P. Stroobant, M. D. Waterfield and E. Rozengurt, *EMBO J.* **3**, 939 (1984).
87. I. Zachary and E. Rozengurt, *PNAS* **82**, 7616 (1985).
88. J. C. Willey, J. F. Lechner and C. C. Harris, *Exp. Cell Res.* **153**, 245 (1984).
89. S. Weber, J. E. Zukerman, D. G. Bostwick, K. G. Bensch, B. I. Sikic and T. A. Raffin, *J. Clin. Invest.* **75**, 306 (1985).

90. D. N. Carney, F. Cuttitta, T. W. Moody and J. D. Minna, *Cancer Res.* **47**, 821 (1987).
91. F. Cuttita, D. N. Carney, J. Mulshine, T. W. Moody, J. Fedorko, A. Fischler and J. D. Minna, *Cancer Surv.* **4**, 707 (1985).
92. R. T. Jensen, T. Moody, C. Pert, J. E. Rivier and J. D. Gardner, *PNAS* **75**, 6139 (1978).
93. T. W. Moody, C. B. Candace, J. E. Rivier and M. R. Brown, *PNAS* **75**, 5372 (1978).
94. J. M. Westendorf and A. Schonbrunn, *Endocrinology* **110**, 352 (1982).
95. P. Dicker and E. Rozengurt, *Nature* **276**, 723 (1978).
96. M. K. L. Collins and E. Rozengurt, *J. Cell. Physiol.* **112**, 42 (1982).
97. E. Rozengurt and M. K. L. Collins, *J. Pathol.* **141**, 309 (1983).
98. R. T. Jensen, S. W. Jones, K. Folkers and J. D. Gardner *Nature* **309**, 61 (1984).
99. J. M. Lundberg, A. Sario, E. Brodin, S. Rosell and K. Folkers, *PNAS* **80**, 1120 (1983).
100. I. Zachary and E. Rozengurt, *BBRC* **137**, 135 (1986).
101. I. Zachary and E. Rozengurt, *JBC* **262**, 3947 (1987).
102. I. Zachary and E. Rozengurt, *EMBO J.*, in press (1987).
103. E. Rozengurt and J. W. Sinnett-Smith, *J. Cell. Physiol.* **131**, 218 (1987).
104. A. P. Palumbo, P. Rossino and P. M. Comoglio, *Exp. Cell Res.* **167**, 276 (1986).
105. J. J. Letterio, S. R. Coughlan and L. T. Williams, *Science* **234**, 1117 (1986).
106. P. McCaffrey, W. Ran, J. Campisi and M. R. Rosner, *JBC* **262**, 1442 (1987).
107. R. Bravo, H. Macdonald-Bravo, R. Muller, D. Hubsch and J. M. Almendral, *Exp. Cell Res.* **170**, 103 (1987).
108. Y. Nishizuka, *Nature* **308**, 693 (1984).
109. U. Kikkawa and Y. Nishizuka, *Annu. Rev. Cell Biol.* **2**, 149 (1986).
110. P. J. Parker, L. Coussens, N. Totty, L. Rhee, S. Young, E. Chen, S. Stabel, M. D. Waterfield and A. Ullrich, *Science* **233**, 853 (1986).
111. U. Kikkawa, Y. Ono, K. Ogita, T. Fujii, Y. Asaoka, K. Sekiguchi, Y. Kosaka, K. Igarashi and Y. Nishizuka, *FEBS Lett.* **217**, 227 (1987).
112. L. Coussens, P. J. Parker, L. Rhee, T. L. Yang-Feng, E. Chen, M. D. Waterfield, U. Francke and A. Ullrich, *Science* **233**, 859 (1986).
113. J. G. Muir and A. W. Murray, *J. Cell. Physiol.* **130**, 382 (1987).
114. M. Castagna, Y. Takai, K. Kaibuchi, K. Sano, Y. Nishizuka and U. Kikkawa, *JBC* **257**, 7847 (1982).
115. J. E. Niedel, L. J. Kuhn and G. R. Vandenbark, *PNAS* **80**, 36 (1983).
116. K. L. Leach, M. L. James and P. M. Blumberg, *PNAS* **80**, 4208 (1983).
117. C. L. Ashendel, J. M. Staller and R. K. Boutwell, *Cancer Res.* **43**, 433 (1983).
118. E. Rozengurt, A. Rodriguez-Pena and K. A. Smith, *PNAS* **80**, 7244 (1983).
119. H. Kikkawa, Y. Takai, Y. Tanaka, R. Miyake and Y. Nishizuka, *JBC* **258**, 11442 (1983).
120. P. J. Parker, S. Stabel and M. D. Waterfield, *EMBO J.* **3**, 953 (1984).
121. N. A. Sharkey, K. L. Leach and P. M. Blumberg, *PNAS* **81**, 607 (1984).
122. P. E. Driedger and P. M. Blumberg, *PNAS* **77**, 567 (1980).
123. M. Shoyab, J. E. DeLarco and G. J. Todaro, *Nature* **279**, 387 (1979).
124. W. G. Dunphy, R. J. Kachenburger, M. Castagna and P. M. Blumberg, *Cancer Res.* **41**, 2640 (1981).
125. A. D. Horowitz, E. Greenebaum and I. B. Weinstein, *PNAS* **78**, 2315 (1981).
126. V. Solanki and T. J. Slaga, *PNAS* **78**, 2549 (1981).
127. P. Dicker and E. Rozengurt, *Nature* **287**, 607 (1980).
128. I. B. Weinstein, *J. Supramol. Struct. Cell. Biochem.* **17**, 99 (1981).

129. E. Rozengurt, A. Rodriguez-Pena, M. Coombs and J. Sinnett-Smith, *PNAS* **81**, 5748 (1984).
130. A. Rodriguez-Pena and E. Rozengurt, *EMBO J.* **5**, 77 (1986).
131. A. Rodriguez-Pena and E. Rozengurt, *J. Cell. Physiol.* **129**, 124 (1986).
132. I. Zachary, J. W. Sinnett-Smith and E. Rozengurt, *JCB* **102**, 2212 (1986).
133. F. Vara and E. Rozengurt, *BBRC* **130**, 646 (1985).
134. M. K. L. Collins and E. Rozengurt, *BBRC* **104**, 1159 (1982).
135. M. Collins and E. Rozengurt, *J. Cell. Physiol.* **118**, 133 (1984).
136. A. Rodriguez-Pena and E. Rozengurt, *BBRC* **120**, 1053 (1984).
137. P. J. Blackshear, L. A. Witters, P. R. Girard, U. F. Kuo and S. N. Quamo, *JBC* **260**, 13304 (1985).
138. R. Ballester and O. M. Rosen, *JBC* **260**, 15194 (1985).
139. A. Rodriguez-Pena and E. Rozengurt, *EMBO J.* **4**, 71 (1985).
140. P. J. Blackshear, L. Wen, B. P. Glynn and L. A. Witters, *JBC* **261**, 1459 (1986).
141. K. Kaibuchi, T. Tsuda, A. Kikuchi, T. Tanimoto, T. Yamashita and Y. Takai, *JBC* **261**, 1187 (1986).
142. S. Stabel, A. Rodriguez-Pena, S. Young, E. Rozengurt and P. Parker, *J. Cell. Physiol.* **130**, 111 (1987).
143. C. M. Isacke, J. Meisenhelder, K. D. Brown, K. L. Gould, S. J. Gould and T. Hunter, *EMBO J.* **5**, 2889 (1986).
144. S. R. Coughlin, W. M. F. Lee, P. W. Williams, G. M. Giels and L. T. Williams, *Cell* **43**, 243 (1985).
144a. F. Vara, J. A. Schneider and E. Rozengurt, *PNAS* **82**, 2384 (1985).
145. R. Bravo, M. Neuberg, J. Burckhardt, J. Almendral, R. Wallich and R. Muller, *Cell* **48**, 251 (1987).
146. J. W. Sinnett-Smith and E. Rozengurt, *J. Cell. Physiol.* **124**, 81 (1985).
147. P. Dicker and E. Rozengurt, *J. Cell. Physiol.* **109**, 99 (1981).
148. S. A. Mendoza, J. A. Schneider, A. Lopez-Rivas, J. W. Sinnett-Smith and E. Rozengurt, *J. Cell Biol.* **102**, 2223 (1986).
149. W. Lee, P. Mitchell and R. Tijan, *Cell* **49**, 741 (1987).
150. P. Angel, M. Imagawa, R. Chiu, B. Stein, R. J. Imbra, H. J. Rahmsdorf, C. J. Honat, P. Herrlich and M. Karin, *Cell* **49**, 729 (1987).
151. R. Prywes and R. G. Roeder, *Cell* **47**, 777 (1986).
152. N. Takuwa, Y. Takuwa, W. E. Bollag and H. Rasmussen, *JBC* **262**, 182 (1987).
153. A. Lopez-Rivas, S. A. Mendoza, E. Nånberg, J. Sinnett-Smith and E. Rozengurt, *PNAS* **84**, 5768 (1987).
154. M. J. Berridge and R. F. Irvine, *Nature* **312**, 315 (1984).
155. P. W. Majerus, T. M. Connolly, H. Deckmyn, T. S. Ross, T. E. Bross, H. Ishii, V. S. Bansal and D. B. Wilson, *Science* **234**, 1519 (1986).
156. J. P. Heslop, D. M. Blakeley, K. D. Brown, R. F. Irvine and M. J. Berridge, *Cell* **47**, 703 (1986).
157. T. R. Hesketh, J. P. Moore, J. D. H. Morris, M. V. Taylor, J. Rogers, G. A. Smith and J. C. Metcalfe, *Nature* **313**, 481 (1985).
158. S. A. Mendoza, A. Lopez-Rivas, J. W. Sinnett-Smith and E. Rozengurt, *Exp. Cell Res.* **164**, 536 (1986).
159. M. K. L. Collins and E. Rozengurt, *PNAS* **80**, 1924 (1983).
160. A. Lopez-Rivas and E. Rozengurt, *Am. J. Physiol.* **247**, c156 (1984).
161. R. Bravo, J. Burckhardt, T. Curran and R. Muller, *EMBO J.* **4**, 1193 (1985).
162. E. Rozengurt, A. Legg, G. Strang and N. Courtenay-Luck, *PNAS* **78**, 4392 (1981).
163. E. Rozengurt, *Exp. Cell Res.* **139**, 71 (1982).

164. E. Rozengurt, *J. Cell. Physiol.* **112**, 243 (1982).
165. E. Rozengurt, M. K. L. Collins and M. Keehan, *J. Cell. Physiol.* **116**, 379 (1983).
166. Z.-W. Wang and E. Rozengurt, *J. Cell Biol.* **96**, 1743 (1983).
167. C. O'Neill, P. Riddle and E. Rozengurt, *Exp. Cell Res.* **156**, 65 (1985).
168. E. Rozengurt, M. Murray, I. Zachary and M. Collins, *PNAS* **84**, 2282 (1987).
169. T. Tsuda, Y. Hamamori, T. Yamashita, Y. Fukumoto and Y. Takai, *FEBS Lett.* **208**, 39 (1986).
170. W. Ran, M. Dean, R. A. Levine, C. Henkle and J. Campisi, *PNAS* **83**, 8216 (1986).
171. A. Lopez-Rivas and E. Rozengurt, *BBRC* **114**, 240 (1983).
172. K. Nishikura and J. M. Murray, *MCBiol* **7**, 639 (1987).
173. P. S. Thomas, *PNAS* **77**, 5201 (1980).

Index

in characterization of meiotic mutants,
223–226
radiation damage
to bases, 109–110, 111
conclusions, 121–122
by direct ionization, 106–107
from direct ionization, 106
by free-radical attack, 106–107
indirect effects of, 114
locally multiply damaged sites, 117–118
as lethal sites, 121
OH free-radical damage classes vs
direct ionization classes, 111–112
reaction mechanisms of, 106–107
significance of singly damaged sites,
111–113
singly damaged sites, 110–111
sites of attack, 107–108
to sugar moieties, 108–109
in vivo by direct energy deposition,
103–104
from water free-radicals, 106
size of patch inserted after ionizing
radiation, 118n
synthesis
bombesin stimulation of, 27
significance of c-*fos* and c-*myc*
induction, 285–287, 289
2α-DNA and *FLP*, mitotic recombination,
255
DNA-binding proteins, 8
DNA tumor-virus genes, 73
DNA virus-derived genes, 74
Drosophila insulin receptor-related gene,
tyrosine kinase homology, 162, 163
Drosophila melanogaster Antennapedia, 5′
noncoding region, 175–177
Duchenne's muscular dystrophy, 139

E

E. coli galactosidase (*LACZ*) sequences,
HO-induced gene conversion, 251–255
E1A gene
cell transformation and, 90–91
functional domains, 76
products
activation of E2 promoter-binding
factor (E2F), 86–88
modulation of cellular gene
expression, 84–91

structure, 84–85
suppression of enhancer-driven
transcription, 89–90
transactivation of chromosomal genes,
88–89
transactivation of nonchromosomal
genes, 85–88
Eastern equine encephalomyelitis virus,
interferon and, 31–32
EBNA-2, 175
Ectopic recombination
description, 218–223
frequencies, 218, 219–220
EGF, *See* Epidermal growth factor
eIF-2, 47
eIF-4A
cross-linking, 185
identification, 178–180
isolation, 181
eIF-4A$_c$, 186
eIF-4A$_f$
characteristics of, 182
RNA-dependent ATP hydrolysis and, 186
eIF-4B
characteristics of, 182, 183
cross-linking, 185
mechanism of action, 186–187
eIF-4E, 182
eIF-4F
characteristics of, 182, 183
identification, 181
inactivation, 184
interaction with cap, 199–200
interaction with eIF-4A subunits, 186
24-kDa CBP subunit, phosphorylation
of, 197–198
kinetics of proteolysis, 193
ribosome binding to mRNA and,
191–192
RNA melting activity and, 196
eIF-4G, 183
Ela enhancer, stimulation by *ras*, 79–80
Encephalomyocarditis virus (emC),
inhibition of macromolecular synthesis
by interferon, 33–35
Energy deposition, direct, amount of
damage produced in DNA *in vivo*,
103–104
Enveloped viruses
IFN effect on late stages of replication,
59–62

L

β-Lactamase, site-directed mutagenesis
    with chemical modification
    investigation, 9, 10, 12, 22
β-Lactams, hydrolysis, 14
LACZ sequences, HO-induced gene
    conversion, 251–255
LET ionizing radiation, low, chromosomal
    aberrations from, 115
Linear energy transfer (LET), 96n, 97, 98
Locally multiply damaged sites (LMDS)
    description of, 112
    energy deposition events and, 116
    as lethal sites, 121
    mechanisms of production and
        characteristics, 117–118, 122
    types
        different distributions among strands,
            119–120
        identities of individual damage types,
            120–121
        numbers of lesions per site, 120
LOX/CRE, mitotic recombination of,
    255–256
Luciferase, inactivation, 3

M

Macrophages, IFN-mediated inhibition of
    HSV replication, 53–54
Major histocompatibility antigens, IFN-
    induced expression, 52
Mammalian cells, DNA damage from
    ionizing radiation, 95–122
    direct and indirect effects, 104–106
Mason–Pfizer monkey virus, inhibition by
    IFN, 59
MAT switching
    analysis in presence of mutations or
        inhibitors of cell growth, 247–249
    analysis of HO-induced mitotic
        recombination events
        chromosomal deletion, 249–251
        gene conversion of LACZ sequences,
            251–255
    intermediates of, 245–247
    kinetics, 243–245
    model of, 240–241
    physical monitoring of, 240–256
    transferred sequences, 242–243

Meiotic recombination
    alteration by multiple heterologies,
        233–236
    detection of intermediates
        formation and resolution of branched
            structures arising from
            recombination, 230–232
        formation of heteroduplex DNA,
            228–230
        initiation of recombination meiotic
            hot spots, 226–228
    effect of multiple heterozygosities, 256
    and gene conversion in small interval,
        233–240
    conversion tract length, 236–238
    in Saccharomyces, 212–238
        characterization of meiotic mutants
            by physical analysis of DNA,
            223–226
        detection of intermediates, 226–232
        physical detection
            constraints on crossing-over, 221–223
            ectopic recombination frequencies,
                219–220
            position effects on allelic
                recombination, 219
            timing of, 212–218
        vs mitotic recombination, 211
Membrane ruffling, ras genes and, 75
Mengovirus, inhibition of macromolecular
    synthesis by interferon, 34
Mercuric ion reductase, 8
Metallothionein gene family, ferritin H
    gene and, 147–148
Metallothionein-II, 62
Methanol, 105
3-Methylquercetin, 193
β_2-Microglobulin, 62
Mitogenesis
    bombesin-stimulated, specific high-
        affinity receptors and, 268–269
    serum as stimulus, 290
    significance of c-fos and c-myc
        induction, 285–287
Mitogens, See also specific mitogens
    of Swiss 3T3 cells, 262
Mitotic recombination
    HO-induced
        chromosomal deletion, 249–251
        gene conversion of LACZ sequences,
            251–255